The Modern Creation Trilogy

Volume II

Science
and
Creation

The Modern Creation Trilogy

Volume II

Science
and
Creation

Dr. Henry M. Morris
Dr. John D. Morris

Master
Books

First printing: November 1996
Second printing: November 1997

ISBN: 0-89051-221-3

Acknowledgments

Scientists who have reviewed the manuscript and made valuable suggestions include several faculty members in the Institute for Creation Research Graduate School. Gratitude is expressed to Dr. Duane Gish (Biochemistry), Dr. Larry Vardiman (Physics), and Dr. Ken Cumming (Biology).

Merle Meeter, M.A., former Head of the English Department at Christian Heritage College, assisted in editing the manuscript, as did Mary Smith, B.S. Mrs. Smith also typed the manuscript from the handwritten script. We are deeply indebted to all these dedicated and very capable colleagues.

Table of Contents

Introduction

This second volume of *The Modern Creation Trilogy* focuses especially on the evidences from science that relate to origins. Today, literally thousands of scientists have abandoned the evolutionary model of origins, believing that true science supports the concept of primeval special creation. Furthermore, they are convinced that the Creator is not some impersonal "force" or "cosmic consciousness," as pantheists would allege, but rather an omnipotent, omniscient Person, capable of simply calling the majestic universe into being by His own power and wisdom. That being the reality — or, at least, the premise — it follows that the Creator would have a purpose in so doing, and would be capable of ordering and preserving the universe thus created, and that all creatures are under the ultimate authority of that Creator.

Although there are many today who would insist that a scientist — by definition — cannot believe in special creation, the fact remains that there are indeed thousands of creationists today who would satisfy every definition of a scientist except *that*! They may reject evolution, but they do have bona fide post-graduate degrees in some field of pure or applied science from accredited universities; they have published scientific research papers in their fields; and they make their living by practicing or teaching science.

For example, since its organization in 1963, over a thousand such scientists have become members of the Creation Research Society. This is an American society, but there are similar organizations in England, Germany, Russia, Australia, the Netherlands, and various other countries. The Creation Science Society in Korea is essentially as large as the Creation Research Society in America. In addition, there are probably at least a hundred *local* creation societies active in both this and other countries, almost all led by scientists rather than by preachers or others.

Furthermore, our experience would confirm the fact — even though no actual statistics are available — that there are several times more creationist scientists outside, than inside, the membership of some organized creationist associations. We believe, too, with good reason, that there are a great many scientists who are "closet creationists," but who will not admit it because of peer pressure.

Many of these creationist scientists — including one of the writers (H. Morris) — were once evolutionists. In order to become creationists despite the opposition of their colleagues, they have had to examine the scientific evidences on both sides of this vital issue very carefully, and they have made an informed decision that the creation model of origins is a better scientific model than the evolutionary model. Creationism correlates the known facts of science far better than evolutionism, with fewer unresolved problems.

Now, even though special creationism is clearly taught in the Bible — as shown in Volume 1 of this Trilogy — it can be defended and expounded scientifically without reference to the Bible. It is *not* true that creationism is purely biblical, rather than scientific, as evolutionists often maintain. Creation is no more "religious" than evolution — in fact, *less* so! And evolution is no more "scientific" than creation — in fact, *less* so! Schools could very easily teach scientific creationism with no reference whatever to the Bible or to other religious literature or religious doctrine.

That, in fact, is precisely the purpose of this volume. Just as Volume 1 of the Trilogy explained and defended the *biblical* doctrine of creation without reference to scientific evidence or arguments, so this Volume 2 will set forth the scientific case for creation without reference to the Bible or to any aspect of religion.

Some may complain that the very idea of creation is religious and therefore non-scientific. Surely, however, any fair-minded person can see that evolution is as much a "religious" concept as is creation. Neither model can be *proved*, in the ultimate sense, or even tested scientifically, for the obvious reason that one cannot repeat history in the laboratory, nor can one *observe* actual past history from some imaginary time-machine. Both models of origins are beyond the reach of the scientific method! It is nothing but self-serving prejudice for evolutionists to assert that evolution is *science* just because it denies or ignores the possibility of God, whereas creation is *not* science because it allows that possibility.

In any case, this volume will discuss the evidences from the various sciences that relate to origins. Such evidences are found not only in biology, but also in geology, astronomy, physics, chemistry, and practically every other field of science. We cannot *prove* creation scientifically, but neither can evolutionists prove evolution. We *can* show, however, that the scientific data correlate better with the assumption of creation than with the assumption of evolution, and we can do so without any reference to the Bible.

Furthermore, this can be done without having to rely overmuch on technical jargon. Scientists can, indeed, pursue these topics in much greater depth than we shall do here, but that is not the purpose of this book. It is important that people of all backgrounds — not just scientists — become aware that the real facts in this world (call them science, or whatever) support the real fact of a personal Creator God, to whom all men and women are responsible; for this knowledge should make a real difference in how they order their lives. Consequently, we shall try to explain the relevant scientific evidences in terms understandable and meaningful even to non-scientists. One certainly does not need to be a credentialed scientist to understand the basic scientific evidences supporting creation and refuting evolution. Whenever scientific terms or concepts need to be introduced into the discussion, we shall try to define and explain them in simple terms.

The evolution model, of course, attempts to include everything within its scope, from elementary particles to the most complex interrelationships in the world of living organisms. So does the creation model. Accordingly, this volume must attempt to cover the origin and development of the universe, of plants and animals, and of human societies, and all of the various systems in between. The subject matter must cover the whole range of reality and, therefore, must necessarily be presented only in summary form. Nevertheless, the key evidences will become clear enough, even with this light treatment.

We trust that, when the survey is completed, the reader will agree with thousands of other scientific creationists, that the scientific case against evolution (and, therefore, for creation) is very strong! Since neither creation nor evolution can be *proved*, one's decision will finally be based on what he or she *prefers* to believe. For those who *want* to believe in creation, however, the evidence is far more than adequate to justify ordering their lives in the light of the *overwhelming evidence for special creation.*

Since no scientist — including the writers — can be directly trained and experienced in every field of science, all the arguments and evidences in this volume are documented by citations from scientists who *are* specialists in the particular fields being discussed. Furthermore, in order not to prejudice the case, all such quotations are from books or articles by evolutionary scientists. Since creationists are sometimes charged by evolutionists to be quoting them out of context to make them sound like creationists, we want to assure our readers, at the outset, that all authorities cited are definitely evolutionists! Occasional exceptions are noted as appropriate.

Sources are also given so that readers can refer to them directly if they wish. It is impossible, of course, to quote enough of the context in each instance to give the authors' full treatment, but we have tried to give enough quoted material to indicate accurately the points being made by the respective authors.

Chapter 1

The Scientific Case for Creation: an Overview

Before discussing the detailed scientific evidence relating to origins, it will be good to get a broad overview of the basic facts involved. It is not too much to say that there is literally no scientific evidence whatever — past, present, or future — for any real evolution. Belief in evolution is strictly a matter of faith.

That is a bold statement, and readers will have to judge for themselves after they have seen the evidence. And that, of course, is exactly the point. If evolution is true, then we ought to be able to *see* the evidence. After all, *science* means "knowledge," something that is *known* (the word comes from the Latin *scientia*, meaning knowledge).

But no one has ever *seen* evolution take place. The changes we do see in living species are either "horizontal" changes, at the same level of organized complexity (e.g., different varieties of dogs, different tribes of people, different colors of roses), or "downward" changes (e.g., mutations and extinctions).

Evolutionists may react to this problem by noting that creation can not be "seen" either, and they would be quite right. Real creation of some complex organism out of nothing, or even out of non-living matter, would indeed require a miracle.

Therefore, evolution and creation are on the same ground. Both must be seen with the eye of faith, because neither can be seen taking place with our physical eyes. But this very fact is a strong argument *for* creation and *against* evolution. One could very legitimately *predict*, from the creation model, that we cannot now see creation take place, since it is postulated as a supernatural event completed in the past.

The evolutionist, on the other hand, should expect actually to *see* evolution in action, since by definition it is an altogether natural process and, therefore, should be operating even now in nature. If we really *could* see things evolving from, say, a given species into another species of greater organized complexity, we would all have to believe in evolution. We could verify it by observing it — *that* would be real science!

But since we *cannot* see it functioning, it is not any more "scientific" than creation. Neither evolution nor creation can be seen in operation. Neither can be proved nor disproved, scientifically. It is conceivable that either one — or both — may have occurred in the past, but the past cannot be tested scientifically! A choice between the two can be made only by faith in one or the other.

The Two Models

The fact that we cannot *test* either belief scientifically, however, does not mean that we cannot *discuss* them scientifically. We can define two scientific models: a creation model and an evolution model. Then we can compare the two models in terms of their relative abilities to correlate and explain and, possibly, even predict scientific data. That way, we can arrive at a decision as to which model is *more likely* to be true, even though we can never *prove* it to be true. Which faith is the more *reasonable* faith — faith in a completed creation or faith in an ongoing evolution? If we can correlate and explain the origin of all scientific data in terms of present processes and phenomena, then evolution is reasonable. If, however, these data cannot be explained in terms of present natural processes, then one is justified in assuming that they require completed supernatural processes of the past, and this would make belief in creation the more reasonable faith.

We must use the term "model" or "framework" or "concept" or some other such term, rather than "theory" or "hypothesis" for both evolution and creation. In standard scientific terminology, a "hypothesis" is a statement that can be tested scientifically by some kind of experiment that could refute it if it is wrong. A "theory" is a hypothesis that has been repeatedly tested in various ways, but has not been refuted as yet. Finally, a scientific "law" is a theory that has been tested, with positive results, so often and in so many different ways that it is almost certainly a confirmed fact of science.

Nevertheless, careful scientists will generally agree that even a "law" of science may eventually turn out to be wrong if some experiment not yet performed might refute it. For that reason, no theory or law of science can ever be *proved* in the absolute sense, for even a single negative result in a properly conceived and controlled future experiment might yet disprove it.

With these standard principles of the scientific method in mind, it is truly amazing that so many *scientists* (not to mention the camp followers of science) will state pontifically that "evolution is a proved fact of science." Stephen Jay Gould, for example, speaks of "our confidence in the fact of evolution."[1] Gould is probably the most influential — certainly the most articulate — of the younger evolutionists, those of the "baby boom" generation. He is also the leading advocate of the modern "punctuated-evolution" school of evolutionary thought.

However, the pre-eminent living evolutionist is probably Ernst Mayr, professor of biology at Harvard, a representative of the older generation of evolutionists, and a leader of the evolutionary school of thought known as neo-Darwinism. Mayr has said this:

> Since Darwin, every knowing person agrees that man is descended from the apes. . . . Today, of course, there is no such thing as the theory of evolution; it is the fact of evolution. . . . The only arguments now are over technical problems, but the basic fact of evolution is so clearly established that no scientist worries about it any more.[2]

With all due recognition of the brilliance and eminence of Professor Mayr, such a statement is pure propaganda. Surely he knows better!

Evolution is *not* a *proved fact* of science or history at all. It has never been observed, either scientifically in existing biological activity, or historically in the records of past biological phenomena, as we shall abundantly document later. Furthermore, evolution should not even be considered as a scientific hypothesis, since there is no conceivable experiment that could be devised which might refute it. Two incisive evolutionary biologists pointed this out more than a quarter century ago.

> Our theory of evolution has become . . . one which cannot be refuted by any possible observations. . . . No one can think of ways in which to test it.[3]

---

[1] Stephen Jay Gould, "Darwinism Defined: the Difference between Fact and Theory," *Discover*, vol. 8 (January 1987), p. 65. Gould is a Professor of Geology at Harvard University.

[2] Ernst Mayr, "Interview," *Omni* (March/April 1988), p. 46. It may be noted that Dr. Ken Cumming, Dean and Professor of Biology at the ICR Graduate School, studied biology at Harvard under Dr. Mayr. Nevertheless, Cumming is now a strong and firmly convinced creationist, even after receiving his doctorate in biology at Harvard.

[3] Paul Ehrlich and L. C. Birch, "Evolutionary History and Population Biology," *Nature*, vol. 214 (April 22, 1967), p. 352.

If anyone objects to this generalization, let him try to devise an experiment himself that could disprove evolution. He will find it impossible. As Ehrlich and Birch express it:

> Every conceivable observation can be fitted into it.[4]

No matter what one may see in an experiment, or in the world at large, he can always explain it, if he wants to badly enough, in terms of evolution. He can devise an evolutionary explanation for the long neck of the giraffe or the short neck of the hippopotamus. He can conceive how the bright colors of the butterfly or the dull coloration of the peppered moth might be explained by natural selection. If he sees no evolutionary change in an animal over many generations, he can say that evolution is *normally* represented by "stasis," being interrupted by periods of rapid change occurring at such long intervals that we can never observe them, or else that evolutionary changes occur so slowly in such minute steps that no one can ever see them. *Anything* can be "explained" by evolution!

The preeminent professor of the philosophy of science Karl Popper pointed out that:

> Agreement between theory and observation should count for nothing unless the theory is a testable theory, and unless the agreement is the result of attempts to test the theory. But testing a theory means trying to find its weak spots; it means trying to refute it. And a theory is testable if it is refutable. . . . It is far from clear what we should consider a possible refutation of the theory of natural selection.[5]

Evolutionists commonly respond to creationists who quote Popper by noting that he still believed in evolution. That, of course, is the point. One *believes* in evolution, but he does not *know* it to be true, except by faith — exactly the same way by which creationists *know* creation to be true. As a distinguished zoologist and Fellow of the Royal Society in England has said:

> Belief in evolution is thus exactly parallel to belief in special creation — both are concepts which believers know

[4] Paul Ehrlich and L. C. Birch, "Evolutionary History and Population Biology," *Nature*, vol. 214 (April 22, 1967), p. 352.

[5] Karl Popper, "Science: Problems, Aims, Responsibilities," *Proceedings, Federation of American Societies for Experimental Biology*, vol. 22 (1963), p. 964.

to be true but neither, up to the present, has been capable of proof.[6]

Significantly, this admission was made by a prominent evolutionist selected to write the foreword to the 1971 edition of Charles Darwin's *Origin of Species*.

It is surely true, as Matthews says, that creationists must *believe* in special creation, just as evolutionists must *believe* in evolution. Creation is neither observable, testable, nor refutable. In the terminology of Ehrlich and Birch, "every conceivable observation" can be fitted into the creation model. Therefore, even though creationists "know" creation to be true, as Matthews says, they cannot prove it scientifically, any more than evolutionists can prove scientifically that evolution is true, no matter how strongly they may believe that they know it to be true.

It does seem, by any criterion of fairness and objectivity, that creation and evolution, as the only two models of origins, ought to be considered as equal alternatives to be evaluated objectively in terms of their relative abilities to correlate and explain scientific data.

In this book, therefore, we will be using the terms "creation model" and "evolution model" to denote these two alternative concepts of origins and history. A "model" can neither be proved nor disproved scientifically, but it can be evaluated scientifically in terms of its ability to correlate — and even "predict" — scientific data that can be actually observed or measured. The model can be defined in simple, broad terms to begin with, then modified and extended as necessary to incorporate incoming data. Then, in general, that model which incorporates the greatest number and variety of data, with the smallest number of modifications and extensions to make it fit, and with the smallest number of unresolved questions about how to incorporate the relevant data, is the model *most likely* to be *true*, even though it can never be proved scientifically to be true.

On this basis, we are convinced that the creation model is far superior to the evolution model, and we shall attempt to bring convincing evidence of that evaluation in the ensuing pages. First, however, we need to define the models.

In the very simplest terms, evolutionism is the model that attempts to explain everything without God the Creator, whereas creationism as a model advances the supernatural activity of the Creator as the explanation

---

[6] L. Harrison Matthews, "Foreword" to *Origin of Species by Natural Selection*, by Charles Darwin (London: J. M. Dent and Sons, Ltd., 1971), p. x.

for the more basic entities of science and the most determinative events of history.

A more concrete comparison of the two models is summarized by some such tabulation as that below.

Evolution Model	Creation Model
Continuing Naturalistic Origin of Basic Systems	*Completed Supernatural* Origin of Basic Systems
Net Present *Increase* in Organized Complexity of Basic Systems	Net Present *Decrease* in Organized Complexity of Basic Systems

Another way of contrasting the two models is to emphasize that the evolution model stresses innovation and integration, whereas the creation model is characterized by conservation and disintegration. Therefore, one cannot properly speak of creation by evolution; each of the two terms is, by definition, the opposite of the other. Douglas Futuyma, a leading evolutionary biologist, has made this clear in a dogmatically anti-creationist book written by him.

> Creation and evolution, between them, exhaust the possible explanations for the origin of living things. Organisms either appeared on the earth fully developed or they did not. If they did not, they must have developed from pre-existing species by some process of modification. If they did appear in a fully developed state, they must indeed have been created by some omnipotent intelligence.[7]

Creationists would certainly disagree with much in Futuyma's book, but we would heartily agree with this particular statement. That is, scientists can either explain all things by continuing natural processes, or they cannot — one or the other. If they cannot, then at least *some* things must be explained by completed supernatural processes of the past. The first situation would support the evolution model, the second the creation model.

Professor Futuyma was thinking specifically of biological organisms, but the same contrast would apply to the inorganic realm as well, including the physical cosmos itself. That is, if we can explain the development of the basic chemical elements, and the entire physical universe by ongoing, observable, natural processes, then we can properly

---

[7] Douglas J. Futuyma, *Science on Trial* (New York: Pantheon Books, 1983), p. 197.

believe in cosmic evolution, stellar evolution, and chemical evolution. If not, then we should accept the creation model, attributing the origin of the universe, the basic structure of matter, the stellar heavens, and the solar system, to special creation.

The Elusive Evidence for Evolution

If evolution is really true, then we ought to be able to observe it in action. We should be able to observe new elements evolving, new stars evolving, new kinds of plants and animals evolving, and so on. If these things *could* be observed, then everyone would accept evolution as scientific fact. Even if we could not observe them actually coming into existence, if we could just observe simpler elements evolving into more complex elements, or invertebrates evolving into vertebrates, or anything of that sort, then we would all be evolutionists without even arguing. There might still be arguments between atheistic evolutionists and theistic evolutionists, but there could be no true creationists. All of us could actually see evolution taking place; it would be observable scientific fact!

We see nothing like this, of course, exactly as would be predicted from the creation model. Creation, by definition, is an event or events of the past, and so cannot be observed taking place in the present. Furthermore, instead of evolutionary changes now taking place to generate more complex systems and organisms, as might be expected from the basic definition of the evolution model, what we actually see is a ubiquitous tendency for systems to disintegrate and for organisms, and even entire species, to decay and die! This is another implication from the basic creation model.

Thus, the creation model basically is obviously more realistic than the evolution model. Its predictions are precisely fulfilled, whereas those of the evolution model are never observed at all.

At this point, however, the evolutionist flees for refuge to the safe haven of "time." He assumes that evolution proceeds either so slowly or so rarely (in sudden leaps) that we can never actually see it operating.

In effect, he must so modify his basic model as to make it almost a quasi-creation model. He says that, even though we can't see it, we must believe that it happened in the past. Otherwise, he would have to believe in creation, and to him such an option is incredible!

Not many modern evolutionists are willing to say this as bluntly as did Professor D. M. S. Watson many years ago, although this is what most doctrinaire evolutionists would say if it did not sound so bigoted. Watson asserted the following:

The theory of evolution itself [is] a theory universally accepted not because it can be proved by logically coherent evidence to be true but because the only alternative, special creation, is clearly incredible.[8]

Similarly, the eminent George Wald, a pantheistic evolutionist at Harvard, after showing that the spontaneous generation of life from non-life was essentially impossible, nevertheless said that he continued to believe in it because, as he put it:

The only alternative to some form of spontaneous generation is a belief in supernatural creation.[9]

And *that* Professor Wald could not endure!

Relegating evolution to the distant past, however, simply points up more clearly than ever the fact that evolutionism, despite its pretensions, is not science! Creationists are frank to admit that creation cannot be scientifically tested, because it took place in the past. Evolutionism is in exactly the same boat in this regard, but most evolutionists would choke before admitting it.

Furthermore, in order to make this idea palatable, evolutionists must attach it to an auxiliary model, that of *uniformitarianism*. The geological dogma of uniformitarianism is usually associated with the name of Darwin's fellow scientist and mentor, Sir Charles Lyell, although — like evolutionism — uniformitarianism is really a very ancient belief of pagan philosophers. The famous slogan of this doctrine is that "the present is the key to the past." The assumption is that present processes (erosion, sedimentation, volcanism, glaciation, etc.), operating as they do at present, are sufficient to explain all the geological and other features of the earth.

This uniformitarian assumption, if valid, would mean that the earth must be very old! Since no instance of true "vertical" evolution has ever been observed during all of documented human history, the evolutionary time span needs to be almost infinitely great in order to make "particle-to-people" evolution seem even remotely feasible. Only three hundred years ago, both scientists and theologians in the Occident were satisfied with a few thousand years of earth history, since all human written records extended back only about 5,000 years or so. Such a young earth

---

[8] D.M.S. Watson, "Adaptation," *Nature*, vol. 124 (1929), p. 233. Watson was a prominent British evolutionary zoologist.

[9] George Wald, "Innovation in Biology," *Scientific American*, vol. 199 (September 1958), p. 100. Professor Wald was a Nobel-prize-winning biologist, specializing in bio-optics.

could not, of course, possibly allow for any measurable evolution, and so it became necessary for the radical social philosophers and others who were promoting evolutionary ideas to find ways of returning scholarly thought to the old pagan belief of an essentially infinitely old earth.

Lyell's uniformitarianism provided chronological encouragement for Darwin's evolutionism, and soon nearly the whole scientific world had capitulated to evolutionary uniformitarianism (see Volume 3 of this Trilogy for further discussion of the history of these developments).

But even Lyell's estimate of the great age of the earth soon proved inadequate for the time demands of the evolutionists:

> The fact that the calculated age of the earth has increased by a factor of roughly 100 between the year 1900 and today — as the accepted age of the earth has increased from about 50 million years in 1900 to at least 4.6 aeons today — certainly suggests we clothe our current conclusions regarding time and the earth with humility.[10]

The author of this fascinating observation was, when he wrote it, professor of geology at California Institute of Technology and the Scripps Institute of Oceanography. He himself was, of course, an evolutionist who believed in the earth's great age. Nevertheless, he was aware of the unscientific assumptions in age speculations.

> We will speculate a lot about the first aeon or more of earth's history . . . in the next few years; but in the foreseeable future it will be mostly speculation — essentially geopoetry.[11]

This "geopoetry" is, nevertheless, presented as science by today's scientific establishment and their camp followers in the socio/humanistic fields. These tremendous ages are dependent entirely on the uniformitarian assumption as applied to a select few processes with very slow rates — especially the decay rates of certain chemical elements. Other processes are not acceptable as chronometers because, even with the assumption of uniformity, they will not yield ages big enough to accommodate evolution.

Now it should be obvious that no one can *prove* uniformitarianism to be applicable in prehistoric time, since there were no observers there to observe it. As a matter of fact, it is not valid even in historic time, for

---

[10] A. E. J. Engle, "Time and the Earth," *American Scientist*, vol. 57 (Winter, 1969), p. 461. In this quotation, an "aeon" is a billion years.

[11] *Ibid.*, p. 462.

it is well known that almost all geologic work today is being accomplished in brief "catastrophes" — floods, eruptions, earthquakes, landslides, tsunamis, hurricanes, etc.

Consequently, more and more geologists today are returning to the pre-Darwinian principle of *catastrophism* as the basis of geological interpretations of prehistoric geologic activities that produced the great features of the earth's surface and subsurface formations. This is somewhat embarrassing to them, however, because catastrophism is more naturally associated with creationism than with evolutionism.

A prominent geologist has argued, for example, in a presidential address to his Society of Economic Paleontologists and Mineralogists that geologists should use the term "episodicity" instead of "catastrophism" when referring to these non-uniformitarian events of either past or present, because the latter term is too easily associated with creationism. He voiced his fear as follows:

> What do I mean by "episodic sedimentation?" Episodic was chosen carefully over other possible terms. "Catastrophic" has become popular recently because of its dramatic effect, but it should be purged from our vocabulary because it feeds the neo-catastrophist-creation cause.[12]

Obviously, it is true that creationists are not embarrassed by any evidence of great catastrophes or even global cataclysms of the past, because creationism does not demand vast ages in which to function, as evolution does. By definition, creation does not operate within the natural laws of the present. It constitutes an absolutely unique supernatural event (or events), and can take place instantaneously at such time or times as the omnipotent Creator may choose. There is nothing at all unreasonable about this possibility, except to an atheist who chooses to reject the very strong evidence that such a Creator does exist. (At the very least, anyone should recognize that it is impossible to *prove* that there is no God!)

The great evolutionary protagonist Thomas Huxley admitted this back in Darwin's day:

> "Creation," in the ordinary sense of the word is perfectly conceivable. I find no difficulty in conceiving that, at some former period, this universe was not in existence and that it made its appearance . . . in conse-

---

[12] Robert Dott, "Episodic View now Replacing Catastrophism," *Geotimes*, vol. 27 (November 1982), p. 16.

quence of the volition of some pre-existing being. Then, as now, the so-called *a priori* arguments . . . against the possibility of creative acts, appeared to me devoid of reasonable foundation.[13]

Now, although uniformitarianism in some form is absolutely essential to the evolution model, and catastrophism is more easily assimilated into the creation model, the creation/evolution issue is a different question than the catastrophism/uniformitarian issue. That is, the *fact* of creation is one scientific question; the *time* of creation is another, and the two should be kept distinct, as far as scientific comparisons go. Both questions can be discussed scientifically, without reference to any "religious" questions, and that will be done in this book, but they can also be discussed independently of each other.

In the earlier chapters of this volume, therefore, the scientific case *for* creation and *against* evolution will be elaborated. Then, in later chapters, we shall look at the evidence *for* catastrophism and *against* uniformitarianism. Finally, this will lead to the concept of a relatively young earth, instead of a very ancient earth. Creation is not only the true scientific key to a true understanding of the world and its history, but also to an understanding of a rather recent creation at that.

As noted earlier, it is not possible scientifically to *prove* either evolution or creation. Neither is it possible to *prove* whether the earth and universe are old or young. One must exercise faith in whichever one he or she chooses to believe, and this is not ultimately a scientific decision.

We maintain, however, that faith in creation is a *reasonable* faith, based on sound evidence, whereas faith in evolution is a *credulous* faith, exercised against all evidence! The choice has eternal consequences, one way or the other, and we would urge our readers at least to consider the evidence.

---

[13] Thomas Henry Huxley, quoted in *Life and Letters of Thomas Henry Huxley*, ed. Leonard Huxley, vol. 2 (New York: Macmillan Co., 1903), p. 429.

Chapter 2

Evolution Does Not Occur in the Here and Now

We believe the creation model of origins correlates far better with scientific data than the evolution model. The evolution model suggests that natural processes can bring things into existence and organize them into more complex systems (innovation and integration). The creation model assumes that complex systems came into existence in the past and are being maintained as such in the present (conservation), except that if any "vertical" changes do take place, they necessarily must be in a "downward" rather than in an "upward" direction (disintegration).

In this chapter, we shall show that processes as they exist at present do not naturally "evolve" anything toward higher levels of organization. Things either remain at the same level, or go downhill toward disorganization, unless acted on by some outside organizer that itself had been organized previously (e.g., by human intelligence and skill). Always they bear witness to the principles of conservation or disintegration — not to naturalistic principles of innovation and integration. In other words, all existing processes support the creation model and testify against the evolution model.

In the next three chapters, we shall show that the records of past events give the same testimony. Then the chapter following that will show that the reason that there is no evidence of evolution in either the present or the past is because naturalistic evolution is impossible. The basic laws of all known natural science are laws of conservation and disintegration, exactly in accord with the creation model, and diametrically opposite to what would naturally be predicted from the evolution model.

The Classification of Biological Organisms Today

The obvious place to begin this comparison of model predictions is in the array of living plants and animals in the organic world today. This array is the present product of any past processes of evolution or creation, and so certainly should provide some clue to the nature of those processes.

However, to be truly objective at this point, we need to try as well as we can to empty our minds of any prior knowledge that we possess as to the characteristics of these organisms. We must try to make predictions strictly on the basis of the two models, and then, as it were, venture forth for the first time into the real world to find what is actually there!

The evolution model attempts to explain the entire organic assemblage in terms of natural descent from a common ancestor. Therefore the most obvious prediction from this model would seem to be that all such descendants should be essentially alike. Having come from the same ancestor by the same processes in the same world, there is no immediately apparent reason why any one of these descendant types should be different from any other.

It is not quite so simple, however. As the descendants multiply, they must necessarily occupy more space and, eventually, this space may become large enough to encompass more than one type of environment. Assuming that the hypothetical common ancestor somehow had the genetic capacity to vary from one individual to another (the origin of this variegated genetic "information" also needs to be explained, of course), then the gradually changing environments should elicit gradually diversifying descendants responding to those environments.

Therefore, the organic assemblage predicted by the evolution model need not be one of uniform sameness. However, it does seem that the model predicts at least a *continuum* of all forms of life. There exists a continuum of environments and a common ancestor and a common process of development. Therefore, there should be a continuum of organisms, and a classification system would be impossible.

That this is necessarily the fundamental prediction of the evolution model is obvious from the fact that the discrete gaps between the various kinds of organisms require further explanation. If there were no gaps, but only a continuum of organisms, no other explanation would be needed. Such a continuum, if it existed, would be properly considered an exceptionally clear evidence of past evolution.

The creation model, on the other hand, in its basic form, predicts that special creation, being purposive, would result in a discrete array of clear-cut distinct organisms, each with its own peculiar structure provided for its own particular functions. There would be many similarities, but also many differences. The creative process would have designed similar structures for similar functions and different structures for different functions. Since both fish and men would have need to see, for example, eyes would be provided for both; but fish would receive gills and men would receive lungs, corresponding to the particular environments in which they were created to function.

What, then, do we actually find in nature, a continuum of organisms, or an array of clear-cut kinds? Let the noted evolutionary geneticist Dobzhansky give the answer:

> If we assemble as many individuals living at a given time as we can, we notice at once that the observed variation does not form any kind of continuous distribution. Instead, a multitude of separate discrete distributions are found. In other words, the living world is not a single array of individuals in which any two variants are connected by unbroken series of intergrades, but an array of more or less distinctly separate arrays, intermediates between which are absent or rare.[1]

Professor Dobzhansky could well have ended this sentence with the words, "altogether absent." In the evolution model, similarities (whether in anatomy, embryology, blood chemistry, or whatever) are predicted on the basis of common ancestry. In the creation model, the same similarities are predicted on the basis of a common purposive designer. Gaps and differences are likewise predicted by the creation model as the product of purposive design. Gaps and differences are not predicted at all by the evolution model, except on the basis of subsidiary hypotheses that must be introduced for this specific purpose. Thus, the very existence of a science of taxonomy is a *prediction* of creationism and a *problem* to evolutionism.

The classification system which we still use today (variety, species, genus, family, order, class, phylum, kingdom) was long ago developed primarily by the great biologist Carolus Linnaeus. This system is found by modern biologists to apply effectively to all the extinct plants and animals in the fossil world (the categories did not evolve!) as well as those in the present world. It is very significant, therefore, that Linnaeus was a creationist, and was attempting to show

---

[1] Theodosius Dobzhansky, *Genetics and the Origin of Species* (New York: Columbia University Press, 1951), p. 3, 4. This book is one of the classics of neo-Darwinism.

that the Creator had organized all organisms into these distinct categories for His own purposes, with the very existence of the gaps — rather
than being an evolutionary "continuum" of organisms — serving clearly
as a testimony to His creative purpose for each type of creature.

Yet today we have the anti-creationist Niles Eldredge expressing
the following remarkably unwarranted assessment of this evidence:

> This hierarchy of life — the pattern of internested
> resemblances interlinking all organisms — was perhaps
> Darwin's best argument of all that life has evolved.[2]

One immediately notes that Dr. Eldredge in this evaluation speaks
of the "internested resemblances," but ignores the far more significant
differences. He does, however, at least acknowledge that even the
resemblances are good evidence for a common designer. They by no
means need to be explained by evolution from a common ancestor. Here
is what he says about that:

> Indeed, the only competing explanation for the order
> we see in the biological world, this pattern of nested
> similarity that links up absolutely all known forms of life,
> is the notion of Special Creation: that a supernatural Cre-
> ator, using a sort of blueprint, simply fashioned life with its
> intricate skein of resemblances passing through it. . . . And,
> of course, it was precisely this notion of divine Creation
> that furnished the explanation for all life — its very exist-
> ence, its exuberant diversity and its apparent order — in
> Darwin's day.[3]

A creationist could hardly have said it better. Then, when the
ubiquitous differences are brought into the discussion, these clear-cut
gaps between the categories (especially at the family level and higher),
this complete absence of an evolutionary "continuum" in the organic
realm becomes an all but compelling argument for creation. No wonder
Eldredge must acknowledge that the original systematic biologists, like
Linnaeus, were creationists:

> And though a few of these eighteenth-century sys-
> tematists had vaguely evolutionary notions, nearly all were
> devoutly and orthodoxly religious. They saw the order in
> their material, the grand pattern of similarity running

---

[2] Niles Eldredge, *Time Frames* (New York: Simon and Schuster, 1985), p. 45.
[3] *Ibid.*, p. 29.

through the entire organic realm, as evidence of God's plan of creation.[4]

This evidence, of course, is one of numerous reasons why many modern biologists are also returning to belief in creation.

One of these, in fact, was selected to write the foreword to the special Centennial Edition of Darwin's *Origin of Species*. In this connection, he said:

> Taking the taxonomic system as a whole, it appears as an orderly arrangement of clear-cut entities, which are clear-cut because they are separated by gaps. . . . The general tendency to eliminate, by means of unverifiable speculations, the limits of the categories nature presents to us, is the inheritance of biology from the *Origin of Species*. To establish the continuity required by theory, historical arguments are invoked, even though historical evidence is lacking. Thus are engendered those fragile towers of hypotheses based on hypotheses, where fact and fiction intermingle in an inextricable confusion.[5]

The author of this penetrating and perceptive analysis, Dr. W. R. Thompson, was for many years director of the Commonwealth Institute for Biological Control in Ottawa, Canada. As a very eminent and knowledgeable biologist, he deserved a far more respectful hearing than the evolutionary establishment was willing to give him. His facts, however, are indisputable.

The Unprogressive Nature of Biologic Change

Having considered the array of organisms, let us next consider the nature of the specific processes which have produced these organisms. Here we need to be more precise than merely to label them evolutionary processes or creative processes.

The evolution model should predict some sort of biologic process that impels simple organisms to advance into complex organisms. Particles have become molecules, and molecules have advanced to cells, and simple cells have progressed to become people. Though the process need not necessarily be continuous, since it has somehow presumably evolved particles into people, it must be there. As our hypothetical innocent scientist, entering for the first time into the real world, begins

---

[4] *Ibid.*, p. 33.

[5] W. R. Thompson, "Introduction" to *Origin of Species*, by Charles Darwin (New York: Everyman's Library, Dutton, 1956).

to study its biologic mechanisms, his evolution model would make him expect to observe in action some powerful and pervasive process whose pressures lead inexorably to great advances in complexity and order.

Nothing in the basic model would tell him whether this process operates slowly or rapidly. The actual tempo of evolution would be unknown at first, but it must at least be rapid enough to be observable — else, how could it produce such near-infinite results in finite time? Furthermore, if it is not observable, it is beyond the reach of the scientific method. Absence of such a process must then be considered *prima facie* evidence that evolution is not scientific. If it operated exclusively in the past and cannot be observed in the present, then it is essentially in the same logical category as creation.

We must realize, too, that this process must not be one that merely shuffles things around at the same level, or one that may even lower the level of order and complexity. To account for the supposed development of all things from a common ancestor — say a protozoan or simpler organism — it must be essentially a process that insistently *increases* order and complexity. If we do find such a process clearly and regularly operating in the real world of experimental observation, it can rightly be considered as strong evidence for evolution.

The creation model predicts, on the other hand, that no such process will be observed at all. Since it presupposes that creation of all the basic kinds — including man, the most complex of all — was a completed event of the past, it says explicitly that no natural process of evolutionary development from a simpler kind of organism to a more complex kind of organism can be observed operating today.

On this test, the facts clearly favor the creation model. All biologists know that biological processes today are not producing more highly developed kinds. Actually, they used to call the fact that "like produces like" the biogenetic law.

Different varieties of plants and animals, at the same level of complexity, can easily be developed, either naturally or artificially, but that's all. Sometimes, evolutionists call this phenomenon "micro-evolution," giving the impression that with enough time, it could become "macro-evolution," but this is either wishful thinking or intentional deception. Not the slightest evidence exists that this has ever happened or ever could happen. Therefore, the process should be called, simply, "horizontal variation," or "recombination," at the same level of complexity (e.g., change in color), but should not be termed evolution.

It therefore seems clear that, contrary to Darwin's conception, most of the genetic variation in populations arises not from new mutations at each generation but from the reshuffling of previously accumulated mutations by recombination. Although mutation is the ultimate source of all genetic variation, it is a relatively rare event, providing a mere trickle of new alleles into the much larger reservoir of stored genetic variation. Indeed recombination alone is sufficient to enable a population to expose its hidden variation for many generations without the need for new genetic input by mutation.[6]

Although the author of the above quotation is one of the nation's leading geneticists and a strong anti-creationist, his statement that the phenomenon of variation (or micro-evolution, as some would call it) is normally just recombination of existing genetic attributes is unintentionally confirming an implication of the creation model. A great deal of variation can take place in a species merely by reshuffling genes. *Mutations* (and we shall discuss these shortly) are necessary for real evolution, but these are very rare.

The creation model stresses conservation of the completed creation, and this implies that the Creator would initially build into each created genome a wide range of variability, enabling the specific creature to adapt to a significantly large range of environments without becoming extinct. That is, the phenomenon of "adaptation," often cited as evidence of evolution, is in reality evidence of conservation, rather than evolution. As two recent authors have recognized:

Although Darwinism is often declared to be dead, it refuses to lie down. Darwin did, however, mislead his audience in one way: his best-known work is much more about the origin of adaptations than of species. Since then, there has been much more progress in understanding the causes of adaptive change than of the mechanisms whereby new species are generated.[7]

The wide range of variability available in the population is also indicated as follows by Ayala:

In any case there can be no doubt that the staggering amount of genetic variation in natural populations provides

---

[6] Francisco Ayala, "The Mechanisms of Evolution," *Scientific American*, vol. 239 (September 1978), p. 63. Ayala is a leading modern neo-Darwinian biologist.

[7] J. A. Coyne and N. H. Barton, "What Do We Know about Speciation?" *Nature*, vol. 331 (February 11, 1988), p. 485.

ample opportunities for evolution to occur. Hence it is not surprising that whenever a new environmental challenge materializes — a change of climate, the introduction of a new predator, man-made pollution — populations are usually able to adapt to it.[8]

Ayala used the term "opportunities for evolution," but it would be better to call it simply "adaptation," or, still better, "conservation."

No matter how much variation and adaptation may occur, the change is always "horizontal" at best, and the species remains the same species. In fact, as Gould and other paleontologists have shown, the species seems to remain in a condition of "stasis," or evolutionary stagnation, through a thousand generations or more, even through periods of traumatic environmental change.

Some consider the phenomenon of polyploidy (the sudden doubling or quadrupling of genes in the chromosome) to be an example of speciation. At most, however, no new basic type is generated. Polyploidy applies almost exclusively to plants, and no "new" genes are produced by this process. Most books on evolution do not even mention it. When they do, it is usually called "variation." It clearly contributes nothing to the overall evolutionary history of life.

Moreover, because species often maintain stability through such intense climatic change as glacial cycling, stasis must be viewed as an active phenomenon, not a passive response to unaltered environments.[9]

It does seem remarkable that "stasis" (meaning "remaining unchanged") is now considered by many leading evolutionists to be the key factor in evolution, which process one would think meant "change" if it means anything.

Stasis, as palpable and observable in virtually all cases (whereas rapid punctuations are usually, but not always, elusive), becomes the major empirical ground for studying punctuated equilibrium.[10]

This is fascinating! According to the punctuationist school of thought among evolutionists, the actual evolutionary advances occur

---

[8] Ayala, "The Mechanisms of Evolution," p. 64.

[9] Stephen Jay Gould and Niles Eldredge, "Punctuated Equilibrium Comes of Age," *Nature*, vol. 366 (November 18, 1993), p. 223.

[10] *Ibid.* See chapter 5 for further discussion of stasis.

during the "punctuations" in the equilibrium of a species. But since these are rarely observable (actually, *none* have been observed so far), the mechanism of evolution must be studied by researching the phenomenon of evolutionary stagnation, or *no* evolution. Remarkable!

The creationist is quite comfortable, of course, with the phenomenon of stasis, for that is actually what his model predicts. He is also comfortable with the very rare (actually non-existent) observation of evolutionary jumps, because this also is as expected. One could surely be justified in taking all this discussion of stasis and punctuations as a sort of grudging (or unconscious?) acknowledgment of the validity of creationism.

> The orthodoxy, as is well known, advocated the fixity of species and acts of special creation — the first can be considered as an extreme form of stasis, the latter of jumps. Whereas Darwin himself hinted at the phenomenological similarity between special creation and evolutionary jumps, the implication of this similarity between stasis and the fixity of species should also be considered in the discussion of the development of his theory.[11]

How sad for Charles Darwin! After receiving the adulation of multitudes of followers because he had provided a supposedly scientific alternative to the Creator, explaining the naturalistic origin of species without God, it turns out that the more advanced of his followers have gone full cycle, returning again to the arguments of the creationists, while not yet realizing that that is what they have done. All of Darwin's evidences turn out to be descriptions of creative adaptation, not origin.

> Darwin, it has now become commonplace to acknowledge, never really addressed the "origin of species" in his book of that title.[12]

The Twilight of Natural Selection

Not only did Darwin fail to cite any actual case of the origin of a new species by natural selection (in fact, he couldn't because there haven't been any), but his proposed mechanism for doing this — natural selection — is now usually acknowledged to be tautologous as a supposed explanation for evolution. Its real value turns out to be as a conservative mechanism to keep species as they are, not allowing them

---

[11] Mirko Majer, "Evolution Again," *Nature*, vol. 320 (March 6, 1986), p. 10.

[12] Niles Eldredge, "Progress in Evolution?" *New Scientist*, vol. 110 (June 5, 1986), p. 55.

to deteriorate and then become extinct.

For many years, creationists have been pointing out the logical fallacy involved in attributing evolution to natural selection, stressing the inherently tautologous nature of the whole concept. That is, natural selection was supposed to insure "the survival of the fittest," but the only pragmatic way to define "the fittest" is "those who survive." Thus, the long neck of the giraffe and the short neck of the hippopotamus are both explicable by natural selection, as are both the dull coloration of the peppered moth and the brilliant colors of the bird of paradise. Natural selection "explains" everything, and, therefore, really *explains* nothing!

Creationists had posed a similar objection to the evolutionist's concept of "adaptation." The fact that a particular organism is adapted to its environment tells us nothing whatever about how it *became* adapted. Any organisms not so adapted would not have survived, but this constitutes no proof that the adaptations were produced by evolution. Creationists have never objected to the idea of natural selection as a mechanism for eliminating the unfit, non-adapted organisms. As a matter of fact, creationists long before Darwin were advocating natural selection as a *conservation* principle. The creationist Edward Blyth wrote on this subject at least 24 years before Darwin; and Loren Eiseley, a prominent modern evolutionist, has asserted that Darwin got the whole idea from Blyth. However, evolutionist Stephen Jay Gould has pointed out that *many* earlier creationists held similar views.

> Darwinians cannot simply claim that natural selection operates[,] since everyone, including Paley and the natural theologians, advocated selection as a device for removing unfit individuals at both extremes and preserving, intact and forever, the created type.[13]

> Failure to recognize that all creationists accepted selection in this negative role led Eiseley to conclude falsely that Darwin has "borrowed" the principle of natural selection from his predecessor E. Blyth. The Reverend William Paley's classic work *Natural Theology*, published in 1803, also contains many references to selective elimination.[14]

As a screening device for eliminating the unfit, natural selection is

---

[13] Stephen Jay Gould, "Darwinism and the Expansion of Evolutionary Theory," *Science*, vol. 216 (April 23, 1982), p. 380.

[14] *Ibid.*, p. 386.

a valid concept, and, in fact, represents the Creator's plan for preventing harmful mutations from affecting and even destroying the entire species. And that is *all* it does! Yet evolutionists, especially Darwinians and neo-Darwinians, have long insisted that it somehow "creates" new, better adapted, more fit species.

Creationists have often pointed out that the one concept that Darwin's book *The Origin of Species by Natural Selection* did *not* discuss was the origin of species by natural selection! Darwin's evidences had to do with *varieties*, not *species*, and all else was conjecture. The leading British evolutionist Colin Patterson has pointed out:

> No one has ever produced a species by mechanisms of natural selection. No one has ever gotten near it and most of the current argument in neo-Darwinism is about this question.[15]

This "current argument in neo-Darwinism," interestingly enough, is merely echoing the arguments against neo-Darwinism that have been advanced by creationists for many years. Evolutionist Gould says this:

> The essence of Darwinism lies in a single phrase: Natural selection is the creative force of evolutionary change. No one denies that selection will play a negative role in eliminating the unfit. Darwinian theories require that it create the fit as well.[16]

Herein, of course, we encounter the impotence of natural selection not only to *produce* the fit, but even to *define* the fit! Any definition is bound to be tautologous, definition in a circle.

Now it is remarkable that in the 20 years preceeding 1995 practically all biologists have come to acknowledge this fact of redundancy. Natural selection is a force that somehow causes the survivors to survive. It enables those who adapt to adapt. Those who leave the most surviving descendants are the fittest to leave surviving descendants.

> One of the most frequent objections against the theory of natural selection is that it is a sophisticated tautology. Most evolutionary biologists seem unconcerned about the

---

[15] Colin Patterson, "Cladistics," Interview on British Broadcasting Corporation television program on March 4, 1982; producer, Brian Leek; Interviewer, Peter Franz. Patterson is senior paleontologist at the British Museum of Natural History.

[16] Stephen Jay Gould, "The Return of Hopeful Monsters," *Natural History*, vol. 86 (June/July 1977), p. 28.

charge and only make a token effort to explain the tautology away. The remainder, such as Professors Waddington and Simpson, will simply concede the fact. For them, natural selection is a tautology which states a heretofore unrecognized relation: The fittest — defined as those who will leave the most offspring — will leave the most offspring.

What is most unsettling is that some evolutionary biologists have no qualms about proposing tautologies as explanations. One would immediately reject any lexicographer who tried to define a word by the same word, or a thinker who merely restated his proposition, or any other instance of gross redundancy; yet no one seems scandalized that men of science should be satisfied with a major principle which is no more than a tautology.[17]

The brilliant writer and vitalist philosopher Arthur Koestler has incisively described the quandary of the evolutionists — now widely acknowledged, but still mostly ignored:

> Once upon a time, it all looked so simple. Nature rewarded the fit with the carrot of survival and punished the unfit with the stick of extinction. The trouble only started when it came to defining fitness. . . . Thus natural selection looks after the survival and reproduction of the fittest, and the fittest are those which have the highest rate of reproduction, . . . we are caught in a circular argument which completely begs the question of what makes evolution evolve.[18]

Evolutionary literature is filled with marvelous stories of how organisms came to be so well adapted to their environments. These "just-so-stories," these fairy tales for intellectuals, are, of course, pure imagination. No evolutionist can predict the course of future evolution, but he delights in "retrodicting" the wonders of past evolution! The reader of such tales should always take them *cum grano salis*.

Paleontologists (and evolutionary biologists in general) are famous for their facility in devising plausible

---

[17] Gregory Alan Pesely, "The Epistemological Status of Natural Selection," *Laval Theologique et Philosophique*, vol. 38 (February 1982), p. 74.

[18] Arthur Koestler, *Janus: A Summing Up* (New York: Vintage Books, 1978), p. 170.

stories; but they often forget that plausible stories need not be true.[19]

All one can learn about the history of life is learned from systematics, from groupings one finds in nature. The rest of it is story-telling of one sort or another. We have access to the tips of a tree; the tree itself is theory and people who pretend to know about the tree and to describe what went on with it, how the branches came off and the twigs came off are, I think, telling stories.[20]

Nevertheless, as Koestler points out, even though the whole fabric of Darwinian and neo-Darwinian natural selection, as an explanation of evolution, is today in shreds, most intellectuals continue to hold it as an article of faith.

In the meantime, the educated public continues to believe that Darwin has provided all the relevant answers by the magic formula of random mutations plus natural selection — quite unaware of the fact that random mutations turned out to be irrelevant and natural selection a tautology.[21]

In the meantime, if one is interested in reading a thorough critique, sound both scientifically and epistemologically, of natural selection as a causative and explanatory factor in evolution, the analysis of Professor R. H. Brady, of Ramapo College, is recommended.[22] Norman Macbeth, the Harvard lawyer whose 1971 book *Darwin Retried* was itself (even though not supporting creationism) a devastating critique of neo-Darwinism, says that one of Brady's papers "seemed to me to utterly destroy the entire idea of natural selection as presently conceived."[23]

Despite all the evidence, however, there are still some ardent defenders of the Darwinian faith in gradual evolution through natural

---

[19] Stephen Jay Gould et al., "The Shape of Evolution: A Comparison of Real and Random Clades," *Paleobiology*, vol. 3, no. 1 (1977), p. 34.

[20] Patterson, "Cladistics." Patterson is a leading exponent of the new science of cladistics, which attempts to categorize plants and animals without reference to any evolutionary histories.

[21] Koestler, *Janus: A Summing Up*, p. 185.

[22] Ronald H. Brady, "Dogma and Doubt," *Biological Journal of the Linnaean Society*, vol. 17 (February 1982), p. 79-96.

[23] Norman Macbeth, "Darwinism: A Time for Funerals," interviewed in *Towards*, vol. 2 (Spring 1982), p. 18. The title has reference to the author's conviction that Darwinism and neo-Darwinism will die as soon as their older advocates die.

selection. Some of the most influential of these still-living neo-Darwinists are Ernst Mayr and Edward Wilson at Harvard, Michael Ruse in Canada, and Richard Dawkins in England.

These men and others have published very articulate and persuasive books, especially pointing out the inadequacies of the various proposed saltational and punctuated equilibrium evolutionary mechanisms as proposed by Gould and others. They have also developed some clever analogies and computer simulations, purporting to show how mutations and natural selection might possibly work to generate new species.

The fact remains, however, when one scrutinizes their writings carefully, they still have not provided any *real* evidence of *real* macroevolution, that is, of one species producing a *new* species. Just like Darwin's book, their own books fail to cite any examples of genuinely new and higher species being produced by natural selection. If anyone doubts this, he should just look and see for himself. True macroevolution simply is not occurring today, anywhere in the world, and no computer simulation, clever analogy, or imaginative just-so-story can produce one.

The Wistful Search for Good Mutations

We don't hear as much about genetic mutations today as we used to, though they remain the best hope for a genuine evolutionary mechanism. The problem is that all *observed* mutations seem to be an embarrassment to evolutionists, not an asset. The problem is, that in accordance with the creation model, they all seem to produce "devolution" instead of evolution. As noted before, Ayala acknowledges that fact thus:

> Although mutation is the ultimate source of all genetic variation, it is a relatively rare event.[24]

Mutations are rare, indeed. Even Richard Dawkins, as doctrinaire a neo-Darwinian as there is in the whole world, says:

> In real life, the probability that a gene will mutate [that is, in one generation] is often less than one in a million.[25]

Dawkins' reference to "real life" is in the context of his computer

---

[24] Ayala, "The Mechanisms of Evolution," p. 63.
[25] Richard Dawkins, "Creation and Natural Selection," *New Scientist*, vol. 111 (September 1986), p. 37.

simulations of the mutation/selection process, which led to his famous book *The Blind Watchmaker*. For these studies, he imposed a mutation rate of one each generation instead of one in a million generations, in order to speed up the process. He then had to *assume* that the mutation in each generation would be beneficial and, therefore, would be preserved through succeeding generations.

But if mutations are really rare, good mutations are very, very, very rare! Furthermore, they are quite random in their occurrence, in no way trying to respond to some specific "need" of the organism.

> A mutation can be considered an error in the replication of DNA prior to its translation into protein.[26]

> The forces that give rise to gene mutations operate at random in the sense that genetic mutations occur without reference to their future adaptiveness in the environment.[27]

Random errors, especially in an efficiently functioning organism, would not make it better or more complex. A "beneficial" mutation, even if natural selection is there waiting to conserve one if it comes along, is simply a figment of the evolutionary imagination. None has yet been documented in "real life" — that is, a mutation beneficial to the creature experiencing it. Even if one does occur in, say, every millionth generation, it would not mean much. The same mutation would probably have to occur simultaneously in the "mate" of the organism before it could hope to spread through the population. And that's only *one* mutation in *one* gene. To produce real evolution in a real animal, there would have to be *multitudes* of such preserved beneficial mutations. The concept seems merely to be a commentary on the intense desire of evolutionists to avoid the Creator.

For at least a half-century evolutionists were supremely confident. The "evolutionary synthesis" promulgated by such leaders as Sir Julian Huxley, George Gaylord Simpson, Theodosius Dobzhansky, Ernst Mayr, J. B. S. Haldane, G. Ledyard Stebbins, Sewall Wright, Glen L. Jepsen, and others of similar stature, seemed to have solved all the major problems. The fossil record (allegedly) proved the *fact* of evolution, while mutations and natural selection (supposedly) provided the *mechanism*.

Creationists, however, kept on insisting that the fossil record showed no intermediate evolving forms, that natural selection was

---

[26] Ayala, "The Mechanisms of Evolution," p. 58.
[27] *Ibid.*, p. 59.

impotent and tautologous, and that mutations were all either neutral, harmful, or lethal, so that evolution still was based on no real evidence, either in the past or present. These cogent, scientific arguments were all simply ignored!

But now all this has changed. A new wave of evolutionists has appeared, and these younger scientists are now using all the old creationist arguments themselves — not questioning evolution, of course (*that* is sacrosanct!) — but seeking to change the standard evidences. The fossil sequences have largely given way to protein sequences, and the Darwinian mechanisms (mutations and natural selection) are now being superseded by hopeful monsters and random chance.

The neo-Darwinists are not giving up easily, however, and the waters of the evolutionary sea have become very turbulent.

Neo-Darwinism, of course, concluded that random mutations in the genetic systems of organisms provided the basic materials on which natural selection could act to produce new, better-equipped species. The problem, repeatedly emphasized by creationists, was that mutations are neutral or harmful, not helpful. At least that is true of all known mutations. Evolutionary theory regarding past mutations tends to ignore or denigrate this fact, but it is always emphasized when dealing with environmental hazards that might cause present-day mutations. Many years ago, the Environmental Mutagenic Society made a detailed study of this subject and concurred that mutations should *always* be avoided if possible.

> Most mutations producing effects large enough to be observed are deleterious. . . . Furthermore, the wide variety of mechanisms by which radiations and chemicals induce mutations make it very unlikely that generalized schemes can be devised to protect against mutagens, except by avoiding them in the first place.[28]

The exact nature of gene mutations is still somewhat obscure, since the exact nature of different genes is still somewhat controversial. Whatever it is, however, a mutation represents an unpredictable — evidently random — change in an extremely complex genetic programmed system. Since the program is inadvertently changed, it is essentially a *mistake* in the transmission of genetic information, as noted before.

---

[28] Environmental Mutagenic Society, "Environmental Mutagenic Hazards," *Science*, vol. 187 (February 14, 1975), p. 503.

Being an error process, mutation consists of all possible changes in the genetic material (excluding recombination and segregation).[29]

The Society therefore recommended — as have practically all other scientists — that everything feasible be done to eliminate radiations and mutagenic chemicals from the environment.

Since the vast majority of detectable mutations are deleterious, an artificially increased human mutation rate would be expected to be harmful in proportion to the increase.[30]

Evolutionists are always careful to say that only the "vast majority" of mutations are harmful, leaving open the possibility that some just might be beneficial. The possibilities are exceedingly limited, however.

From the standpoint of population genetics, positive Darwinian selection represents a process whereby advantageous mutants spread through the species. Considering their great importance in evolution, it is perhaps surprising that well-established cases are so scarce; for example, industrial melanisms in moths and increases of DDT resistance in insects are constantly being cited.[31]

As a matter of fact, however, neither of the cases cited is a true mutation. Industrial melanism in moths is simply a recombination of genetic factors already present, and the same is true of the insects.

Insect resistance to a pesticide was first reported in 1947 for the housefly (*Musca domestica*) with respect to DDT. Since then the resistance to pesticides has been reported in at least 225 species of insects and other arthropods. The genetic variants required for resistance to the most diverse kinds of pesticides were apparently present in every one of the populations exposed to these man-made compounds.[32]

The mention of industrial melanism in moths refers to the famous

[29] *Ibid.*, p. 504.
[30] *Ibid.*, p. 512.
[31] Motoo Kimura, "Population Genetics and Molecular Evolution," *Johns Hopkins Medical Journal*, vol. 138 (June 1976), p. 260.
[32] Ayala, "The Mechanisms of Evolution," p. 63.

peppered moth in England, often considered to be the classic example of "evolution in action" today. The story is found in practically every biology textbook, about how the light-colored moth evolved into a dark-colored moth with the advancing industrial revolution and the soot-darkening landscape. But most books do not give the updated version.

> The peppered moth, *Biston betularia*, is a classic example of natural selection in action. As the dark satanic mills blackened the English landscape, the dominant form of the peppered moth changed from light to dark, a case of industrial melanism. Since the Clean Air Acts came into force, industrial pollution has declined. A new study by Sir Cyril Clarke and his associates shows that the light form of the peppered moth has become much more common.[33]

This change, just like that of the insects responding to the pesticide, was not evolution at all, but conservation! The species has an inbuilt genetic potential to vary in color, with both light and dark moths always present in the population, enabling the population as a whole to shift its dominant coloration in response to environmental changes.

No mutations were involved at all, but simply recombinations of genetic inheritances at most, as involved regularly in all species. Mutational changes would take far longer to become fixed in a population than this shifting back and forth of genes already present.

> The first black specimen of *Biston betularia* was caught in Manchester in 1848. By 1895, 98 per cent of the moths in the area were dark, an extremely rapid change given that the peppered moth breeds just once a year.[34]

Because of all these problems, more and more evolutionists are realizing that ordinary mutations, as actually observed in nature, are *not at all adequate* to provide the basis for evolution. Neither will it do to suppose that very small, non-observable mutations, gradually accumulating over long periods of time, could do the job.

> Bacteria, the study of which has formed a great part of the foundation of genetics and molecular biology, are the organisms which, because of their huge numbers,

---

[33] Jeremy Cherfas, "Clean Air Revives the Peppered Moth," *New Scientist*, vol. 109 (January 2, 1986), p. 17., quoting Biological Journal of the Linnaean Society, vol. 26, p. 189.

[34] *Ibid.*

produce the most mutants . . . bacteria, despite their great production of intra-specific varieties, exhibit a great fidelity to their species. The bacillus *Echerichia coli*, whose mutants have been studied very carefully, is the best example. The reader will agree that it is surprising, to say the least, to want to prove evolution and to discover its mechanisms and then to choose as a material for this study a being which practically stabilized a billion years ago.[35]

The same is true of the organism whose mutants have probably been studied more than any other.

The fruit-fly (*Drosophila melanogaster*), the favorite pet insect of the geneticists, whose geographical, biotopical, urban, and rural genotypes are now known inside out, seems not to have changed since the remotest times.[36]

The author of the above evaluations, Pierre Grassé, is not a creationist and, in fact, as France's leading zoologist, held the Chair of Evolution at the Sorbonne (France's leading university) for over 20 years. His opinion of mutations as an explanatory cause of evolution is summarized below:

The opportune appearance of mutations permitting animals and plants to meet their needs seems hard to believe. Yet the Darwinian theory is even more demanding: a single plant, a single animal would require thousands and thousands of lucky, appropriate events. Thus, miracles would become the rule: events with an infinitesimal probability could not fail to occur. . . . There is no law against day-dreaming, but science must not indulge in it.[37]

This is surely an insightful evaluation, and Grassé's fellow-evolutionists would do well to pay attention to it. Mutations and natural selection must have been energized by a continuous succession of miracles if they really do constitute the explanation of evolution. It is small wonder that the new school of evolutionists is strenuously searching for a better explanation.

Yet, despite this knowledge, such an influential evolutionary

---

[35] Pierre P. Grassé, *Evolution of Living Organisms* (New York: Academic Press, 1977), p. 87.
[36] *Ibid.*, p. 130.
[37] *Ibid.*, p. 103.

spokesman as Stephen Jay Gould still considers the variations produced on such organisms as the fruit fly to be the first of the three best kinds of evidence for evolution.

> Our confidence in the fact of evolution rests upon copious data that fall, roughly, into three great classes. First, we have the direct evidence of small-scale changes in controlled laboratory experiments of the past hundred years (on bacteria, on almost every measurable property of the fruit fly *Drosophila*), or observed in nature (color changes in moth wings, development of metal tolerance in plants growing near industrial waste heaps), or produced during a few thousand years of human breeding and agriculture.[38]

These phenomena are nothing but normal variations, however, having nothing to do with real evolution. Biologists may like to call them "micro-evolution," but Gould is out of character citing them as evidence for macro-evolution. He and his fellow punctuationists have persistently argued that micro-evolution is "de-coupled" from macro-evolution, the first never becomes the second!

In regard to the multitude of experiments that have been performed on the fruit-fly, the comments of Jeremy Rifkin, who is an anti-Darwinian evolutionist, are cogent:

> The fruit fly has long been the favorite object of mutation experiments because of its fast gestation period (twelve days). X-rays have been used to increase the mutation rate in the fruit fly 15,000 percent. All in all, scientists have been able to "catalyze the fruit fly evolutionary process such that what has been seen to occur in *Drosophila* (fruit fly) is the equivalent of many millions of years of normal mutations and evolution." Even with this tremendous speed-up of mutations, scientists have never been able to come up with anything other than another fruit fly.[39]

These fruit-fly experiments, conducted now for many years in many labs all over the world, not only have never produced anything other than fruit flies, but have not even been able to generate a better fruit

---

[38] Stephen Jay Gould, "Darwinism Defined: The Difference between Fact and Theory," *Discover* (January 1987), p. 65.

[39] Jeremy Rifkin, *Algeny* (New York: Viking Press, 1983), p. 134.

fly! All the mutant varieties so generated have been either lethal, harmful, or neutral in any presumed struggle for existence in nature.

Summarizing this type of present-day so-called "evolution in action," some of the studies (e.g., peppered moth) are nothing but confirmation of the "conservation" implications of the creation model. Others (e.g., fruit flies) confirm the "deterioration" implications of the creation model. None of the studies relate in any degree whatever to true macro-evolution, which is the only point at issue between creationists and evolutionists. Instead they are all beautiful evidences in support of the basic stability of created organisms. These fruit flies have all either remained essentially the same as created in the beginning or else disintegrated and sometimes become extinct, in exact conformance with the definition of the creation model.

Imperfections as Evolution

The second of Gould's three prime evidences for evolution has to do with the fossil record, which will be shown in the next chapter to be much better understood also in terms of the creation model. His third evidence can be considered here. It is the most bizarre of all; yet he considers it the most important of all:

> Third, and most persuasive in its ubiquity, we have the signs of history preserved within every organism, every ecosystem, and every pattern of biogeographic distribution, by those persuasive quirks, oddities, and imperfections that record pathways of historical descent.[40]

Gould's reasoning here is that, if there were a Creator, He would have made everything "perfect," so evidence of imperfections in plants and animals (not even to mention moral imperfections in human beings) indicates that they must have come about by evolution instead of creation.

Not many other evolutionists have picked up on this particular "evidence," for obvious reasons. They have been accustomed to arguing ever since Darwin that the marvelous "adaptations" of organisms to their environments is a strong evidence of the effectiveness of natural selection. Gould, however, sounds almost like a creationist when he deals with this evidence (lest anyone misunderstand, however, he is decidedly *not* a creationist!).

> The order of life and the persistence of nearly all basic anatomical designs throughout the entire geological

---

[40] Gould, "Darwinism Defined," p. 68.

history of multi-cellular animals record the intricacy and resistance to change of complex development programs, not the perfection of adaptive design in local environments.[41]

For a hundred years and more, the remarkable adaptations of organisms to their environment have been considered to be strong indicators of the efficiency of "natural selection." The supposed selection of favorable variations, provided by random beneficial mutations is the essence of Darwinism, and especially of neo-Darwinism, and has long been accepted by most evolutionists as the basic mechanism through which new species evolve. In fact, the reason for Darwin's success in the first place was that his theory seemed to provide a mechanism for explaining away the apparent evidences of design in nature. The remarkable relations of plants and animals to each other and to their environments has often been presented in ecstatic language as proof of the marvelous ability of natural selection. Actually, as already noted, many recent evolutionists have admitted that the very concept of natural selection as an agent of "evolution" is unscientific tautology. Those organisms that "survive" are *assumed* to have been the "fittest" by that fact.

Creationists, of course, have always argued that, while natural selection is a real process that serves to eliminate unfit organisms, it could never create the complex, wonderfully adapted organisms found in the living world. As noted above, Stephen Jay Gould has recently acknowledged that even William Paley, the great Christian advocate of design and "natural theology," taught *this* type of natural selection more than half a century before Darwin.[42] Creationists have argued persuasively that complex adaptations are evidence of creative design, not of chance variations, and Gould has even admitted this. The British scientist Jeremy Cherfas has recently echoed Gould's thesis as follows:

> In fact, as Darwin recognized, a perfect Creator could manufacture perfect adaptations. Everything would fit because everything was designed to fit.[43]

This admission, however, does not mean at all that Gould or Cherfas or their fellow evolutionists have decided actually to believe in

---

[41] Stephen J. Gould, "Through a Glass, Darkly," *Natural History* (September 1989), p. 24.

[42] Stephen Jay Gould, *Science* (April 23, 1982), p. 386.

[43] Jeremy Cherfas, *New Scientist* (May 17, 1984), p. 29.

creative design. They have simply decided that adaptations do not prove evolution after all.

> It is in the imperfect adaptations that natural selection is revealed, because it is those imperfections that show us that structure has a history. If there were no imperfections, there would be no evidence of history, and therefore nothing to favor evolution by natural selection over creation.[44]

This is an amazing admission! The main evidence against creation and for evolution is that natural selection does not work! If there were no "imperfect" structures in nature, all the evidence would favor creation. No wonder evolution has to be imposed by authority and bombast, rather than by reason, if this is its only real evidence!

As a matter of fact, this argument from imperfections is merely a new wrinkle on the old discredited argument from vestigial organs. These are structures that were believed to have atrophied from once-useful structures to useless vestiges. S. R. Scadding, of the Zoology Department at Guelph University, comments on this argument thus:

> Haeckel makes clear why this line of argument was of such importance to early evolutionary biologists. . . . It seemed difficult to explain functionless structures on the basis of special creation without imputing some lack of skill in design to the Creator.[45]

Actually, there are probably no real vestigial organs, and probably no imperfect adaptations in nature. Scadding points out that the former list of nearly 100 such organs in humans has now dwindled to almost nothing.[46] The same could be shown for most of Gould's alleged "imperfections." But even if there really are any vestiges or imperfections, this would be evidence for degeneration, not for evolution.

It should be perfectly obvious that "imperfections" are an extraordinarily weak evidence for evolution. They are, instead, explicit confirmations of one of the two basic descriptors of the creation model — namely, that any "vertical" changes in the originally created organisms would be "downward" changes from their original forms.

Gould is right in inferring that an omnipotent, omniscient Creator would create perfect creations in the beginning. Each creature would be created with structures perfectly designed for its created environment.

---

[44] *Ibid.*

[45] S. R. Scadding, *Evolutionary Theory* (May 1981), p. 174.

[46] *Ibid*, p. 175.

This does not mean, however, that there would never be later changes in either the environment or the organism or both. The creation model simply states that, *if* such changes occur, they will necessarily be in the direction of imperfection. One cannot improve perfection!

Thus, whatever "imperfections" may exist in present-day organisms, they are *not* evidence of evolution but of deterioration. Many such changes have even led to atrophy and extinction, but this is precisely the opposite of evolution!

The greater marvel is that so few imperfections do exist. The Creator's conservation measures have enabled organisms to adapt to a wide variety of changing environments, and it is difficult to find any structure in any plant or animal that is not beautifully equipped to function at least adequately in fulfilling its purpose.

Neither adaptations nor imperfections speak of evolution, but, rather, of primeval creation followed by conservation supplemented occasionally by deterioration or extinction, exactly in accord with the creation model!

Chapter 3

Evolution Never Occurred in the Long Ago

Professor Pierre Grassé of the famous Sorbonne University in Paris, once recognized as Europe's leading zoologist, was convinced that evolution had stopped in the present age.

The evolution of all zoological groups was initially highly productive, then slowed down and is now restricted to the creation of new species.[1]

Grassé was editor of the 28-volume encyclopedia *Traite de Zoologie*, and he taught the courses on evolution at the Sorbonne, yet he believed that evolution was limited today to ordinary variation and possibly speciation, exactly as we have shown in the preceding chapter. The great evolutionary advances had all occurred in the past, according to him, and could now be seen only in the fossils.

Naturalists must remember that the process of evolution is revealed only through fossil forms . . . only paleontology can provide them with the evidence of evolution and reveal its course or mechanisms.[2]

The fossil record has long been considered as the main evidence for evolution. As noted in the preceding chapter, Gould considered it to be one of the three arguments for proofs of evolution: the first being the

---

[1] Pierre Grassé, *Evolution of Living Organisms* (New York: Academic Press, 1977), p. 82.
[2] *Ibid.*, p. 4.

small changes of the present (which Grassé thought were trivial), and the third the imperfections in organisms (an anomalous type of evidence, which seemed to occur mainly to Gould). With respect to the fossil record, Gould maintained this conclusion:

> Second, we have direct evidence for large-scale changes, based upon sequences in the fossil record.[3]

In this chapter, therefore, we shall look in some depth at this supposedly definitive evidence of evolution.

Fossils: the Alleged Proof of Evolution

Obviously, the fossil record is the most important test of the two models, especially of evolution. Since vast spans of geologic time have been found necessary to allow evolutionary changes of significance, the question of what actually did happen in ancient eras is of primary importance.

The creation model, of course, must predict that the array of organisms preserved as fossils will correspond to the same classification system as applicable to present-day plants and animals. Since all the basic categories (species, genera, families, etc.) were created in the beginning, these categories must have persisted relatively unchanged ever since and into the present, with the exception of any that may have become extinct. Therefore, essentially the same kingdoms, phyla, classes, orders, etc., would apply to *fossil* classification, as apply to *modern* classification. The same sorts of "gaps" between different kinds of organisms in the present world would be anticipated in the fossils.

The creation model does not preclude extinction of types of plants or animals, any more than it precludes the death of individuals, but it does preclude the development of entirely new types from older types, either in the present or in the past. Therefore, it predicts that there will be no true transitional forms, from one type into another type, found in the fossil record. There may well be many variations within types, including transitions from one variety to another variety, and possibly from one species to another, but no true transitional intermediates from one basic type to another. It predicts that, whenever a new type of plant or animal first appears in the fossils, it will already be a fully typical representative of that type.

These are rather rigid constraints that we have placed on the creationist predictions, and they ought to give a clear indication as to its probable validity. No preliminary forms, no transitional forms, clear

---

[3] S. J. Gould, "Darwinism Defined," *Discover*, vol. 8 (January 1987), p. 68.

gaps between types, same taxonomic categories as at present, etc., — all of which are *explicitly different* from the predictions of evolution.

That is, if evolution is true, and if all organisms really have gradually developed from one or a few primeval, simple ancestral forms during the geologic ages, then the evidence for that development ought to be found in the fossil record of the past if it is found anywhere. There must have been many preliminary forms, and there must have been many transitional forms, and there should be at least a statistical sampling of these preserved in the fossils.

Though some gaps certainly are to be expected, because of the accidental nature both of fossilization and of fossil discoveries, such gaps should at least be randomly distributed between the present kinds of animals and the transitional forms. Gaps in the fossil record should not be the same kinds of gaps as those in the present taxonomic system, and there should be many true transitional intermediates found as fossils — if the evolution model has any value as a predictive system.

In fact, if evolution is true, even the basic taxonomic categories should have been evolving, and there should be evidence of these changes in the fossils.

That these predictions are the obvious and basic predictions of the evolution model can be appreciated if one stops to imagine what the reaction would be if real transitional forms were actually found! That is, if the fossil record really did yield an abundant sampling of true incipient and transitional forms, if actually there were changing taxonomies, if the fossil gaps were not regular and systematic but only statistical — all of this would be hailed as striking, indisputable proof of evolution. Such an array of evidence would, indeed, be hard for the creation model to refute.

Since, however, this type of evidence is *altogether lacking* in the fossil record, auxiliary conditions have to be imposed on the evolutionist predictions. Evolutionists may assume, for instance, that evolution took place explosively, in small populations, giving little opportunity for fossilization of the transitional forms. Additional assumptions must be introduced, then, to account for such evolutionary spurts, since the process today is apparently too slow to observe at all. The sudden appearance of all the basic taxonomic categories, or phyla, approximately a half-billion years or so ago in the Cambrian, with no fossil record of their prior development, is especially hard to incorporate into the evolution model.

No such auxiliary assumptions and conditions are needed for the creation model! All of its predictions are explicitly confirmed by the fossil record exactly as it stands. Even the general order of appearance of the various fossils in the geologic strata is anticipated in the creationist framework, but this will be considered later.

It may be well at this point, however, to document (from evolutionary writers) the fact that there are no incipient or transitional forms in the fossils. Paul Moody, in a standard textbook used widely for many years, said:

> So far as we can judge from the geologic record, large changes seem usually to have arisen suddenly . . . fossil forms, intermediate between large subdivisions of classification, such as orders and classes, are seldom found.[4]

As a matter of fact, they are *never* found!

That the dearth of intermediate forms extends even to smaller divisions was confirmed by Davis, in a very influential neo-Darwinian reference anthology:

> The sudden emergence of major adaptive types as seen in the abrupt appearance in the fossil record of families and orders, continued to give trouble. A few paleontologists even today cling to the idea that these gaps will be closed by further collecting, but most regard the observed discontinuity as real and have sought an explanation.[5]

In his day, Darwin attributed these gaps to the limited number of fossils collected. This explanation is no longer adequate.

> There is no need to apologize any longer for the poverty of the fossil record. In some ways it has become almost unmanageably rich and discovery is outpacing integration. . . . The fossil record nevertheless continues to be composed mainly of gaps.[6]

Finally, no less an authority than the leading neo-Darwinian paleontologist, George Gaylord Simpson, acknowledges the regular systematic existence of these gaps in the fossil record:

> In spite of these examples, it remains true, as every paleontologist knows, that *most* new species, genera, and

---

[4] Paul A. Moody, *Introduction to Evolution* (New York: Harper and Row, 1962), p. 503.

[5] D. Dwight Davis, "Comparative Anatomy and the Evolution of Vertebrates," in *Genetics, Paleontology and Evolution*, ed. Jepsen, Mayr and Simpson (Princeton, NJ: Princeton University Press, 1949), p. 74.

[6] T. N. George, "Fossils in Evolutionary Perspective," *Science Progress*, vol. 48 (January 1960), p. 1, 3.

families, and that nearly all categories above the level of families, appear in the record suddenly and are not led up to by known, gradual, completely continuous transitional sequences.[7]

Note that the same classification categories existed throughout the long ages of the fossil record as originally worked out for existing plants and animals. The system itself showed no signs of evolving. Furthermore, most of the major categories (down through at least the families) have remained clearly distinct since their first appearance in the record.

Now evolutionists may believe that the gaps still result from the rarity of fossil deposition and discovery. Or perhaps, as most think, the gaps result from spurts of explosive evolution caused by periods of intensified cosmic radiation or something else. The fact is, the gaps are still *there*, and this is a primary prediction of the *creation model*.

Never are fossils of creatures found with incipient eyes, with half-way wings, with half-scales turning into feathers, with partially-evolved forelimbs, or with any other nascent or transitional characters. Yet there must have been innumerable individuals that possessed such features, *if* the neo-Darwinian model of evolutionary history is correct. It seems very strange that the fossilization process selected only those individuals for preservation that already had completed particular stages of evolutionary progress, and yet preserved these in great abundance and variety. Was Nature somehow ashamed of her evolutionary embryos?

The creation model predicts directly that the fossil record will be composed of the same classification categories as those of the present world, with the same kinds of gaps between the categories, and with no evidence of gradual transitions between these categories. This is exactly what is found. Creationists, therefore, believe that the fossil record, while not absolutely impossible of reconciliation with the evolution model, does conform much more simply and directly to the creation model.

It is noteworthy that the above quotations from Moody, Davis, George, and Simpson were all taken from publications during the reign of neo-Darwinism, before the advent of the modern school of punctuationism. It was almost universally taught during those years that evolution proceeded slowly and gradually, produced by the accumulation of the small, rare, beneficial mutations that had been preserved by natural selection.

---

[7] George Gaylord Simpson, *The Major Features of Evolution* (New York: Columbia University Press, 1953), p. 360. Emphasis his.

Even though mutations always seemed to be either harmful or neutral, it was believed that there must be some good ones, and that these could be preserved and accumulated by natural selection through a sort of ratchet mechanism that would allow the bad ones to be discarded. This, of course, was wishful thinking of a high order, but the philosophy was that, in a billion years, anything could happen.

Even then, however, it was recognized that there were practically no true transitional forms among the fossils, as indicated by the above quotations. Nevertheless, since it was obvious that no real evolution of consequence could be observed taking place today, it was necessary to use the fossils as evidence that it had occurred in the past. A widely used textbook on evolution has emphasized this fact:

> While many inferences about evolution are derived from living organisms, we must look to the fossil record for the ultimate documentation of large-scale change. In the absence of a fossil record, the credibility of evolutionists would be severely weakened. We might wonder whether the doctrine of evolution would qualify as anything more than an outrageous hypothesis.[8]

These so-called "circumstantial" evidences will be reviewed later, but it is obvious that the fossil record is the definitive evidence for evolution, such as it is.

And just what is that evidence? Its formal expression is summarized in a tabulation known as the "geologic column," which purports to represent the types of plants and animals living in the various geological ages of the past billion years or so. This standard column may be found in many textbooks of general geology, historical geology or evolution, and in many textbooks of biology or general science, so it is assumed that the reader is at least somewhat familiar with the concept.

The "column" supposedly represents an idealized cross-section through the earth's sedimentary crust, from the surface down to the crystalline "basement" rocks. These sedimentary rocks (sandstones, shales, conglomerates, limestones, etc.) have been deposited by processes of sedimentation (erosion from some source, then transportation — usually by water, though sometimes by ice or wind — and finally by deposition and lithification). Such rocks often contain "fossils" (bones, shells, footprints, etc.) of the plants or animals that were living at the time of rock formation. Presumably, the earliest ages with their fossils are

---

[8] Steven M. Stanley, *Macroevolution: Pattern and Process* (San Francisco, CA: W. H. Freeman, 1979), p. 2.

preserved at the bottom of the column, proceeding up through later ages, to the most recent ages and their fossils on the top.

When one looks uncritically at this standard representation of the geologic column — or geological-time table, as it is also called — it does, indeed, give a superficial appearance of evolution over the geological ages. With only one-celled organisms at the bottom, then marine invertebrates, then fishes, amphibians, reptiles, birds, mammals, and finally man at the top, it *seems* to be telling the story of evolution during past ages, even though we do not see it taking place today.

But this appearance is strictly superficial. When one begins to look more closely at the fossil record, the evidence for evolution — and even for the geological ages themselves — soon vanishes. For the present discussion, however, we shall assume that the various divisions and sequences in the geological column are real, and we shall look only at the fossils themselves. We can sidestep the question of time by employing the alternate names for the divisions — that is, using "system" instead of "period," and "series" instead of "epoch." These are legitimate alternate terms, used quite regularly by working geologists, stressing the actual physical nature of the rocks, rather than the imaginary "ages" assigned to them.

A great abundance of fossils exist, surely enough to show evidence of evolutionary transitions if they ever really happened. Billions and billions of fossils have been preserved, often in great fossil "graveyards," found all over the world, from every so-called age. Many of these represent animals that are now extinct, but probably most are merely fossilized varieties or closely related species or genera of animals and plants that are still living today. If any transitional or intermediate types ever existed, they should — like all the others — be found in reasonable statistical abundance among this profusion of remains.

They are not, however! The predictions from the creation model (see page 18) are precisely verified by the actual fossil record. Consider just a few typical statements from knowledgeable evolutionists:

> The oldest truth of paleontology proclaimed that the vast majority of species appear fully formed in the fossil record and do not change substantially during the long period of their later existence. . . . In other words, geologically abrupt appearance followed by subsequent stability.[9]

Since 1859 one of the most vexing properties of the

---

[9] Stephen Jay Gould, "Opus 200," *Natural History*, vol. 100 (August 1991), p. 14.

fossil record has been its obvious imperfection. . . . The inability of the fossil record to produce the "missing links" has been taken as solid evidence for disbelieving the theory.[10]

All paleontologists know that the fossil record contains precious little in the way of intermediate forms; transitions between major groups are characteristically abrupt.[11]

The point emerges that, if we examine the fossil record in detail, whether at the level of orders or of species, we find — over and over again — not gradual evolution, but the sudden explosion of one group at the expense of another.[12]

This last reference is from the presidential address at the 1976 meeting of the British Geological Association. In that same address, the eminent geologist Dr. Ager made the following pungent comment:

It must be significant that nearly all the evolutionary stories I learned as a student . . . have now been debunked.[13]

It would be easily possible to multiply statements like these about the ubiquitous absence of transitional forms in the fossil record, statements made by evolutionists themselves, but those above clearly make the point. The point is that, out of the many billions of fossils known to be preserved in the sedimentary rocks of the earth's crust, including representatives of many still-living types of plants and animals, *no true transitional fossil forms* have yet been discovered!

This is a very perplexing situation, if any such transitional forms ever existed at all. It is certainly not the situation that a doctrinaire evolutionist would have predicted ahead of time. In fact, Charles Darwin himself was troubled by the lack of transitional forms. In his day, he could attribute this dearth simply to the limited number of fossils known at that time (the first dinosaur fossil had only recently been discovered). He actually predicted that the missing transitional forms would be

---

[10] A. J. Boucot, *Evolution and Extinction Rate Controls* (Amsterdam: Elsevier Scientific Publishing Co., 1975), p. 196.

[11] Stephen Jay Gould, "The Return of Hopeful Monsters," *Natural History*, vol. 86 (June/July 1977), p. 24.

[12] Derek W. Ager, "The Nature of the Fossil Record," *Proceedings of the British Geological Association*, vol. 87, no. 2 (1976), p. 133.

[13] *Ibid.*, p. 132.

discovered through further fossil exploration. But, of course, they have not been found, and creationists predict that they never will be found, because they never existed!

Now all of this precisely discredits the evolution model and precisely supports the creation model. The fossil record has been touted as the main evidence for evolution, but, instead, it denies evolution. No wonder, therefore, that in a recent review article by a professor of zoology at the famed Oxford University — and an explicitly anti-creationist article at that — we are told that the fossil record is irrelevant to the issue!

> In any case, no real evolutionist, whether gradualist or punctuationist, uses the fossil record as evidence in favor of the theory of evolution as opposed to special creation.[14]

Isn't that interesting! We noted earlier that Pierre Grassé concluded that "the process of evolution is revealed only through fossil forms."[15] Yet Ridley says that no evolutionist should use the fossils to prove evolution. Two top-flight European zoologists at the two most prestigious universities in Europe are in diametric disagreement on such a definitive evolutionary argument as this. Grassé says that only the fossils can provide evidence of evolution; Ridley says that the fossils do not provide evidence of evolution. So which is right?

They are both right. Grassé is correct in saying that, since evolution does not occur today, the fossils must be used to show whether it occurred in the past. Ridley is also correct when he says that the fossils don't show any such evidence. There is, therefore, no evidence anywhere that evolution has ever occurred at all, either in the present or in the past.

The needed intermediate forms are still missing after 200 years of intensive fossil collecting. The paleontologist says that we cannot find them because evolution occurred in spurts, so rapidly that only a few intermediates ever existed. The modern geneticist, however, says that evolution proceeds so slowly and gradually that we cannot actually observe it taking place. We can't see evolution in the present because it goes too slow; we can't see it in the past because it went too fast. We can't *observe* it anywhere! Therefore, as "true scientists," we must "walk by faith, not by sight." Otherwise, we would become creationists! So they seem to be saying.

---

[14] Mark Ridley, "Who Doubts Evolution?" *New Scientist*, vol. 90 (June 25, 1981), p. 831.
[15] Grassé, *Evolution of Living Organisms*, p. 4.

Where Are the Evolutionary Transitions?

Many evolutionists will object vigorously to the foregoing analysis. We often hear one say: "That's absurd! There are *many* evolutionary intermediate forms in the fossils."

Well, where? Let us explore, one by one, the supposed evolutionary advances in progressing from amoeba to man, in search of transitional forms.

We begin with the one-celled organisms in the Proterozoic rocks at the bottom of the geological column, ignoring the question for the moment of where *they* came from. It is true that numerous types of fossil bacteria and protozoan animals have been documented in these supposedly very ancient rocks. It is also true that many of these simple organisms still exist today, not having changed noticeably in the billion or so years since they are presumed to have first appeared. We have already mentioned the notorious *E. coli* bacteria, which are still (uncomfortably) very much with us after all that time. There are others.

> Many of the prokaryotes from Spitzbergen and related areas exhibit characteristics of morphology, development and behavior (as inferred from their orientation in the sediments) that render them virtually indistinguishable from cynanobacteria and other bacteria that live in the comparable habitats today. . . . Some Spitzbergen eukaryotes resemble modern prasinophyte (green) algae, whereas others bear closer resemblance to the so-called chromophyte algae such as the dinoflagellates that are ubiquitous in modern oceans.[16]

It does seem odd that these and other "billion-year" old organisms, which tend to multiply quite rapidly, would remain so unaffected by evolutionary pressures for so long, if evolution is true. Presumably, however, at least one did change, because the rocks of the Cambrian "period" (or system) team with multitudes of marine invertebrate animals of great complexity and fantastic variety — worms, brachiopods, starfish, jellyfish, trilobites, and a host of others. These may well be the most abundant of all the fossils.

Yet, out of the billions of fossils of Precambrian protozoa and billions of Cambrian metazoan fossils, *nowhere* has there *ever* been found a transitional form from a Precambrian one-celled animal to a Cambrian many-celled invertebrate.

---

[16] Andrew H. Knoll, "End of the Proterozoic Eon," *Scientific American*, vol. 265 (October 1991), p. 64–65.

If any event in life's history resembles man's creation myths, it is this sudden diversification of marine life when multi-cellular organisms took over as the dominant actors in ecology and evolution. Baffling (and embarrassing) to Darwin, this event still dazzles us and stands as a major biological revolution on a par with the invention of self-replication and the origin of the eukaryotic cell. The animal phyla emerged out of the Precambrian mists with most of the attributes of their modern descendants.[17]

As we shall see in a later chapter, the "invention of self-replication and the eukaryotic cell" — that is, the origin of life — is indeed a complete mystery, in fact, explicable only by what amounts to a miracle of creation! And evidently the transition from one-celled organisms to the great variety of many-celled invertebrates would also require something like a miracle. In any case, there are no transitional forms to show that this tremendous evolutionary jump ever took place. Stephen Gould has the following comment:

Studies that began in the early 1950s and continue at an accelerating pace today have revealed an extensive Precambrian fossil record, but the problem of the Cambrian explosion has not receded, since our more extensive labor has still failed to identify any creature that might serve as a plausible immediate ancestor for the Cambrian fauna. . . . Where, then, are all the Precambrian ancestors — or, if they didn't exist in recognizable form, how did complexity get off to such a fast start?[18]

Try creation, Dr. Gould! His mention of an "extensive Precambrian fossil record" is a reference to the so-called "Ediacaran fauna," a complex of strange metazoan fossils that are radically different from any of the Cambrian invertebrates. These unique creatures likewise have no transitional connection with any of the Precambrian protozoa. As Gould

---

[17] Stefan Bengston, "The Solution to a Jigsaw Puzzle," *Nature*, vol. 345 (June 28, 1990), p. 765. Richard Dawkins has a revealing comment in his *Blind Watchmaker* (New York: Norton, 1986), "Both schools of thought agree that the only alternative explanation of the sudden appearance of so many complex animal types in the Cambrian era is divine creation, and both would reject this alternative" (p. 230). That is, both gradualists and punctuationists believe that this vast gap is due to the incomplete fossil record, rather than to creation.

[18] Stephen Jay Gould, "A Short Way to Big Ends," *Natural History*, vol. 95 (January 1986), p. 18.

says, neither is there any transitional form connecting *any* of the Ediacaran fossils with *any* of the Cambrian invertebrates.

The only defense that evolutionists have tried to offer for the absence of any transition to the Cambrian animals is that the latter were the first ones with "hard parts" to be preserved. That, however, is a poor excuse. None of the Precambrian fossils had hard parts. Furthermore, many of the larger Cambrian fossils did not have hard parts (e.g., jellyfish), yet their fossils are available in considerable numbers.

The same is true of animals in later ages, too. For example, note the following recent discussion:

> In certain circumstances the organic tissues themselves can survive for geologically significant periods of time.[19]

> Mineralized skeletons are not ubiquitous in the animal kingdom. Two-thirds of existing phyla lack any mineralized hard parts.[20]

> The discovery in Waukesha, Wisconsin, of the first significant assemblage of soft-bodied animals from the Silurian period, 400 million years ago, extends the known time range of some taxa back several millions of years.[21]

Surely, if there were any ancestors of the Cambrian invertebrates in the Protorozoic (Precambrian) sediments, some of them would have soft parts in the process of evolving into hard parts, because they had acquired hard parts by the Cambrian "period." But even if they didn't, surely some of these soft-bodied "ancestors" could have been preserved somewhere. If so, they have not been found as yet.

Furthermore, since two-thirds of the existing phyla do not have hard parts capable of mineralization, as Briggs says, this means that many more modern animals that have not yet been found in the fossil record probably were there all the time, but just did not leave any record.

Finally, note this summary statement by Briggs, who is a leading British paleontologist, about the abundance of fossils whose soft parts have been preserved in the Cambrian rocks:

> From the beginning of the Cambrian the number of

---

[19] Derek E. G. Briggs, "Extraordinary Fossils," *American Scientist*, vol. 79 (March/April 1991), p. 135.
[20] *Ibid.*, p. 136.
[21] *Ibid.*, p. 137.

known sites displaying significant soft-part preservation exceeds 60, and for each of these major sites there are many minor ones.[22]

It is also very significant, as mentioned before, that the taxonomic categories themselves have not evolved since the beginning. The same classification system developed by Linnaeus and others to categorize modern plants and animals applies also to the plants and animals of the Cambrian and Precambrian periods, except that a number of the Cambrian phyla have become extinct (note that extinction is not evolution!). Once the great explosion of Cambrian phyla took place, no new phyla ever evolved after that.

> Described recently as "the most important evolutionary event during the entire history of the Metazoa," the Cambrian explosion established virtually all the major animal body forms — *Baupläne* or phyla — that would exist thereafter, including many that were quickly "weeded out" and became extinct. Compared with the 30 or so extant, some people estimate that the Cambrian explosion may have generated 100. The evolution innovation of the Precambrian/Cambrian boundary had clearly been extremely broad.[23]

This "explosion" has no real evolutionary explanation. As far as all appearances go, these 30 (or 100) phyla seem to have been created fully developed to begin with.

> If ever we were to expect to find ancestors to or intermediates between higher taxa, it would be in the rocks of late Precambrian to Ordovician times, when the bulk of the world's higher animal taxa evolved. Yet transitional alliances are unknown or unconfirmed for any of the phyla or classes appearing then.[24]

The Chordates and the Vertebrates
Not long ago, it was believed that the earliest vertebrates evolved

---

[22] *Ibid.*, p. 139.

[23] Roger Lewin, "A Lopsided Look at Evolution," *Science*, vol. 241 (July 15, 1988), p. 291.

[24] James W. Valentine and Douglas H. Erwin, "Interpreting Great Developmental Experiments: The Fossil Record," in *Development as an Evolutionary Process* (Alan R. Lias, Inc., 1987), p. 84.

in the Silurian period. Now, however, it is generally agreed that the vertebrate phylum (or sub-phylum, if preferred), like all the other phyla, was present in the Cambrian itself.

> Discoveries of fragmentary phosphatic plates, interpreted as pertaining to heterostracans, from numerous localities in Late Cambrian and early Ordovician marine limestone extend the vertebrate record back to more than 500 million years before the present. . . . Fossil evidence of pre-vertebrate chordate evolution is still scanty and equivocal.[25]

> The presence of cellular bone in the Late Cambrian-earliest Ordovician genus Cordylodus predates the earliest previously recorded occurrence of vertebrate hard tissues by around 40 million years.[26]

> The addition of the conodonts increases the number of well-established Cambro-Ordovician vertebrate genera by a factor of 30, from 5 to nearly 150.[27]

The origin of true fishes, of course, is still a mystery to evolutionists. Exactly which marine invertebrate "evolved" into a fish is completely unknown, because no intermediate forms have ever been found. This is surely strange, because the transition from an animal with hard parts on the outside (e.g., shells) to one with hard parts on the inside (e.g., bony skeleton) must have been a very long and difficult transition; therefore, surely some of these transitional animals must have been buried and fossilized somewhere! Multiplied billions of both invertebrate fossils and fish fossils have been preserved, but apparently no intermediate forms. How does the evolution model accommodate this anomaly?

It doesn't, of course, but it perfectly fits the creation model. The evolution model should be rejected on this basis alone.

> How this earliest chordate stock evolved, what stages

---

[25] James A. Hopson and Leonard B. Radinsky, "Vertebrate Paleontology: New Approaches and New Insights," *Paleobiology*, vol. 6 (Summer 1980), p. 256. See also "A Fish from the Upper Cambrian of North America," by J. Rapetski (*Science*, vol. 200, 1978), p. 529.

[26] I. J. Sansom et al., "Presence of the Earliest Vertebrate Hard Tissues in Conodonts," *Science*, vol. 256 (May 29, 1992), p. 1310.

[27] D. E. Briggs, "Conodonts: A Major Extinct Group Added to the Vertebrates," *Science*, vol. 256 (May 29, 1992), p. 1286.

it went through to eventually give rise to truly fish-like creatures we do not know . . . there is a gap of perhaps 100 million years we will probably never be able to fill.[28]

But whatever ideas authorities may have on the subject, the lung fishes, like every other major group of fishes that I know, have their origins firmly based in *nothing*.[29]

All three subdivisions of the bony fishes appear in the fossil record at approximately the same time. . . . How did they originate? What allowed them to diverge so widely? . . . And why is there no trace of earlier, intermediate forms?[30]

The answer to all such questions, obviously, is that of direct creation, but evolutionists automatically reject this possibility. As we proceed up the theoretical geological "column," we find the same types of gaps between the various classes of vertebrates, as the gaps between the various phyla. That is, there are no transitional forms between the fish and the amphibians, between amphibians and reptiles, between reptiles, and the mammals and birds. These gaps apply between all the classes just as they do between all the phyla.

Students of evolutionary history have observed repeatedly that in an adaptive radiation, the major subgroups appear early and at about the same time. . . . Nearly all living phyla of marine invertebrates that have reasonably good fossil records have first occurrences either in the late Precambrian or early to middle Cambrian. At the class level there are 27 paleontologically important living groups and all have documented occurrences which are Silurian or older. . . . The same relative pattern can be seen in the geologic records of vertebrates and land plants, although origins are generally displaced in time toward the recent.[31]

In other words, practically all classes, as well as all phyla, have existed unchanged since their earliest appearance far back in "geological

---

[28] F. D. Ommanney, *The Fishes* (Life Nature Library, 1964), p. 60.

[29] Errol White, "A Little on Lungfishes," *Proceedings of the Linnaean Society of London*, vol. 177 (January 1966), p. 8.

[30] Gerald T. Todd, "Evolution of the Lung and the Origin of Bony Fishes: A Causal Relationship," *American Zoologist*, vol. 26, no. 4 (1980), p. 757.

[31] David M. Raup, "On the Early Origin of Major Biologic Groups," *Paleobiology*, vol. 9, no. 2 (1983), p. 107.

time." Furthermore, the "time" of first appearance is continually being pushed back further with new fossil discoveries.

> Experience has shown that as more fossils are discovered, the first occurrences of major groups tend to be pushed back in time.[32]

To be more specific, the first amphibians are already recognizable as true amphibians.

> No clearly intermediate form in the fish-tetrapod transition has been discovered.[33]

The same applies to the transition from amphibians to reptiles.

> Unfortunately not a single specimen of an appropriate reptilian ancestor is known prior to the appearance of true reptiles. The absence of such ancestral forms leaves many problems of the amphibian-reptile transition unanswered.[34]

Furthermore, each of the orders among the amphibians is completely different from the others, with no intermediates, and the same is true of the reptilian orders and the orders of fishes. This fact could be documented at length, but that seems unnecessary, since no vertebrate paleontologist would dispute it. The same is true of the classes and orders among the invertebrates. Wherever we look in the fossil record, the transitional forms so essential to evolutionary theory are missing. These facts, on the other hand, fit the creation model perfectly!

Alleged Transitional Forms

The same absence of transitional forms is found between classes of the "higher" vertebrates — that is, between reptiles and mammals, and between reptiles and birds — although both birds and mammals are believed by evolutionists to have evolved from reptiles.

However, it is at this point that evolutionists commonly interject their classic examples of alleged transitional forms, namely the mammal-like reptiles and the reptile-like birds, especially *Archaeopteryx*. Whenever a creationist asks an evolutionist for examples of fossil transitions, it is almost inevitable that these two (in addition to the

---

[32] *Ibid.*, p. 113.

[33] Hopson and Radinsky, "Vertebrate Paleontology," p. 258.

[34] Lewis L. Carroll, "Problems of the Origin of Reptiles," *Biological Reviews of the Cambridge Philosophical Society*, vol. 44 (1969), p. 393.

supposed ape-men, a topic that will be discussed later) are the ones that will be cited.

Now if evolution were really true, there should be multitudes of transitional forms available to document it. In fact, one might properly suppose (if it were not for his awareness of the real world) that *every* living organism would be in some kind of transition. So why is it that evolutionists can suggest only two or three possible (but exceedingly doubtful) transitional forms? To creationists, the answer is obvious. Evolution is false!

Terrestrial vertebrates (reptiles, mammals, birds) are easy enough to distinguish when they are living, but since they all have somewhat similar functions, their basic skeletal structures would naturally be created to be somewhat similar.

Consider the "transition" between reptiles and mammals:

> Recent mammals and reptiles are easily distinguished by the differences of anatomical, physiological, reproductive and adaptive features, but in the reptile-mammal transition documented by the late Triassic fossils, the distinction is not clear-cut. . . . The presence of a squamosal-dentary articulation forming part or all of the joining between the skull and lower jaw is now used as the main practical diagnostic criterion for the class mammalia. . . . This distinction in the jaw articulation was found to be inadequate, however.[35]

All the mammal-like reptiles are extinct, though they were numerous and quite varied in the past, so it is not possible to examine and evaluate their characteristic soft biology. It is the latter by which living mammals and reptiles are distinguished today, not by the bones in the ear-jaw system.

There is no reason whatever to assume that the mammal-like reptiles were animals in the process of being transformed from reptiles to mammals. They originated simultaneously with the other orders of reptiles, with no clear indication of ancestry.

> Each species of mammal-like reptile that has been found appears suddenly in the fossil record and is not preceded by the species that is directly ancestral to it. It disappears some time later, equally abruptly, without

---

[35] Sankar Chatterjee, "An Ictidosaur Fossil from North America," *Science*, vol. 220 (June 10, 1983), p. 1151.

leaving a directly descended species.[36]

Not only was their origin without any indication of reptilian ancestry, but also their extinction was without any mammalian descendants, at least so far as the evidence goes.

> The transition to the first mammal, which probably happened in just one or, at most, two lineages, is still an enigma.[37]

> Those searching for specific information useful in constructing phylogenies of mammalian taxa will be disappointed.[38]

The various orders of mammal-like reptiles (pelycosaurs, therapsids, theriodonts, cynodonts, etc.) were apparently quite successful in their respective environments. There is no reason at all not to conclude that they had been *created* for those environments. Some were the size of a rat, some as large as a rhinoceros, with hundreds of different species. Other reptilian orders, of course, have survived, while all the mammal-like reptiles became extinct even earlier than the dinosaurs, for reasons unknown.

> If therapsids were so diverse and so successful, what became of them? As in the case of more recent extinctions, the answer is not fully known.[39]

In fact, Tom Kemp, curator of zoology at the Oxford University Museum, and one of the top authorities on the mammal-like reptiles, has concluded that each type was destroyed by a separate sudden mass extinction, followed by a very sudden evolution of a new type. The reviewer of Kemp's definitive book on these creatures notes this aspect in particular:

> Major evolutionary change was restricted to the short interval between the mass extinction and completion of the

---

[36] Tom Kemp, "The Reptiles that Became Mammals," *New Scientist*, vol. 93 (March 4, 1982), p. 583.

[37] Roger Lewin, "Bones of Mammals' Ancestors Fleshed Out," *Science*, vol. 212 (June 26, 1981), p. 1492.

[38] R. Eric Lombard, Review of *Evolutionary Principles of the Mammalian Middle Ear*, by Tom S. Kemp (Berlin: Springer-Verlag, 1978), in *Evolution*, vol. 33 (no. 4), p. 1230.

[39] "Adding Flesh to Bare Therapsid Bones," *Science News*, vol. 119 (June 20, 1981), p. 389.

sudden radiation. . . . The rapid rates of morphologic change accompanying the subsequent radiations are attributed to mutations of "regulator genes" — in effect, the production of "hopeful monsters" — with natural selection playing only a minor role in the process.[40]

This concept of mass extinction and sudden appearance of seemingly parent-less new orders might give support (as Kemp suggests) to the punctuated equilibrium school of Gould and Eldredge. A still better explanation, however, is special creation of each type, fully functional in all its parts and already adapted to its intended purpose by its Creator.

The even more well-known evolutionary scenario of *Archaeopteryx* as a reptile-bird transition form has a similar creationist explanation. This "primitive" bird is almost always the first example cited when one asks an evolutionist for an example of an evolutionary transition.

Archaeopteryx was a relatively small bird, supposedly representing a lizard-type reptile in the process of evolving into a bird. It had teeth and claws like a reptile, but wings with feathers like a bird. Probably no more than seven fossils of this creature have been found, only three of which show the feather impressions and essentially the complete animal. The first two to be found were offered by a Bavarian doctor as evidence of evolution soon after the publication of Darwin's *Origin of Species*. He had obtained them apparently from a fossil-rich limestone bed in Germany.

In 1985, the British astronomer Fred Hoyle and an Israeli scientist, Lee Spetner, made studies on these two specimens, which resulted in allegations that the fossils were fraudulent, with chicken feathers pressed into a cement matrix that was then applied to two genuine fossils of a small dinosaur. Hoyle and Spetner, along with Hoyle's colleague N. Wickramasinghe, then published papers[41] and a small book showing their evidence of the fraud.

Hoyle and Spetner presented what seemed like a strong case for the fabrication of the "Piltdown Bird," as many started calling it, in reference to the famous Piltdown Man hoax of previous fame. As might be expected, however, this charge against such a key "proof" of evolution could not be allowed to stand, and evolutionists everywhere were

[40] James A. Hopson, "Synapsids and Evolution," Review of *Mammal-like Reptiles and the Origin of Mammals* (New York: Academic Press, 1982, 364 p.), in *Science*, vol. 219 (January 7, 1983), p. 50.

[41] Fred Hoyle and N. Wickramasinghe, "*Archaeopteryx*, the Primordial Bird?" *Nature*, vol. 324 (December 18/25, 1986), p. 622. See also Gail Vines, "Strange Case of *Archaeopteryx* 'Fraud,'" *New Scientist*, vol. 105 (March 14, 1985), p. 3.

indignant. A number of papers purportedly refuting the fraud allegation were published, and the furor has died down now, with *Archaeopteryx* still offered in proof of evolution by most evolutionists. Unfortunately, these fossils now have been locked away in the basement of the British Museum of Natural History, no longer accessible to public view or further research.

Assuming that it is a genuine fossil of a real animal, there is still no good evidence that it is a transitional form. It was a true bird, not a half-reptile. It had feathered wings, and that is what makes a bird. In fact, just before the alleged fraud exposure, an international conference on *Archaeopteryx* was assembled in Germany to evaluate its status.

> At the end of the three days of presentations, Charig orchestrated a concerted effort to summarize the ideas for which consensus exists. The general credo runs as follows: *Archaeopteryx* was a bird that could fly, but it was not necessarily the direct ancestor of modern birds. . . . A communiqué expressing the unanimous belief of all participants in the evolutionary origin and significance of *Archaeopteryx* was adopted, in order to forestall possible misuse by creationists of apparent discord among scientists.[42]

If nothing else, this conference points up the desperate need felt by evolutionists for a proof of evolution.

And yet, they unanimously acknowledged that *Archaeopteryx* was a bird, though probably not the ancestor of modern birds. That particular link is still missing.

The ornithologist Alan Feduccia has made many studies and written several articles on *Archaeopteryx*. He has shown that it had aerodynamically efficient feathers, just as much so as modern birds. The "claws" — which some cite as evidence of reptilian kinship — actually show that its habitat was arboreal, like that of other birds. Note his conclusion:

> *Archaeopteryx* probably cannot tell us much about the early origins of feathers and flight in true protobirds, because *Archaeopteryx* was, in the modern sense, a bird.[43]

[42] Peter Dodson, "International *Archaeopteryx* Conference," *Journal of Vertebrate Paleontology*, vol. 5 (June 1985), p. 179.

[43] Alan Feduccia, "Evidence from Claw Geometry Indicating Arboreal Habits of *Archaeopteryx*," *Science*, vol. 259 (February 5, 1993), p. 792.

Incidentally, the claws of this animal have no relation to those of reptiles. A number of modern birds also have wing claws. One of these is the hoatzin, which also has a strange "kinship" with cows and sheep, employing foregut fermentation in its digestive system like any big ruminating mammal. With respect to the claws, a short review article notes:

> [Stuart D. Strahl, of the New York Zoological Society's Wildlife Conservation International] adds that some ornithologists call the "hoatzin" primitive because of its archaeopteryx-like claws; but he prefers to think of it as "highly specialized." Sivans, ibis, and many other birds, he notes, have wing claws; they just never make use of them.[44]

As far as the teeth of *Archaeopteryx* are concerned, modern birds do not have teeth, but that is not to say that the Creator could not have made some birds with teeth (not all reptiles have teeth, incidentally, so teeth are not *necessarily* a reptilian characteristic). There are other extinct toothed birds, and the teeth of *Archaeopteryx* were like those of other toothed birds — not at all like those of reptiles. One example, recently discovered in China, not only had teeth and claws, but it is "younger" than *Archaeopteryx*.

> The recent discovery of an articulated fossil bird about 20 to 15 m. y. younger than *Archaeopteryx*, has opened a new window on early Avian evolution. . . . The Chinese bird was arboreal . . . Other characters establish the fossil avian as the second most primitive bird next to *Archaeopteryx*, such as the presence of toothed jaws.[45]

A very recent bird find in Mongolia had hands and arms like those of digging animals, as well as teeth, and is dated as only half as old as *Archaeopteryx*.

> Mongolian and U.S. researchers have found a 75-million-year-old, bird-like creature with a hand so strange it has left paleontologists grasping for an explanation. . . . Paul Sereno of the University of Chicago notes that *Monoychus* had arms built much like those of digging animals. Because moles and other diggers have keeled

---

[44] J. H., "What's a Hoatzin?" *Scientific American*, vol. 261 (December 1989), p. 30.

[45] Paul C. Sereno, "Ruling Reptiles and Wandering Continents: A Global Look at Dinosaur Evolution," *GSA Today*, vol. 1 (July 1991), p. 144.

sternums and wrists reminiscent of birds, the classification of *Monoychus* becomes difficult, he says.[46]

Possibly, birds evolved from moles instead of from reptiles!

Actually, *Archaeopteryx, Monoychus,* and every other type of bird, reptile, mammal, and whatever, give every indication of being special creations of the God of creation, each with its own distinctive structure designed for its own specific purpose in the creation. With respect to the classic "transitional form," *Archaeopteryx,* even such doctrinaire evolutionists as Eldredge and Gould recognize that it is not really transitional.

> At the higher level of evolutionary transition between basic morphologic designs, gradualism has always been in trouble. . . . Smooth intermediates between *Baupläne* are almost impossible to construct, even in thought experiments. There is certainly no evidence for them in the fossil record (curious mosaics like *Archaeopteryx* do not count).[47]

Archaeopteryx is a "mosaic" of useful and functioning structures found also in other creatures, not a "transition" between them. A true transitional structure would be, say, a "sceather" — that is, a half-scale, half-feather — or a "ling" — half-leg, half-wing — or, perhaps a half-evolved heart or liver or eye. Such transitional structures, however, would not survive in any struggle for existence. No wonder these authors say that one could not conceive of such a thing even in a "thought experiment."

The same applies to the mammal-like reptiles and other transitional forms that have occasionally been suggested, such as the coelacanth fish and the lungfish, both of which are occasionally proffered as about to become amphibians, as well as the ichthyostegids (the fish-like amphibians) and the seymourians (amphibian-like reptiles). All such creatures are really "mosaics," not "transitions."

A wondrous example of a modern mosaic creature is the famous duck-billed platypus. It has fur, and it suckles its young like a mammal, lays eggs, and possesses a duck-bill like a bird, spends most of its time in water like an amphibian, has a poison sac like a reptile, and can pick up electric signals like nothing else.

---

[46] Monastersky, R., "A Clawed Wonder Unearthed in Mongolia," *Science News*, vol. 143 (April 17, 1993), p. 245.

[47] Stephen Jay Gould and Niles Eldredge, "Punctuated Equilibria: the Tempo and Mode of Evolution Reconsidered," *Paleobiology*, vol. 3 (Spring 1977), p. 147.

> To be a platypus sports an unbeatable combination for strangeness . . . its obvious melange of reptilian (or birdlike), with obvious mammalian, characters . . . a superbly well-designed creature for a particular, and unusual, mode of life. . . . The platypus is one honey of an adaptation.[48]

The platypus is certainly not a transitional form, nor some kind of hybrid. Neither are there any fossil transitional forms in the process of becoming a platypus. As Gould says (perhaps without thinking, since he does not believe in design — only in chance), it is "superbly well designed" for its "unusual mode of life." It is hard for evolutionists even to invent a "just-so story" to explain a platypus!

Thus, there are no transitional forms leading up to the mammals. Furthermore, each of the 32 orders of mammals (rodents, insectivores, ungulates, primates, etc.) is drastically different from all others, with no intermediates!

However, it is within the mammalian orders themselves that evolutionists have professed to have some real paleontological evidence of evolution. The famous horse series, from *Eohippus* to *Equus*, is perhaps the most exploited. More recently, it seems to have been pre-empted in prominence by the whale supposedly evolving from a land mammal. Most important of all is the so-called case for *human evolution*. These will all be discussed in the next chapter.

---

[48] Stephen Jay Gould, "To Be a Platypus," *Natural History*, vol. 94 (August 1985), p. 10, 14-15.

Chapter 4

Neither Did It Happen in the Recent Past

The Tertiary "period" is the so-called age of mammals and, finally, man. The great dinosaurian reptiles had all died, they say, at the end of the Cretaceous "period," and the mammal-like reptiles even before that, so the mammals were then free to proliferate everywhere, so the story goes.

The best-publicized evolutionary series during this period is that of the horses, although the elephants and others supposedly went through changes also. The best case for evolution, at least in the past, has been the horse series, so we shall consider that first of all, as typical of the others.

The Horse Family Bush

According to the traditional scenario, there was first a small multi-toed animal denoted as *Eohippus*, the "dawn horse," living in the Paleocene epoch about 60 million years ago. *Eohippus* is supposed to have evolved through a long series of other horses (called *Mesohippus*, *Miohippus*, *Pliohippus*, etc.), finally culminating in the modern horse *Equus*.

With the advance from one stage to another, the succession of horses increased in size, while their hooves devolved from five toes to three to one. This presumed "family tree" of horses has long been presented as one of the key proofs of evolution.

In recent years, however, all this has changed, and the horse tree has become a bush, with no one horse clearly descended from any other. The first in the series, *Eohippus*, was probably more like a hyrax than a horse, and should not even be included in the group at all. He is now again being called *Hyracotherium* (which was the name given by its first discoverers, before certain North American paleontologists got the quaint notion that this little creature might be the ancestor of the horses, and perhaps also of the elephant).

Furthermore, this animal was quite stable, in terms of the standard geological column. Paleontologist Stephen Stanley notes the following:

> Those who in the past have contemplated the formation of the modern horse by gradual evolution, beginning with this early genus, must now contend with the fact that at least two species of *Hyracotherium* lasted for several million years without appreciable change.[1]

As a matter of fact, there has been much less change than evolutionists wish for, since *Hyracotherium* is clearly much the same as our modern hyrax. With respect to the modern horse, *Equus*, Stanley notes that it also has been highly stable:

> It is notable that the evidence of great stability for species of *Hyracotherium* is complemented at the other end of equid phylogeny, by data showing that ten species of horses lived through most or all of Pleistocene time.[2]

As far as the intermediate horses are concerned (*Mesohippus*, *Miohippus*, *Merychippus*, *Pliohippus*, etc.), it is now well-known that they no longer diagram into a tree, but a "bush." There is much overlapping, and each is separated from the others without intermediate forms between. In the John Day strata of Oregon, the three-toed grazer *Merychippus* has been found in the same formation with the single-hoofed *Pliohippus*, for example. *Pliohippus* has also been found to be contemporaneous with the three-toed *Hipparion* in the Great Basin area, supposedly for several million years. No wonder David Raup says:

> The record of evolution is still surprisingly jerky and, ironically, we have even fewer examples of evolutionary transition than we had in Darwin's time. By this I mean that some of the classic cases of Darwinian change in the fossil record, such as the evolution of the horse in North America,

---

[1] Stephen M. Stanley, "Macroevolution and the Fossil Record," *Evolution*, vol. 36, no. 3 (1982), p. 464.
[2] *Ibid.*

have had to be discarded or modified as a result of more detailed information.[3]

Once the little hyrax is taken out of the horse series, the remaining horses in the series could all well be viewed either as different varieties of the original created horse type or as separate created horse types. There is certainly no clear evidence that any one of them is the evolutionary ancestor of any other! For all that anyone can show to the contrary, their times could all have overlapped, or even all been the same. Dr. Stephen Stanley, one of the nation's top paleontologists and author of an important book on macro-evolution, has evaluated the significance of these fossil horses as follows:

> The horse is the most famous example — the classic story of one genus turning into another, turning into another. Now it's becoming apparent that there's an overlap of these genera, and that there were many species belonging to each one. It's a very bushy sort of pattern that is, I think, much more in line with the punctuational model; there isn't just a simple, gradual transition from one horse to another. This is now becoming fairly well known.[4]

As a matter of fact, many natural history museums have completely revised their horse evolution exhibits in recent years. Although evolution is still assumed, it is not much emphasized any more in these exhibits. A "bush" does not lend itself as easily as a "tree" to evolutionary inference. Stephen Gould even regards the horse as an evolutionary failure, since all its "relatives" in the bush have become extinct.

> If a clade has been markedly unsuccessful and now lies at the brink of extinction with but one surviving twig, then our anagenetic biases click in, and we often read the single extant path as an anagenetic trend. Thus we celebrate little, many-toed *Eohippus* marching towards the large, noble single-toed *Equus*. But *Equus* is the sole survivor of a tree once lush and vibrant (in an early Tertiary world with few artiodactyls and abundant perissodactyls). We speak of the anagenesis of horses only because our

[3] David M. Raup, "Conflicts between Darwin and Paleontology," *Field Museum of Natural History Bulletin*, vol. 50 (January 1979), p. 25. Raup is Curator of Geology at the Field Museum.

[4] Stephen Stanley, "Resetting the Evolutionary Timetable," Interview by Neil A. Campbell, *Bioscience*, vol. 36 (December 1986), p. 726.

biases abstract bushes as ladders. And the clade of horses has been so depleted that only one lineage remains to be misread as the terminus of a trend. All our textbooks cite horses as the prototypical evolutionary trend, but there is no classical tale about the evolutionary "trend" of antelopes, rodents, or bats — though these are the true success stories of mammalian evolution by the more appropriate criterion of increasing representation.[5]

This is an interesting line of reasoning, but it really has nothing whatever to do with genuine evolution. Whether one wants to talk about horses or rodents or any other mammalian order, there are a number of similar types within each group, but no evolutionary "tree" apparent in any one of them! Each order is completely distinct from all others and from any possible predecessors. Even within each order, the various members are all clearly distinct from each other, with no real transitional structures or transitional series anywhere. The "trees" found in evolutionist textbooks are all artificially constructed by selective picking off the family bush.

The Tale of the Walking Whale

The problem of marine mammals has been of great frustration to evolutionists. Mammals are supposed to have evolved only on land, by way of some uncertain reptilian ancestry, so the problem is how to account for whales and dolphins and other mammals that live in the sea. Many imaginative scenarios have been devised, whereby some ungulate or other terrestrial animal gradually went back to the sea again, with legs either mutating back into flippers or else becoming vestigial, and with a new apparatus for breathing. Here is the amazing tale of the whale:

> The whale's ascendancy to sovereign size apparently began sixty million years ago when hairy, four-legged mammals, in search of food or sanctuary, ventured into water. As eons passed, changes slowly occurred. Hind legs disappeared, front legs changed into flippers, hair gave way to a thick smooth blanket of blubber, nostrils moved to the top of the head, the tail broadened into flukes, and in the buoyant water world, the body became enormous.[6]

---

[5] Stephen Jay Gould, "Trends as Changes in Variance: A New Slant on Progress and Directionality in Evolution," *Journal of Paleontology*, vol. 62, no. 3 (1988), p. 321.

[6] Victor B. Scheffer, "Exploring the Lives of Whales," *National Geographic*, vol. 50 (December 1976), fold-out display.

The evolution of the dolphin proceeded in similar fashion, they say:

> Dolphins evolved at least 50 million years ago from land mammals, that may have resembled the even-toed ungulates of today, such as cattle, pigs and buffaloes. After taking to the sea, dolphins became progressively better adapted to life in the water: their ancestral fur was replaced by a thick coat of blubbery fat, they became sleek and streamlined . . . their forelimbs were modified into steering paddles and . . . many species evolved a dorsal fin.[7]

These fascinating scenarios have not been gleaned from some child's book of fairy tales, as one might suppose, but from sober scientific articles in respected journals. They do lend themselves easily to cynical comment by creationists, and evolutionists have longed for *some kind* of transitional fossil to add a touch of credibility to them.

Philip Gingerich of the Museum of Paleontology at Michigan University has been a leader in this search.

> Not far from the Khyber Pass in the arid Himalayan foothills of Pakistan, University of Michigan paleontologist Philip D. Gingerich found a skull and several teeth and came to the startling conclusion that they belonged to an ancient walking whale.[8]

He deduced that the skull and teeth belonged to a whale because of certain similarities to primitive whale fossils from India. As to how this skull indicated that the whale was walking, this was admittedly a guess based on the terrestrial nature of the sediments around it.

On a later trip, Gingerich found more fossil remains of the cranial area of this "whale," which had been named *Pakicetus*, and concluded that its ancestor was a hoofed wolf-like mammalian carnivore named *Mesonyx*. Again, however, no fossils of the body or leg bones were found.

> We do not yet know anything about the post-cranial anatomy of early Eocene whales.[9]

---

[7] Bernard Wursig, "Dolphins," *Scientific American* (March 1979), p. 138.

[8] "Whales with Legs," *Science Digest* (November/December 1980), p. 25.

[9] Philip D. Gingerich et al., "Origin of Whales in Epicontinental Remnant Seas: New Evidence from the Early Eocene of Pakistan," *Science*, vol. 220 (April 22, 1983), p. 405.

It was also found that *Pakicetus* was probably unable to hear under water, making it still more doubtful that it was a whale.

But Gingerich was persistent. In 1989, he turned his attention to a number of fossils from Egypt of a creature named *Basilosaurus*. As the name suggests, this was originally identified as a marine reptile when it was first excavated and described early in the 19th century. It was a long serpent-like sea creature, but did have certain mammal-like characteristics (as have various other extinct reptiles). When limb and foot bones were found by Gingerich near to articulated skeletons of *Basilosaurus*, he assumed that he had found his long-sought walking whale! He did acknowledge, however, that:

> The inferred posture and range of motion of the hind limb of *Basilosaurus* are unusual for a mammal. . . . [They] appear to have been too small relative to body size to have assisted in swimming, and they could not possibly have supported the body on land.[10]

These limbs were obviously not mere vestiges, however, as they were too complex and well formed, with no suggestion of degeneracy. Accordingly (assuming that the limbs actually belonged to *Basilosaurus*), the following was concluded:

> Thus hind limbs of *Basilosaurus* are most plausibly interpreted as accessories facilitating reproduction.[11]

Gingerich and his associates probably have the right interpretation of the use of these limbs as "guides during copulation, which may otherwise have been difficult in a serpentine aquatic mammal." But how does that make it a whale, let alone a walking whale? Most likely, it should continue to be regarded as a sea-going "king lizard," which is the meaning of its name. Nevertheless, the evolutionists really needed a transitional form to make whale evolution seem somewhat feasible, so they still insist that that is what it is:

> Temporal and morphological intermediates are direct and important evidence of transition in evolution: an Eocene whale with functional hind limbs narrows the gap considerably between generalized Paleocene land mammals that used hind limbs in locomotion and Oligocene–Recent

[10] Philip D. Gingerich, B. Holly Smith, and Elwyn L. Simons, "Hind Limbs of Eocene *Basilosaurus*: Evidence of Feet in Whales," *Science*, vol. 249 (July 13, 1990), p. 155.
[11] *Ibid.*, p. 156.

modern whales that lack pelvic limbs.[12]

Still more recent fossil digs in Pakistan turned up a strange fossil mammal with both front and hind limbs. It was called *Ambulocetus*,[13] and may have been able both to swim in water and walk (like a sea lion) on land. It seems to have had a very long tail, without flukes. It was found in a much higher stratum than *Pakicetus*, so could hardly have been ancestral to it, even as it could hardly have been a descendant of it.

To a creationist, it would seem most reasonable that *Pakicetus* is an extinct wolf-like mammal, that *Basilosaurus* is an extinct marine reptile, that *Ambulocetus* is an extinct animal of no apparent affinity with anything else, and that *none of them* have any evolutionary connection with either modern or extinct whales. All were specially created with specific structures suitable for their particular environments, but they became extinct when their environments changed or when some catastrophe befell them.

Evolutionists indeed are desperate for transitional forms between major types of animals, and calling these odd creatures examples of transitional animals illustrates just how desperate they are. Nevertheless, the evidence surely, to one not bound to naturalistic preconceptions, is overwhelmingly on the side of creationism in this matter of marine mammals and their alleged relatives.

Now if *Archaeopteryx* and the horses and the mammal-like reptiles do not constitute transitional forms (and, as we have shown, they do not), and if these are the ones most cited by evolutionists as examples of transitional forms (and they are), then we are abundantly justified in concluding that there are *no real transitional forms* anywhere at all in the fossil record. This is amazing, if evolution is true. Statistically, there should be many transitional forms. In fact, if evolution is really true, it would seem logical that *all* creatures, living and extinct, should be transitional forms, in the process of evolving into new, higher forms. And yet there are none!

Men, Monkeys, and Missing Links

Of all the supposed evolutionary family trees, the one leading to man should be best documented. As the most recent evolutionary arrival, pre-human fossils have been exposed to decay processes for the shortest period of time, and so should be better preserved and easier to find than any others. Furthermore, since they are of greatest interest to man, more people have been looking for them than for any other kinds of fossils.

---

[12] *Ibid.*
[13] See *Science*, vol. 263 (1994), p. 180, 210-212.

Consequently, if there are any real transitional forms anywhere in the fossil record, they should be most abundantly documented in the line leading from the first primate to modern man. Certainly, the finds in this field have been more publicized than in any other.

And yet after over 100 years of intensive searching, none have been found! The links are still missing. A few "hominid" bones and teeth have been found, which some anthropologists (not all, by any means) have argued were in the line of human evolution, but all of these are very doubtful, highly controversial, and extremely fragmentary. The general public has no idea just *how* fragmentary!

> The fossils that decorate our family tree are so scarce that there are still more scientists than specimens. The remarkable fact is that all the physical evidence we have for human evolution can still be placed, with room to spare, inside a single coffin.[14]

And the obvious comment that one is almost compelled to make is that a coffin is exactly *where* it should be placed!

One of the nation's leading paleoanthropologists, Yale's David Pilbeam, makes a similar comment about the scarcity of data:

> Human paleontology shares a peculiar trait with such disparate subjects as theology and extraterrestrial biology; it contains more practitioners than objects for study.[15]

There are not very many practitioners either, for that matter. Physical anthropology has had an impact on human thought far outweighing the normal influence of a very small and otherwise insignificant discipline. More recently, Pilbeam has admitted the following:

> I know that at least in paleoanthropology, data are still so sparse that theory heavily influences interpretations. Theories have, in the past, clearly reflected our current ideologies instead of the actual data.[16]

---

[14] Lyall Watson, "The Water People," *Science Digest*, vol. 90 (May 1982), p. 44. More precisely, Colin Tudge has recently said that: "All that paleoanthropologists have to show for more than 100 years of digging are remains from fewer than 2000 of our ancestors. They have used this assortment of jawbones, teeth, fossilized scraps . . . to piece together a line of human descent going back 5 to 8 million years to the time when humans and chimpanzees diverged from a common ancestor," *New Scientist*, vol. 146 (May 20, 1995), p. 24.

[15] David Pilbeam and Stephen J. Gould, "Size and Scaling in Human Evolution," *Science*, vol. 186 (December 6, 1974), p. 892.

[16] David Pilbeam, "Rearranging Our Family Tree," *Human Nature* (June 1978), p. 45.

Pilbeam, of course, is referring not to evolution in general, but to particular ideas about the sequences of human evolution. He is not about to become a creationist! Nevertheless, it seems odd that evolutionists can be so sure about evolution, when they admittedly know nothing as to how it works or what course it has followed.

Actually, no more is known about the evolution of apes (pongids) than that of man.

> Unfortunately, the fossil record of pongids is nonexistent, making a glaring deficiency in the whole story.[17]

How is it, then, that evolutionists are so dogmatically insistent that apes and people have a common ancestor? So far as all real evidence goes, apes have always been apes and people have always been people. Yet, such anthropologists as Donald Johanson and the Leakeys have become world famous because of their excavation of a few handfuls of bones in Africa, which they claim give evidence of human evolution. Interestingly enough, Richard Leakey and Johanson have disagreed heatedly as to where their respective finds (known popularly as Lucy, Skull 1470, Handy Man, etc.) fit in the line of human evolution, but they are united in their opposition to any suggestion of human creation.

Some evolutionists (including evolutionist debaters) are so anxious to persuade people about man's evolution that they have deliberately ignored the physical evidence in order to arrange these so-called hominid fossils into what *looks like* an evolutionary family tree. They have, for example, taken all relevant data on cranial capacities, from the 500 c.c. capacities of the australopithecines (and modern gorillas) to the 1500 c.c. skulls of modern man, and published them in a graphical sequence purporting to show the gradual increase in brain size as man evolved. However, this "evolutionary line" is not a "time line," for the dates assigned to these skull fragments are widely divergent, with considerable evidence that *Australopithecus*, *Homo erectus*, and *Homo sapiens* have all lived contemporaneously in the past.

As a matter of fact, one could arrange the skull sizes of *living* human beings in a similar series, increasing from as low as 700 c.c. to over 2000 c.c., and this would have nothing whatever to do with evolution, since cranial capacity has no necessary correlation at all with human intelligence or mental ability — still less with the soul/spirit complex that completely separates man from all animals.

The fact is that, even after a century of intensive searching and special pleading, there is still no real fossil evidence of human evolution!

17 *Ibid.*, p. 43.

Not surprisingly, despite the diligent research done in East Africa by paleontologists Richard Leakey and Donald Johanson, there are gaping holes in the evolutionary record, some of them extending for four to six million years.

> Modern apes, for instance, seem to have sprung out of nowhere. They have no yesterday, no fossil record. And the true origin of modern humans — of upright, naked, tool-making, big-brained beings — is, if we are to be honest with ourselves, an equally mysterious matter.[18]

Even the professional paleoanthropologists, though still firmly committed to an evolutionary faith, are in disarray as to the actual fossil histories.

> All this makes a much more complex picture of hominoid evolution than we once imagined. It no longer resembles a ladder but is, instead, more like a bush. . . . Hominids evolved, as did many other mammal groups, with diverse and overlapping radiations. There is no clear-cut and inexorable pathway from ape to human being.[19]

> Anthropologists are like the blind men looking at the elephant, each sampling only a small part of the total reality.[20]

> The simple idea of evolution, which it is no longer thought necessary to examine, spreads like a tent over all those ages that lead from primitivism into civilization. Gradually, we are told, step by step, men produced the arts and crafts, this and that, until they emerged in the light of history. Those soporific words "gradually" and "step-by-step," repeated incessantly, are aimed at covering an ignorance which is both vast and surprising. One should like to inquire: Which steps? But then one is lulled, overwhelmed, and stupefied by the gradualness of it all, which is at best a platitude, only good for pacifying the mind, since no one is willing to imagine that civilization appeared in a thunderclap.[21]

---

[18] Lyall Watson, "The Water People," p. 44.

[19] David Pilbeam, "Rearranging Our Family Tree," p. 44, 45.

[20] Alan Mann, as quoted in "Puzzling Out Man's Ascent," *Time* (November 7, 1977), p. 77. Mann is an anthropologist at the University of Pennsylvania.

[21] Giorgio de Santillana and Hertha von Dechend, *Hamlet's Mill* (Boston, MA: Gambit, Inc., 1969), p. 68.

The quotations above are from articles or books written two decades or more ago, but anthropologists continue to wrangle and speculate on these matters year after year.

> Paleoanthropologists seem to make up for a lack of fossils with an excess of fury, and this must now be the only science in which it is still possible to become famous just for having an opinion. As one cynic says, in human paleontology the consensus depends on who shouts loudest.[22]

> The study of human origins seems to be a field in which each discovery raises the debate to a more sophisticated level of uncertainty.[23]

The fervent arguments between Richard Leakey and Donald Johanson have been mentioned. More recently Johanson has been feuding vigorously with other anthropologists — especially Dr. Garniss Curtis and Tim White — on the staff at the University of California at Berkeley, leading to a lawsuit and almost to blows.[24] The arguments generally have to do with competition over funding and over priorities, as well as whose "ape-man" find is the oldest and most important. To an outsider, it does seem that every paleoanthropologist has his (or her) own agenda and ax to grind.

> The subjective element in this approach to building evolutionary trees, which many paleontologists advocate with almost religious fervor, is demonstrated by the outcome: there is no single family tree on which they agree. On the contrary, almost every conceivable combination and permutation of living and extinct hominoids has been proposed by one cladist or another.[25]

The authors of the above complaint against any cladistic approach to an evolutionary tree are, in turn, promoting their own biomolecular approach. They are certainly correct, however, in noting the numerous evolutionary lineages proposed for human beings.

---

[22] J. S. Jones, "A Thousand and One Eves," *Nature*, vol. 345 (May 31, 1990), p. 395.

[23] Christopher B. Stringer, "The Legacy of Homo Sapiens," *Scientific American*, vol. 268 (May 1993), p. 138.

[24] David J. Jefferson, "This Anthropologist Has a Style That is Bone of Contention," *Wall Street Journal* (January 31, 1995), p. 1.

[25] Jerald Loewenstein and Adrienne Zihlman, "The Invisible Ape," *New Scientist*, vol. 120 (December 3, 1988), p. 58.

> If placed on top of one another, all these competing versions of our evolutionary highways would make the Los Angeles freeway system look like County Road 41 in Elkhart, Indiana.[26]

Any discussion of specific fossils is out of date nearly as soon as published, so it is almost redundant to critique the hominids currently in vogue. The once-fashionable names of Java Man, Piltdown Man, Nebraska Man, Heidelberg Man, Rhodesia Man, Peking Man, and others that used to be offered as proof of man's evolution are nowadays all but ignored in anthropological discussions. Neanderthal Man and Cro-Magnon Man are now universally accepted as *Homo sapiens*. Even *Ramapithecus* is currently out of favor as an early hominid, being recognized now as simply an orangutan. All of the anthropologists agree, however, when it comes to fighting creationism.

We do need to consider in a little more detail the hominids that are currently in favor with most paleoanthropologists.

The Australopithecines

When one of the writers (H. Morris) was in school, it was commonly taught that the three conclusive proofs of human evolution were Piltdown man, Peking man, and Java man. These famous discoveries, however, are an embarrassment and are rarely taken seriously. Piltdown man was a hoax, Peking man has been lost for 50 years, and Java man was later admitted by its discoverer to be an artificial construct of a human thighbone and the skull of a gibbon. Other former "stars" in the ape-man extravaganza were Nebraska man (an extinct pig) and Neanderthal man (now universally acknowledged to be modern man).

The current "lead" in this long-running play is a supposed hominid (ape-man) named *Australopithecus* (meaning "ape of the south"), associated with a varied collection of fossil evidence, including Louis Leakey's *Zinjanthropus*, Richard Leakey's Skull 1470 and Donald Johanson's Lucy, as well as Mary Leakey's Laetoli fossil footprints. Although there has been sharp disagreement between Johanson and the Leakeys as to their "finds'" exact role in evolution, they all now maintain that these so-called "australopithecines" walked erect, like men, even though they had ape-like brains and skulls.

Nevertheless, the evidence against this view is growing. Dr. Yoel Rak describes the significance of the first-discovered australopithecine ear bone.

---

[26] "Whose Ape Is It, Anyway?" *Science News*, vol. 125 (June 9, 1984), p. 361.

It is substantially different from that of a modern man, and the dissimilarity exceeds that between the ear bones of *Homo sapiens* and the African apes. The new incus ("anvil") is of interest particularly in view of the unique advantages that ear ossicles (bones) have for taxonomic and phylogenetic (evolutionary) studies. The only other fossil hominid ear ossicles are from latseh and are indistinguishable from those of modern man.[27]

That the australopithecines were simple apes of some kind is evident also from their skulls, which have long been recognized as having the brain capacity (about 500 cubic centimeters) of a true ape. It was long believed, however, that their brains were at least probably human-like in shape. This now also turns out to have been quite wrong.

I expected the australopithecine natural endocasts to appear like miniature replicas of human brains because that had been the prevalent view in the scientific literature since 1925.... My analysis of the seven known australopithecine endocasts shows Radinsky's hunch was right: all of the convolutions that they preserve were apelike.[28]

Although some scientists and many popular writers believe that man is descended from the australopithecines, many do not.

Interestingly, despite almost a decade of technically sophisticated analyses of australopithecine remains, there is still considerable controversy over their functional and phylogenetic significance — in particular whether they are too divergently specialized to be considered suitable ancestors for *Homo*.[29]

The most sophisticated of these analyses were performed by Solly Zuckerman, Charles Oxnard, and their colleagues. These multivariate statistical analyses were computerized and highly detailed, showing almost conclusively that the australopithecines were some form of extinct ape, and that they did *not* walk erect. Oxnard's evaluation was summarized as follows:

---

[27] Yoel Rak, "Ear Ossicle of *Australopithecus Robustus*," *Nature*, vol. 279 (May 3, 1975), p. 62.

[28] Dean Falk, "The Petrified Brain," *Natural History*, vol. 93 (September 1984), p. 38.

[29] James A. Hopson and Leonard B. Radinsky, "Vertebrate Paleontology: New Approaches and New Insights," *Paleobiology*, vol. 6 (Summer 1980), p. 263.

> Although most studies emphasize the similarity of the australopithecines to modern man, and suggest, therefore, that these creatures were bipedal toolmakers . . . a series of multivariate statistical studies of various postcranial fragments suggests other conclusions.[30]

The conclusion was, essentially, that *Australopithecus* was an extinct ape, more like the orangutan than like any other living creature.

Some have argued, however, that Mary Leakey's 1978-79 finds of fossil footprints proved that *Australopithecus* did walk erect. These footprints indicated a bipedal creature, but the only reason for identifying them with *Australopithecus* was the fact that they were found in Africa and were dated radiometrically to correspond to the *assumed* age of *Australopithecus*. Consider, however, the following evaluation of them:

> The uneroded footprints show a total morphological pattern like that seen in modern humans. . . . Spatial relationships of the footprints are strikingly human in pattern. . . . The Laetoli hominid trails at site G do not differ substantially from modern human trails made on a similar substrate.[31]

In other words, these trails are indistinguishable from trails of true human footprints. Why, then, try to make them out to be australopithecine footprints? Why not draw the much more reasonable conclusion, either that the dates are wrong, or else that man lived at the same time as the australopithecines?

Further evaluation of these footprints continues to favor the conclusion that they must be human tracks. The University of Chicago anthropologist Russell Tuttle has been studying them for some ten years. He says:

> In sum, the 3.5-million-year-old footprint trails at Laetoli site G resemble those of habitually unshod modern humans. None of their features suggest that the Laetoli hominids were less capable bipeds than we are.[32]

They could *not* have been made by any of the australopithecines,

---

[30] Charles Oxnard, *Nature*, vol. 258 (1975), p. 389.

[31] P. H. Busse and K. E. Heikes, "Evolutionary Implications of Pliocene Hominid Footprints," *Science*, vol. 208 (April 11, 1980), p. 175.

[32] Russell Tuttle, "The Pitted Pattern of Laetoli Feet," *Natural History* (March 1990), p. 64.

as many have assumed they were. Recent detailed studies of the actual mechanics of australopithecine anatomy, made at the Natural History Museum of Paris, have conclusively demonstrated this.

> The present results lead to the conclusion that the bipedalism of *Australopithecus* must have differed from that of *Homo* . . . the australopithecine walk differed significantly from that of humans, involving a sort of waddling gait, with large rotatory movements of the pelvis and shoulders around the vertebral column. . . . A previous paper has suggested that the pelvic proportions of *Australopithecus* could provide some arguments for an arboreal locomotion. The results of the present study suggest amplification of this opinion.[33]

It does seem that true humans were living at the same time as the australopithecines, and that the Laetoli footprints were made by *them*, *not* by the hominids, regardless of the "age" of the tracks.

The latter conclusion, while contrary to the usual evolutionary prejudices, is not really so far-fetched, even in the framework of the standard geologic ages. It is now rather generally agreed by anthropologists that australopithecines were contemporaries of *Homo erectus*, even though some believe that the latter had evolved from the former. If that is the case, why could not *Homo sapiens* have been contemporaneous with both? Richard Leakey, for example, has described localities where fossils of *Homo erectus* and *Australopithecus* were found at the same level. But then he also reminds us of the following discovery, originally noted by his father Louis Leakey, but thereafter mostly ignored.

> At one locality, remains of a stone structure — perhaps the base of a circular hut — were uncovered; there is an excellent date of 1.8 million years for this.[34]

Now a circular stone hut could hardly have been constructed by anyone but a true human being, but the stratigraphic level of this structure was *below* the levels of fossils of both *Australopithecus* and *Homo erectus*! And then, how about the remarkable intimations from the new science of cladistics, especially when correlated with the assumed

---

[33] Christine Berg, "How Did the Australopithecines Walk? A Biomechanical Study of the Hip and Thigh of *Australopithecus afarensis*," *Journal of Human Evolution*, vol. 26 (April 1994), p. 271.

[34] Richard Leakey, "Hominids in Africa," *American Scientist* (March/April 1976), p. 177.

chronology of continental drift?

After showing that "cladograms" (diagrams of assemblages of physiologic and morphologic similarities, used to deduce relationships) of birds, butterflies, reptiles, and plants correspond globally with the chronology of splitting and drifting continents, two specialists in this field proceeded to show that cladograms of human beings, when classified according to race, language, and biochemistry, show exactly the same type of correlation. But the primeval super-continent is supposed to have split and initiated the development of these relationships about 80 million years ago. Consequently, these authors pose the following question:

> Would we not have to consider the possibility that humans also are that old, and have been affected by the same events?[35]

This would mean that man is not only as old as the australopithecines, but also as old as the dinosaurs! To the creationist, of course, this is eminently reasonable. Many "anomalous" human fossils and artifacts have been reported throughout the geologic column, but these have been commonly ignored or explained away by evolutionists.

But that is another story. The point we emphasize here is that the fossil record of man and the apes, like that of all other creatures, is one that testifies to the stability of the basic created kinds, variation within the kinds, occasional extinction of kinds, with clear-cut and permanent gaps between the kinds. There has never been any *real* evolution.

The Enigma of Homo Erectus

Another group of fragmentary fossils, collectively known as *Homo erectus*, is believed by many paleoanthropologists to be intermediate between *Australopithecus* and *Homo sapiens*. Peking man and Java man, once believed to be in this group, are now mostly ignored. However, other fossils of *Homo erectus* have since been found in both Asia and Africa, and possibly even in Australia. These have been so identified mostly by their brain capacities, usually in the 700–800 c.c. range.

This factor alone, however, does not prove anything, since a considerable number of fully normal modern human beings are known to have skull capacities in this range. Furthermore, many modern people

---

[35] Gareth Nelson and Norman Platnick, *Systematics and Biogeography* (New York: Columbia University Press, 1981). Of course, if evolutionists cannot be persuaded by fossil footprints, they will probably not be influenced by cladograms.

have heavy brow ridges and low sloping foreheads, so these features don't mean much either. One problem has been that the apparent ages of *Homo erectus* remains have often overlapped the dates assigned to *Australopithecus*, so that the two families are known now to have been living contemporaneously, and even in the same geographical areas.

There is no doubt that *Homo erectus* ("erect man") had an upright posture. That he was truly human, rather than an erect ape, has possibly been confirmed by studies of the brain endocast from the skull known as "1470," discovered a number of years ago by Richard Leakey.

> An endocast from the Kenya National Museum, a *Homo habilis* specimen known as ER 1470, reproduces a human-like frontal lobe, including what appears to be Broca's area.[36]

Since this part of the brain (Broca's area) is known to control speech, and is uniquely human, it seems possible that at least this particular *Homo erectus* specimen was a true man, even though his cranial capacity was just over 750 c.c. This skull remains controversial (ER 1470 is even considered by some anthropologists to be an australopithecine) and is still commonly called *Homo habilis*, assumed intermediate between *Australopithecus* and *Homo erectus*. Nevertheless, as Falk says:

> If we wish to identify one prime mover of human brain evolution, the endocast from ER 1470, with its human-like frontal lobes that contain what appears to be Broca's speech area in the left hemisphere, confirms what is suggested by comparing the behavior of apes and humans: it is language.[37]

The fact that *Homo erectus* was a true man, rather than an ape-human intermediate of some kind, has been further confirmed by the discovery in late 1984 of the most complete *Homo erectus* skeleton found to date, a boy estimated to be 12 years old, excavated in Kenya, and believed by evolutionists to have lived about 1.6 million years ago, as based on radiometric dating of the ash deposits in which it was found by anthropologists Richard Leakey and Alan Walker.

> The new find reveals that these ancient people had bodies virtually indistinguishable from our own. . . . The

---

[36] Dean Falk, "The Petrified Brain," p. 38.
[37] *Ibid.*, p. 39.

skeleton showed that the boy stood 5 feet 6 inches, taller than many of today's 12 year olds.[38]

Except for the brain size (about 880 c.c.), the skull and jaw-bone looked "much like a Neanderthal."[39] Neanderthal man, of course, is now acknowledged by all evolutionary anthropologists to be true man, *Homo sapiens*. Therefore, while *Australopithecus* was simply an ape of some kind, it is almost certain that *Homo erectus* was a true man, similar in some ways to the extinct Neanderthal tribe. Quite possibly, fossils have been identified as *Homo erectus*, rather than *Homo sapiens*, simply because they happened to be members of the human race whose brain sizes were at the low end of the normal spectrum of brain-size variation, but otherwise they were probably normal human beings.

Further studies of this Kenya fossil seem to support the possibility that — except for the very old date assigned to it and the African location — it could almost be grouped with the Neanderthals, which are now universally recognized as *Homo sapiens*. At any rate, the *Homo erectus* designation groups it and all others of that type within the family of *Homo* — that is, "man." In the absence of any living members of that "tribe," it is impossible to say anything about their language or other means of communication.

Language, of course — that is, the ability to communicate in abstract, symbolic, intelligible speech, whether verbal or written — is the one essential attribute that distinguishes true man from apes or other animals. And, as just noted, *Homo erectus* meets that test, even if his cranial capacity was at the lower end of the human spectrum. (And even *that* is within the range of modern man!)

That does bring up the subject of Neanderthal man. Although their brain capacity was somewhat *above* the modern average, many have argued that the heavy Neanderthal jawbones would have made speech impossible for them. This has turned out to be wrong:

> Paleontologists in Israel have discovered a fossil bone which shows that Neanderthals may have been just as capable of speech as modern humans. The bone, known as the hyoid, is from a Neanderthal who lived between 50,000 and 60,000 years ago. The hyoid, a small v-shaped bone, is a key part of the vocal apparatus in modern human beings. . . . According to B. Arensberg and Yoel

---

[38] Boyce Rensberger, "Human Fossil is Unearthed," *Washington Post* (October 19, 1984), p. A1.

[39] *Ibid.*

Rak of Tel Aviv University and their colleagues, the fossil hyoid, in size and shape is just like a modern human's (*Nature*, vol. 338, p. 758). The positions of the muscle attachments are also similar. The researchers believe that, despite their heavy jawbones, Neanderthals spoke a language.[40]

In February, at the annual meeting of the American Association for the Advancement of Science, University of Kansas paleoanthropologist David Frayer presented a survey of accumulating data, including the discovery of the hyoid bone and a new reconstruction of an old Neanderthal skull, in launching a new attack on the idea that Neanderthals couldn't speak.[41]

It was already well-known that both Neanderthal man and Cro-Magnon man not only were human in anatomy and brain size, but also buried their dead, made tools, grew flowers, painted pictures, and showed other aspects of a truly human culture. Neanderthal's somewhat stooped posture, heavy skull, and other physical peculiarities may have been the result of disease or dietary deficiencies — possibly even old age — but they certainly were within the range of modern human attributes. We are warranted in concluding that Neanderthal, Cro-Magnon, and *Homo erectus* were *all created human beings*, whereas *Australopithecus* was a *created* but now *extinct* ape.

The Uniqueness of Human Language

The most important physical ability distinguishing man from apes and other animals is undoubtedly his remarkable capacity for language. The ability to communicate with others of his own kind in abstract, symbolic speech is unique to man, and the evolutionist has never been able to bridge the tremendous gulf between this ability and the grunts and barks and chatterings of animals.

Some researchers have, of course, made extravagant claims as to the potentiality of teaching chimpanzees to speak, for example, or have developed highly imaginative speculations as to how animal noises may have evolved into human languages. Such notions are, however, not based on real scientific observation or evidence.

Man's brain is quite different from that of chimpanzees, especially

---

[40] Sarah Bunney, "Neanderthals Weren't So Dumb After All," *New Scientist*, vol. 123 (July 1, 1989), p. 43.

[41] Ann Gibbons, "Neanderthal Language Debate: Tongues Wag Anew," *Science*, vol. 256 (April 3, 1992), p. 33.

in that portion which controls speech. Isaac Asimov noted this in these words:

> Once speech is possible, human beings can commu-
> nicate thoughts and receive them; they can consult, teach,
> pool information. . . . Once speech was developed, then the
> evolution of intelligence proceeded rapidly. The chimpan-
> zee lacks Broca's convolution, but it may have the germs
> of communication, which could develop rapidly if it ever
> evolved that part of the brain.[42]

Realistically, however, one does not acquire a brain capable of abstract thought and intelligent speech (even if "Broca's convolution" *is* really all that the brain needs to do this) merely by allowing "evolution" to create one because it might be helpful. Two top authorities on supposed human evolution, David Pilbeam and Stephen Gould, anthropologist at Yale and invertebrate paleontologist at Harvard, respectively, have pointed out that man's brain shape is not a mere scaled-up replica of the ape's, but is qualitatively distinct in critical ways.

> *Homo sapiens* provides the outstanding exception to
> this trend among primates, for we have evolved a relatively
> large brain and small face, in opposition to functional
> expectations at our size. . . . *Australopithecus africanus* has
> a rounded braincase because it is a relatively small animal;
> *Homo sapiens* displays this feature because we have evolved
> a large brain and circumvented the expectations of nega-
> tive allometry. The resemblance is fortuitous; it offers no
> evidence of genetic similarity.[43]

Though creationists do not share the credulous faith of evolutionists that man's unique brain has simply "evolved," they do concur with the inference that this uniqueness has placed an *unbridgeable gap* between man and any of the animals.

Evolutionist George Gaylord Simpson admitted that there is little possibility of tracing an evolutionary connection between animals and men, as far as language is concerned.

> Human language is absolutely distinct from any sys-

---

[42] Isaac Asimov, "Chimps Tell Us About Evolution," *Science Digest*, (November 1974), p. 89.

[43] David Pilbeam and Stephen Jay Gould, "Size and Scaling in Human Evolution," *Science*, vol. 186 (December 6, 1974), p. 899-900.

tem of communication in other animals. . . . It is still possible, but it is unlikely, that we will ever know just when and how our ancestors began to speak.[44]

Since Simpson was a biologist and paleontologist, rather than a linguistics scientist, certain of the younger speculative linguists may feel that he was speaking out of his field, and that it may yet be possible to trace such an evolutionary origin of human language. However, many modern linguistic specialists today would acknowledge Dr. Noam Chomsky, Professor of Linguistics at the Massachusetts Institute of Technology, to be the world's foremost linguist, and according to Gunther Stent, Dr. Chomsky has said:

> Human language appears to be a unique phenomenon, without significant analogue in the animal world.[45]

As to whether the gap between animal noises and human language was ever bridged by evolution, Dr. Chomsky asserts the following:

> There is no reason to suppose that the "gaps" are bridgeable. There is no more of a basis for assuming an evolutionary development of "higher" from "lower" stages, in this case, than there is for assuming an evolutionary development from breathing to walking.[46]

In other words, there is no comparison at all!

Chomsky and many other modern linguists have found, not only that there is no connection between animal sounds and human speech, but also that there is a deep commonality between the basic thought patterns of all men, regardless of how diverse their individual languages may be. That is, there is a fundamental connection between all human languages, but *no connection at all* between human language and animal "language."[47]

Dr. Gunther S. Stent (professor of molecular biology at the University of California in Berkeley) has drawn the further inference from Chomsky's studies that man has a certain fundamental being that is incapable of being reached by scientific analysis.

---

[44] George Gaylord Simpson, "The Biological Nature of Man," *Science*, vol. 152 (April 22, 1966), p. 476, 477.

[45] Gunther S. Stent, "Limits to the Scientific Understanding of Man," *Science*, vol. 187 (March 21, 1975), p. 1054.

[46] *Ibid.*, p. 68.

[47] Noam Chomsky, *Language and Mind* (New York: Harcourt, Brace, Jovanovich, Inc., 1972), p. 67.

Chomsky holds that the grammar of a language is a system of transformational rules that determines a certain pairing of sound and meaning. It consists of a syntactic component, a semantic component, and a phonological component. The surface structure contains the information relevant to the phonological component, whereas the deep structure contains the information relevant to the semantic component, and the syntactic component pairs surface and deep structures.[48]

Chomsky and his associates have developed what they call *structural linguistics*, with its concepts of the "deep" structure and the "surface" structure. The latter involves the ordinary phenomena of different languages and their translation one into the other. The mere fact that people are able to learn other languages is itself evidence of the uniqueness and fundamental unity of the human race. No such possibility exists between man and animals.

The "deep structure" is the basic self-conscious thought structure of the man himself, and his intuitive formulation of discrete thoughts and chains of reasoning. The vocal sounds that he uses to transmit his thoughts to others may vary widely from tribe to tribe, but the fundamental thought system is there, and is universal among mankind.

The semantic component has remained invariant and is, therefore, the "universal" aspect of the universal grammar, which all natural languages embody. And this presumed constancy through time of the universal grammar cannot be attributable to any cause other than an innate, hereditary aspect of the mind. Hence, the general aim of structural linguistics is to discover this universal grammar.[49]

Presumably, if this "universal grammar" could ever be ascertained, it would supply the key to man's original language — perhaps even its phonology and syntactical structure, as well as its semantic content.

Evolutionists, as well as creationists, have in recent years come to believe in the monophyletic origin of all the tribes and races of mankind. Most of the earlier evolutionists, however, believed in man's polyphyletic origin, thinking that each of the major "races" had evolved

---

[48] Stent, "Limits to the Scientific Understanding," p. 1054.
[49] Chomsky, *Language and Mind*, p. 68.

independently from a different hominid line. This idea, of course, easily leads to racism, the belief that one race is innately superior to another race. That is, if each race has had a long, independent evolutionary history, slowly developing its distinctive character by the lengthy process of random mutation and natural selection, then it is all but certain that there has been a differential rate of evolution between the different races, with some evolving to higher levels than others. That such racist beliefs were held by all nineteenth-century evolutionist scientists (Darwin and Huxley included) has been thoroughly documented.[50]

Modern evolutionists, however, repudiate racism, which has become sociologically unpopular in the 20th century. Although they are now in practically complete agreement that all present groups of men came originally from one single population of ancestral men, they are currently in complete confusion as to exactly what that lineage may have been. In any case, man has always been man, culturally and linguistically, as well as physically and mentally.

Consider this ancestral human population, whenever and however it first appeared — whether several million years ago, newly arrived by an unknown evolutionary process from unknown evolutionary ancestors, or only several thousand years ago. In either event, they must have constituted an originally coherent body of true men, all with the same language and culture.

The question then is, how did the different languages ever develop? If the "semantic component" of language, as Chomsky puts it, is still the same for all men, how did the "phonologic component" ever become so diverse and variegated? Gradual changes are understandable (as in the gradual accretion of Latin words, Greek words, Germanic words, etc., to produce the modern English language), but how could such vastly different linguistic systems as the Indo-European languages, the agglutinative languages of the Africans, and the tonal languages of the Mongols ever develop from a single ancestral language?

Furthermore, the *more ancient* languages seem to be the *more complex* languages, as do the languages of the more apparently "primitive" tribes living today.

> Even the peoples with least complex cultures have highly sophisticated languages, with complex grammar and large vocabularies, capable of naming and discussing anything that occurs in the sphere occupied by their speakers.

---

[50] John S. Haller, Jr., *Outcasts from Evolution* (Urbana, IL: University of Illinois Press, 1971).

The oldest language that can reasonably be reconstructed is already modern, sophisticated, complete from an evolutionary point of view.[51]

Not only so, but the history of any given language, rather than representing an increasingly complex structure, as the structure of its users supposedly evolved into higher levels of complexity, seems, instead, to record an inevitable decline in complexity.

The evolution of language, at least within the historical period, is a story of progressive simplification.[52]

It seems necessary to assume either of two alternatives in order to explain these strange linguistic phenomena:

1. An original population of men, at least 100,000 years ago and possibly up to four million years ago, with a highly complex language and culture. This original population (its origin completely unknown and apparently inexplicable on evolutionary grounds) somehow broke up into a number of separate populations, each then developing independently of the others for such a very long time that its extreme peculiarities of linguistic phonology and syntax could emerge as a deteriorative remnant of the ancestral language.
2. An original population of men several thousand years ago. This population once used the postulated complex common-ancestral language, but somehow broke up into the assumed smaller populations. However, this breakup was not a slow evolutionary process over hundreds of thousands of years, but rather was accomplished in some kind of traumatic separation, accomplished essentially instantaneously by a sudden transmutation of the one phonology into a number of distinctively and uniquely different phonologies.

Neither of these alternatives is amenable to an evolutionary interpretation, since neither accounts for the original ancestral complex language, and since both involve a subsequent deterioration (rather than evolution) of language complexity. The former, however, is favored by evolutionists because the great time spans involved seem more suitable to a uniformitarian philosophy, and because the latter clearly involves

---

[51] Simpson, "Biological Nature of Man," p. 477.
[52] Albert C. Baugh, *A History of the English Language* (New York: Appleton-Century-Crofts, Inc., 1957), p. 10.

catastrophic, even supernaturalistic intervention in human history.

The long-time-span interpretation, however, necessarily involves the evolution model once again in its racist connotations. For how are populations going to be separated long enough to develop such drastically different languages, without also developing drastically different physical features and mental abilities? As long as they were together, or even closely enough associated to be in communication with each other (and such association would surely be to their mutual advantage), they would retain an essentially common language, would intermarry, and thereby retain common physical and mental characteristics as well.

Yet the languages and cultures and physical features are, indeed, quite different, and have been so since the dawn of recorded history! A genetics professor at Stanford says:

> When we look at the main divisions of mankind, we find many differences that are visible to the unaided eye. . . . It is highly likely that all these differences are determined genetically, but they are not determined in any simple way. For example, where skin color is concerned there are at least four gene differences that contribute to variations in pigmentation.[53]

If such an apparently simple and obvious difference as skin color is determined in such a complex fashion, and if all such gene factors have developed originally by mutation (as evolutionists believe), then a very long period of racial segregation must have been necessary.

> The simplest interpretation of these conclusions today would envision a relatively small group starting to spread not long after modern man appeared. With the spreading, groups became separated and isolated. Racial differentiation followed. Fifty thousand years or so is a short time in evolutionary terms, and this may help to explain why, genetically speaking, human races show relatively small differences.[54]

Furthermore, if obvious differences such as skin color and facial morphology can arise by mutation and selection in 50,000 years, then

---

[53] L. L. Cavalli-Sforza, "The Genetics of Human Populations," *Scientific American*, vol. 231 (September 1974), p. 85.

[54] *Ibid.*, p. 89. From what has been noted, however, it is obvious that even the author's 50,000 year estimate is much too small in the evolution framework. Even this shorter time, however, would surely involve significant racist connotations.

surely subtle differences in mental abilities could also arise in such a time, and these would have considerably more selection value for survival than would skin pigmentation. The inferences for racism are again very obvious and ominous!

As a matter of fact, as creationists have repeatedly pointed out, there is no empirical evidence of mutations that confer any kind of "beneficial" effect in the natural environment upon either the individuals or the populations that experience them. The various physical changes (skin color, etc.) can be much more easily explained as *created* genetic factors that were latent in the human genetic system ever since the creation, but which could become openly expressed only in a small population being forced to reproduce by inbreeding after segregation from its ancestral population.

If the initial population were somehow forced to break up into small reproductively isolated populations, only a relatively small number of generations would be required to allow distinctive physical characteristics (all representing created genetic factors already present, though latent, in the larger population) to become manifest and fixed in different combinations in the different tribal clans.

The enforced segregation would most expeditiously be arranged by the postulated sudden transmutation of the ancestral phonology (spoken language) into a number of uniquely different phonologies. No other traumatic changes would be necessary, as the physical changes would easily and quickly develop genetically from the linguistic segregation.

Furthermore, no basic change in human nature would be involved. All would still "think" in the same way and would still be, distinctively, men. The "deep structure" of human consciousness and communicative ability would be unaffected even by a traumatic change in the "surface structure." Dr. Stent makes an incisive comment in this connection.

> Hence it is merely the phonological component that has become greatly differentiated during the course of human history, or *at least since the construction of the Tower of Babel*.[55]

Whether or not Dr. Stent believes in the confusion of tongues at Babel as a real event of history, it is at least symbolic to him of the fact that there must have at one time been some such division, and that no normal evolutionary development could accomplish it! To the creation-

---

[55] Stent, "Limits to the Scientific Understanding," p. 1054.

ist, of course, Babel is not only symbolic, but actual. The supernatural confusion of phonologies, with its resultant tribal dispersions throughout the world, and its logical genetic consequences in the rapid emergence of distinctive tribal characteristics, fits all the known facts of philology, ethnology, and archaeology perfectly.

Furthermore, man's universal semantic consciousness is at once an attestation of his uniqueness in the living world, and of the inability of naturalistic science to comprehend this deep inner nature of man. Dr. Stent himself recognizes this as follows:

> No matter how deeply we probe into the visual pathway, in the end we need to posit an "inner man" who transforms the visual image into a precept. And as far as linguistics is concerned, the analysis of language appears to be heading for the same conceptual impasse as does the analysis of vision.[56]

Chomsky and the other structural linguists have found it necessary to postulate a "deep structure" of self-consciousness, but they do not know where this "inner man" comes from, nor how it functions. Materialistic science can explain much with its chemical and physical equations, but it flounders when it reaches the domain of "soul" and "spirit." Stent continues as follows:

> That is to say, for man the concept of "meaning" can be fathomed only in relation to the self, which is both ultimate source and ultimate destination of semantic signals. But the concept of the self . . . cannot be given an explicit definition. Instead, the meaning of "self" is intuitively obvious. It is another Kantian transcendental concept, one which we bring *a priori* to man just as we bring the concepts of space, time, and causality to nature.[57]

The concept of "self" may be intuitively obvious, but its *cause* is not so obvious, at least not to an evolutionist. Its reality is found to be necessary, even by naturalistic science, but as an "effect," it requires an adequate "cause," and no naturalistic cause is available to explain it. A supernatural Creator is required!

All of which leads to the conclusion that the *ultimate* purpose of language is not merely for communication between man and man, but even more for communication between man and his maker.

---

[56] *Ibid.*
[57] *Ibid.*, p. 1057.

Chapter 5

Evolution Never Happened at All

We have seen that the predictions of the creation model have been precisely confirmed with respect to the systems and processes of the present, and also with respect to the fossil record of the past. That is, there have always been distinct types of plants and animals, with clear-cut and apparently permanent gaps between them. Each type is highly complex and is organized to function in its environment. There is no evolutionary flux apparent at all, except for small "horizontal" changes at the same level of complexity. Each organism thus has the ability to adapt (within limits) to changing environments without becoming extinct.

All of this is predictable from the creation model, and it does not at all support the evolution model. Nevertheless, it does not *prove* creation, and evolutionists are perpetually modifying their model to try to make it fit the data. In recent years, there has been a widespread shift to a "saltational" model of evolutionary change, which purportedly predicts such "gaps" in the record. To creationists, this ploy seems to be a reluctant and unacknowledged recognition that the creationists' predictions were right after all. It is essentially just a desperate attempt to account for creation without a Creator, and it still will not work!

Punctuated Equilibrium — Evolution's Last Stand

The mystery of the ubiquitous lack of transitional forms has not silenced doctrinaire evolutionists. They used to explain these gaps by the lack of fossils, but fossils are so abundant now that they know the gaps are real! Consequently, many have fallen back (though not all) to a concept of evolution by quantum leaps.

One of the most noticeable aspects of the theory of evolution, therefore, is its own continuing evolution! One would think that after almost 150 years of intensive study of supposed evolutionary mechanisms, everyone should know by now how it works. But the fact is that evolution is no better understood now than it was in the days of Charles Darwin. Evolutionists protest (too much, in fact) that they *know* evolution is true, but it must be embarrassing for them to have to admit repeatedly that they still don't understand its mechanism!

The latest idea is *stasis* — that is, stability, "standing still." Paleontologist Steven M. Stanley (Johns Hopkins University) says:

> The [fossil] record now reveals that species typically survive for a hundred thousand generations, or even a million or more, without evolving much. We seem forced to conclude that most evolution takes place rapidly, when species come into being by the evolutionary divergence of small populations from parent species. After their origins, most species undergo little evolution before becoming extinct.[1]

Similarly, Harvard University paleontologist Stephen Gould has said this:

> Thus, our model of "punctuated equilibria" holds that evolution is concentrated in events of speciation and that successful speciation is an infrequent event punctuating the stasis of large populations that do not alter in fundamental ways during the millions of years that they endure.[2]

This is certainly fascinating. *Evolution*, which means "change," is characterized mainly by *stasis*, which means "no change!" The "punctuations" that produce new species occur so rapidly and so rarely that they can never be observed. Since we can never observe evolution in action, it is presumed to happen very rapidly when we are not looking. No wonder it has been so hard to learn how evolution works!

All this brings us to the amazing new concept known as *punctuated equilibrium*. This idea was introduced in this country only in 1971 by Niles Eldredge and Stephen Jay Gould (though it had previously been popular in Russia), but it is now rapidly gaining dominance over the field as far as evolutionary theory is concerned. It is the product *not* of any

---

[1] Steven M. Stanley, *The New Evolutionary Time-table: Fossils, Genes and the Origin of Species* (Basic Books, Inc., 1981), preface.

[2] Stephen Jay Gould, "Is a New and General Theory of Evolution Emerging?" *Paleobiology*, vol. 6, no. 1 (1980), p. 125.

evidence — but rather of *lack* of evidence — for evolution. Since the universal absence of transitional forms in both the fossil record and the living world had shown that slow-and-gradual evolution was invalid, and since the traditional mutation/selection mechanism of neo-Darwinism had proved impotent to generate anything of consequence, many evolutionists have finally decided that they must resort to *revolutionary evolutionism*.

The only alternative seems to be creationism, and that, to the leaders of evolutionary thought, is unthinkable heresy. So, instead of turning to God, they attribute the generation of each new kind of organism to some mysterious genetic upheaval, some remarkable embryonic saltation, some lucky leap of jumping genes, transforming a decadent population of organisms in equilibrium, through a dynamic punctuation in that equilibrium, to a new and higher degree of biologic existence! Thus, paradoxically, the main characteristic of evolution has become stability, and evolutionism is now an oxymoron. The mechanism of evolution is long periods of equilibrium punctuated by brief but dynamic episodes of chance upheavals, which heave things up instead of down.

This is an amazing excursus into the logic of wonderland. Since species survive indefinitely without significant change (except extinction), therefore, they evolve very rapidly! Creationists, of course, have long emphasized this stability of basic types. That is exactly what the "creation model" predicts: primeval completed creation and subsequent conservation of the biologic kinds. But evolutionists reject creationism not because of the testimony of science, but because of their commitment to naturalism.

Because of this innate rebellion against the concept of creation, the modern school of evolutionists has turned to a theory for which there is no mechanism and no evidence! Stanley and others like to emphasize what they call "quantum speciation," since there is no evidence for gradual evolution, even at the species level. If the origin of new species is inexplicable, however, the origin of higher categories (genera, families, orders, etc.) is far more so. We have already quoted Gould on the impossibility of accounting for the origin of the *Baupläne* (phyla) by any form of gradualism (see page 70).

The evolutionist has long used mutations as his explanation of the origin of new features in organisms. The main problem has been that real mutations always turn out to be harmful. In fact, individual creatures that experienced significant mutations were once commonly called "monsters" (or "aberrations" or "freaks"), since they were seriously handicapped — if they survived at all.

In the 1930s and 1940s, two leading scientists proposed that occasional "hopeful monsters," as they called them, must have been the means by which evolution had advanced. Europe's top paleontologist, O. H. Schindewolf, and Richard Goldschmidt, one of America's outstanding geneticists, vigorously promoted this idea, pointing out that everything known about genetics and paleontology showed that slow-and-gradual evolution *had* not occurred and *could* not occur. However, neo-Darwinism prevailed at the time, and the hopeful-monster idea was mostly ridiculed, despite the high reputations of its advocates.

Now, however, evolutionists finally are acknowledging that slow-and-gradual evolution really doesn't work after all, and the "hopeful monster" is being taken seriously. Gould has actually written a key article called "The Return of Hopeful Monsters" (*Natural History*, July 1977), predicting that Goldschmidt soon will be vindicated. Stanley also has referred to this concept in several places. For instance, he illustrates it with a familiar example:

> Schindewolf believed that a single *Grossmutation* could instantaneously yield a form representing a new family or order of animals. This view engendered such visions as the first bird hatching from a reptile egg.[3]

Regardless of the terminology that may be preferred, however — hopeful monster, *Grossmutation*, quantum speciation, punctuated equilibrium, or whatever — the facts are still the same. There are no transitional forms, and there is no known mechanism that will accomplish gradualistic evolution. Consequently, if one will not accept creation, he simply has to believe in some as-yet-undiscovered mechanism that will cause new and more complex organisms to evolve all at once — or at least so rapidly as to leave no record of the few intermediate steps. No such example has been recorded in all human history (stories of frogs turning into princes are not found in history books!), but there seems to be no other alternative.

Is the punctuated-equilibrium/hopeful monster concept really a plausible option? It would seem that, if slow-and-gradual evolution must be rejected for lack of evidence, then sudden evolution must be *even more vigorously rejected*, for its evidence is not only missing, but inconceivable. One of the most revered of the neo-Darwinians, population geneticist Sewall Wright, has protested as follows:

---

[3] Stephen M. Stanley, *Macroevolution: Pattern and Process* (San Francisco, CA: W. H. Freeman and Co., 1979), p. 35; see also p. 159.

The reorganization required for the origin of the highest categories may seem so great that only "hopeful monsters" will do. Here, however, we must consider the size and complexity of the organisms. Such changes would probably have been impossible except in an organism of very small size and simple anatomy. I have recorded more than 100,000 newborn guinea pigs and have seen many hundreds of monsters of diverse sorts, but none were remotely "hopeful," all having died shortly after birth if not earlier.[4]

Can anyone seriously believe that the first bird really hatched out of a *reptile egg*? Actually, there would have to be at least two such hopeful monsters — one male and one female — occurring simultaneously in the same population, in order to assure survival of the new type. It would seem that one could as easily believe in a fairy godmother with a magic wand!

Evolutionists sometimes insist that the punctuated equilibrium concept applies only to sudden change at the species level, and so should not be confused with the hopeful-monster idea, which presumably would apply, if at all, only to higher categories. However, Gould and other punctuationists have frequently referred to the sharp gaps between phyla, classes, orders, and families as evidence in favor of punctuated equilibrium. At any rate, the fact remains that there are no true transitional forms (with transitional structures) between these higher categories.

Considerable resistance to this punctuated equilibrium concept is evident among evolutionists (as well there should be!), but it has probably become the dominant view. We have already noted the admitted difficulty of even imagining viable intermediate forms in the gradualistic evolutionary alternative, as well as the complete lack of fossil evidence for it. If evolutionists were really willing to take the scientific evidence seriously, they would have to conclude that *neither* gradual upward evolution *nor* saltational upward evolution has ever occurred, and that neither ever could occur.

But this conclusion would make them creationists! That would be too much for them emotionally and spiritually, so they continue to insist that evolution is a fact, hoping that they can impose their humanistic faith on others by weight of authority and peer pressure.

---

[4] Sewall Wright, "Character Change, Speciation, and the Higher Taxa," *Evolution*, vol. 36, no. 3 (1982), p. 440.

Even though Gould more recently has denied believing in Goldschmidt's "hopeful monster" concept, he, nevertheless, has defended its main thesis:

> As a Darwinian, I wish to defend Goldschmidt's postulate that macroevolution is not simply microevolution extrapolated and that major structural transitions can occur rapidly without a smooth series of intermediate stages.[5]

Of course, both Goldschmidt and Gould were driven to such an extremity as hopeful monsters by the intractable facts of the fossil record, which they have been honest enough to acknowledge. Gould concedes this in another article:

> The extreme rarity of transitional forms in the fossil record persists as the trade secret of paleontology. . . . We fancy ourselves as the only true students of life's history, yet to preserve our favored account of evolution by natural selection we view our data as so bad that we never see the very process we profess to study.[6]

The creationist, however, does not have to invent such whimsical and bizarre explanations for the gaps in the fossils. The creationist *predicted* the gaps! They provide positive evidence for the creation model.

Creationists are not the only ones who recognize the absurdity of making this complete absence of evolutionary transitional forms a basic feature of the new evolution model! Evolutionist philosopher Larry Azar raises this question in *Bioscience*:

> I can understand the inherent difficulty in attempting to discover intermediate forms. My problem concerns the *methodology* of science: If an evolutionist accepts gaps as a prerequisite for his theory, is he not arguing from a lack of evidence? If a biologist teaches that between two existing fossils there was a non-existing third (and perhaps several others), is he not really like the man of religious faith who says: "I believe, even though there is not evidence"?[7]

---

[5] Stephen Jay Gould, "The Return of the Hopeful Monsters," *Natural History*, vol. 86 (June/July 1977), p. 24.

[6] Stephen Jay Gould, "Evolution's Erratic Pace," *Natural History*, vol. 86 (May 1977), p. 14.

[7] Larry Azar, "Biologists, Help!" *Bioscience*, vol. 28 (November 1978), p. 714.

Two hundred years of systematic fossil collecting, with billions of fossils now known, yet all the supposed evolutionary links are still missing links! The laws of science demonstrate that evolution is impossible, and the fossil record demonstrates that it never occurred even if it *were* possible. Evolution is nothing but a naive and credulous religious faith in the omnipotence of matter — a faith exercised blindly, in spite of the universal evidence against it.

Despite the lack of transitional forms, however, and in spite of the strong arguments by Gould and others for a punctuationist theory of evolution, there are still a number of leading evolutionists who cling to the gradualistic, or neo-Darwinian, school of thought. One of the key scientists defending this supposedly orthodox evolutionary viewpoint is England's Richard Dawkins, who presents that faith as follows:

> Darwin's own bulldog, Huxley, as Eldredge reminds us again, warned him against his insistent gradualism, but Darwin had good reason. His theory was largely aimed at replacing creationism as an explanation of how living complexity could arise out of simplicity. Complexity cannot spring up in a single stroke of chance: that would be like hitting upon a combination number that opens a bank vault. But a whole series of tiny chance steps, if non-randomly selected, can build up almost limitless complexity of adaptation. It is as though the vault's door were to open another chink every time the number on the dials moved a little closer to the winning number. Gradualness is of the essence. In the context of the fight against creationism, gradualism is more or less synonymous with evolution itself. If you throw out gradualism, you throw out the very thing that makes evolution more plausible than creation.[8]

Although Dawkins is an atheist and also a bitter foe of creationism, we creationists would certainly have to agree with his critique of punctuationism and its implied concession to creationism. If evolution by gradual accumulation of favorable chance mutations seems highly unlikely, evolution by quantum leaps seems *altogether impossible*, except by special creation at each jump.

In fact, many observers have viewed the heated arguments between the gradual evolutionists and the punctuational evolutionists in terms more of politics than of science. Those advocating "evolution by

---

8 Richard Dawkins, "What Was All the Fuss About?" *Nature*, vol. 316 (August 22, 1985), p. 683.

revolution" are aligned with Marxism and communism, whereas those promoting gradual evolution with its survival-of-the-fittest implications tend to be aligned (at least in the minds of their opponents) with 19th-century social Darwinism, including racism, laissez-faire capitalism, and possibly even fascism.

Michael Ruse, the Canadian Darwinist philosopher, and Edward Wilson, the Harvard sociobiologist, have been (with Dawkins and others) leaders on the neo-Darwinist side. A detailed review of this conflict and its background was recently published in *Isis*, the history of science journal.

> Ruse (along with others among Gould's critics) has no hesitation in assigning Gould's advocacy of punctuated equilibria theory and the support it has received in large part to politics, both internal and external to science. He identifies an internal struggle among paleontologists and other evolutionists, especially geneticists, for cognitive standing in evolutionary theorizing. . . . Gould's advocacy of punctuated equilibria theory, Ruse claims, is connected with its congruency with the Marxist ideology of dialectical materialism.[9]

Be that as it may, the punctuationists do have one strong evidence in their favor, namely, the gaps in the fossil record. That is why most paleontologists today seem to favor the punctuated-equilibrium concept. They are well aware that the gaps are real, not just an artifact of the incompleteness of the fossil record, as the gradualists still assume.

> There are too many places where the fossil record is complete enough that we ought to see transitions occurring. Even in these cases we see very few good examples of higher taxa evolving by gradual change.[10]

Very few, indeed! He should have said, "no examples."

> Evolution happens rapidly in small, localized populations, so we're not likely to see it in the fossil record.[11]

Stanley goes on to refute the best example that others have cited of

[9] Eveleen Richards, "A Political Anatomy of Monsters, Hopeful and Otherwise," *Isis*, vol. 85 (September 1994), p. 379.

[10] Steven Stanley, "Resetting the Evolutionary Timetable," Interview by Neil A. Campbell, *Bioscience*, vol. 36 (December 1986), p. 725.

[11] *Ibid.*

such gradual change: namely, the fossil horses of the Tertiary. If *that* example is invalid, we can be confident that there are *none* that are valid. Evolutionists would certainly use any that *were*.

> Eldredge and Gould, by contrast, decided to take the record at face value. On this view, there is little evidence of modification between species, or of forms intermediate between species, because neither generally occurred. A species forms and evolves almost instantaneously (on the geological time scale) and then remains virtually unchanged until it disappears, yielding its habitat to a new species.[12]

Evolutionary Stagnation

It is interesting to observe the great emphasis that Gould and his colleagues are now placing on what they call "stasis." As we have noted, this seems a strange way to prove evolution. A species that is not changing is surely not evolving into something else. It seems that the main purpose of this emphasis on "evolutionary stagnation" is as an argument against their gradualist opponents, but stasis surely doesn't contribute much to evolution! On the other hand, it strongly supports a prediction from the creation model: namely, the conservation of the various types once they have been created.

But note what Gould and Eldredge say about stasis in relation to their own theory of evolution:

> Stasis, as palpable and observable in virtually all cases (whereas punctuations are usually, but not always, elusive) becomes the major empirical ground for studying punctuated equilibrium. . . . Although punctuated equilibrium deals directly only with stability of species through time, the higher-level analogue of non-trending in higher clades has also graduated from an undefined non-subject to a phenomenon worth documenting.[13]

Gould's unique style of gloating comes to the surface in a review article published in his monthly column in *Natural History*.

> Stasis is now generally recognized as an intriguing puzzle by evolutionists. No definitive resolution is in sight,

---

[12] Peter J. Smith, "Evolution's Most Worrisome Questions," *New Scientist*, vol. 116 (November 19, 1987), p. 59.

[13] Stephen J. Gould and Niles Eldredge, "Punctuated Equilibrium Comes to Age," *Nature*, vol. 366 (November 18, 1993), p. 223.

but geneticists and embryologists have offered their counsel, and I am tickled that our much maligned profession (dull, descriptive paleontology) has provided such a puzzle to kings of the theoretical mountain.[14]

The concept of stasis interrupted at rare intervals by evolutionary jumps, also, in the thinking of Gould and his associates, does away with the idea that evolution implies progress. It is all just a matter of chance, chaotic shuffling, and contingency:

> Nonetheless, contemporary science has massively substituted notions of indeterminacy, historical contingency, chaos and punctuation for previous convictions about gradual, progressive, predictable, determinism.[15]

Note Gould's implicit and self-serving assumption that his personal views constitute "contemporary science."

Assisted by Elizabeth Vrba, Gould also attempts to explain presumed evolutionary progress by invoking a mysterious "hierarchy" concept, a *deus ex machina* obviously designed to salvage his dubious evolutionary faith.

> The concept of progress has been particularly vexatious throughout the history of evolutionary biology. . . . Hierarchy may resolve the issue by explaining life's weak and impersistent vector of progress as the result of deeper structural principles more inclusive than natural selection. . . . Although we can as yet only see "through a glass darkly" into the working of genes and the lives of species in macroevolution, we already glimpse enough to know that the expanded hierarchy is a reality.[16]

Exactly how such a "hierarchy" of "sorting and selection" might be invoked to explain "life's weak vector of progress" is suggested here by Niles Eldredge:

> But if species do not change much in the course of their existence, how then do we explain large-scale, long-term change in evolution? . . . Perhaps trends are best explained by a net production or survival of species that

[14] Stephen Jay Gould, "Opus 200," *Natural History* (August 1991), p. 16.

[15] Gould and Eldredge, "Punctuated Equilibrium Comes to Age," p. 227.

[16] Elizabeth Vrba and Stephen J. Gould, "The Hierarchical Expansion of Sorting and Selection," *Paleobiology*, vol. 2 (Spring 1986), p. 226.

have a feature (such as large brains) towards one end of the spectrum of variation among a series of closely related species. There may be a higher-order culling device — analogous to natural selection but operating at a higher level — that underlies much of the macroevolutionary patterns seen in the history of life.[17]

Well, yes, "perhaps" . . . "there may be" some such way of "explaining" how evolution might have happened, even if all the hard evidence goes against it. One should remember, though, that the actual "patterns seen in the history of life" are precisely predictable from the creation model.

On the other hand, one must also remember that evolution by jumps is not based on evidence, but on lack of evidence!

Gould and Eldredge (1977) contend that: "Phyletic gradualism was an *a priori* assertion from the start — it was never 'seen' in the rocks . . ." (p. 115). By the same token . . . punctuated equilibrium . . . is not based on empirical evidence but on the apparent lack of evidence — gaps in the fossil record.[18]

The Need for Extinctions

Another important cog in the punctuational model is that of extinction. The idea is that a long-stationary population must become extinct before a new type can expand and take over the vacated ecological niche. This is presumably a part of the "chaos" that Gould would invoke to generate new organisms. His colleague, Eldredge, also favors extinctions, as does Peter Smith:

Extinctions disrupt eco-systems and reset the evolutionary clock: significant amounts of evolutionary change are positively correlated with episodes of ecological recovery following extinction.[19]

Using examples from throughout the fossil record, both marine and continental, Eldredge thus demonstrates convincingly that extinction is the motor of species evolution,

---

[17] Niles Eldredge, "Progress in Evolution?" *New Scientist*, vol. 110 (June 5, 1986), p. 57.

[18] Brian J. Alters and William F. McComas, "Punctuated Equilibrium: the Missing Link in American Education," *American Biology Teacher*, vol. 56 (September 1994), p. 337.

[19] Eldredge, "Progress in Evolution?" p. 57.

and that without it, there could be no development.[20]

Isn't evolution marvelous? The way it happens is for species not to change for a long, long time, and then suddenly to become extinct so that a new species can appear and be preserved by an unidentified culling device higher than natural selection.

One would think that, with such explanations, it would be evolutionism itself that would become extinct! However, real evolutionists are committed religiously to evolutionism, and they will continue to believe in it, or at least to promulgate it, no matter what the evidence shows against it.

It is worth noting in passing that, if "extinction is the motor of evolution," as Eldredge says, and if speciation takes place rapidly, as Gould and Stanley maintain, then we ought to be observing many species evolving today. Norman Myers, an ecologist especially concerned with preserving the environment, often points out the frequency of extinctions.

> We are surely losing one or more species a day right now out of the five million (minimum figure) on earth.[21]

There have, of course, been many extinctions during acknowledged human history, a history that is more or less equated by evolutionists with the Pleistocene and recent epochs. One thinks of the mastodon, sabertooth tiger, cave bear, moa, aurochs, etc. If we are losing one species a day, that would suggest that well over a million species have become extinct during human history! Such extinctions are supposed to be evolution's "motor," but not one *new* species is documented in all human history. It seems that, if the motor is running, it's running backwards.

Presumably, evolution occurs while we are not watching. Evolutionists used to tell us that we could not see it because it goes too slow. Now, it turns out that we cannot see it because it goes too fast:

> If in a given time interval, there are dramatically new forms appearing — new genera, for example — and at the same time the species are quite stable, then we must conclude that . . . the origin of new genera must come via rapid branching events. Maybe in some cases an entirely new genus forms via one event or in some cases by way of three or four events.[22]

---

[20] Smith, "Evolution's Most Worrisome Questions," p. 59.

[21] Norman Myers, "The End of the Lines," *Natural History*, vol. 94 (February 1985), p. 2.

There are even larger gaps to account for, of course, at the family level and higher. Evolutionists are generally quite silent on *that* problem.

The bottom line, of course, is that there is no real scientific evidence that evolution has ever occurred at all, either gradualistically or punctuationally, in past or present. Two eminent evolutionary geologists, though still committed firmly to evolutionism, have made the following cogent observation:

> We conclude that the probability that species selection is a general solution to the origin of higher taxa is not great, and that neither of the contending theories of evolutionary change at the species level, phyletic gradualism or punctuated equilibrium, seem applicable to the origin of new body plans.[23]

A creationist could not have said it better!

Living Fossils

The punctuationists have laid great stress on the phenomenon of stasis, but they have really only scratched the surface. The basic types of living plants and animals have actually been in a period of practical stasis ever since they first appeared in the fossil record. Many types have existed unchanged throughout the whole geologic column, and the geological ages that it is supposed to represent. Others have deteriorated and/or become extinct, but none have ever evolved into higher types, so far as the record shows.

Not infrequently, some certain animal that was supposed to have become extinct in a previous geological "age" will turn up still alive and well in the present world. Even though no fossils of the organism had been found in strata from the intervening ages, it was surely alive during those ages, and so it is now recognized as a "living fossil."

Many of these living fossils have been identified, and more keep turning up all the time. One of the most famous of the living fossils has been the coelacanth fish, which supposedly became extinct in the Cretaceous period about 70 million years ago, but which suddenly turned up still alive and well in the Indian Ocean near Madagascar.

Other such publicized living fossils include the Metasequoia dawn redwood tree (previously thought to be extinct since the Miocene epoch, 20 million years ago), the tuatara, or beakhead reptile (supposedly

---

[22] Stanley, "Resetting the Evolutionary Timetable," p. 724.

[23] James W. Valentine and Douglas H. Erwin, "Interpreting Great Developmental Experiments: The Fossil Record," in *Development as an Evolutionary Process* (Alan R. Lias, Inc., 1987), p. 96.

extinct since the Cretaceous), the segmented mollusk Neopilina (extinct, it was thought, since the Devonian, 300 million years ago), and the brachiopod shellfish Lingula (presumed extinct for about 400 million years, since the Ordovician).

Recently, a key "index fossil" from the Ordovician period has been identified as still living.

> All paleontologists dream of finding a "living fossil." Noel Dilly, it seems, has done so and an account of the discovery appears in a recent issue of the *Journal of Zoology*. A trawl from deep water off New Caledonia, half way between Brisbane and Fiji, has brought to light an extant pterobranch (a colony forming hemichordate) that has an astonishing physical resemblance to graptolites, a group considered to have been extinct since the Carboniferous, 300 million years ago. . . . graptolites are arguably the most important zone fossils of the lower Paleozoic (570–360 million years before present).[24]

A "zone fossil," or "index fossil," is one that is believed to be so identified with a specific geologic "age," that its presence in a rock is generally believed to date the rock. Graptolites have long been used to date Ordovician rocks, but now it seems that they must also have been present *in all the other* "ages." The same is true of a number of the other "living fossils."

As a matter of fact, the very term is misleading, since most other living plants and animals also have fossil representatives. In that sense they are *all* living fossils.

As noted before, even many of the one-celled creatures of the Precambrian are still living today:

> Both blue-green algae and bacteria fossils dating back 3.4 billion years have been found in rocks from South Africa. . . . Even more intriguing, the pleurocapsalean algae turned out to be almost identical to modern pleurocapsalean algae at the family and possibly even at the generic level.[25]

This is typical of many bacteria-fossil finds. Precambrian rocks

---

[24] Sue Rigby, "Graptolites Come to Life," *Nature*, vol. 362 (March 18, 1993), p. 209.

[25] "Ancient Alga Fossil Most Complex Yet," *Science News*, vol. 108 (September 20, 1975), p. 181. See also "Static Evolution," *Science News*, vol. 145 (March 12, 1994), p. 168-169.

have also yielded fossils of modern soil bacteria, as well as the very common modern *E-coli* cells, and various others.

> This is truly the "age of bacteria." . . . The number of *Escherichia coli* cells in the gut of each human being exceeds the number of humans that has ever lived on this planet.[26]

Gould is here making the point that in all the assumed four-billion-year history of life, the bacteria have been the most successful survivors in the struggle for existence, and they have changed hardly at all in four billion years.

The same principle is found among the marine invertebrates of the Paleozoic. No one yet has found a living trilobite, but stay tuned! Many of the other ancient invertebrates are still alive.

> Nearly all living phyla of marine invertebrates that have reasonably good fossil records have first occurrences either in the late Precambrian or early to middle Cambrian. At the class level there are 27 paleontologically important living groups and all have documented occurrences which are Silurian or older.[27]

Now Professor David Raup of the University of Chicago and the Field Museum of Natural History is one of the nation's leading paleontologists. He goes on to point out that the same phenomena are found among the vertebrates and the land plants. He also says:

> Experience has shown that as more fossils are discovered, the first occurrences of major groups tend to be pushed back in time.[28]

Stephen Gould makes the following significant observation:

> The order of life and the persistence of nearly all basic anatomical designs throughout the entire geological history of multicellular animals record the intricacy and resistance to change of complex development programs.[29]

---

[26] Stephen Jay Gould, "The Evolution of Life on Earth," *Scientific American*, vol. 271 (October 1994), p. 87.

[27] David M. Raup, "On the Early Origins of Major Biologic Groups," *Paleobiology*, vol. 9, no. 2 (1983), p. 107.

[28] *Ibid.*, p. 113.

[29] Stephen Jay Gould, "Through a Lens, Darkly," *Natural History* (September 1989), p. 24.

Undoubtedly, more living fossils among the many phyla of the marine invertebrates will come to light with further marine exploration.

> Scientists searching the South Pacific ocean beds have found living prehistoric creatures, thought to have died out 66 million years ago. Dr. Dennis Gordon, a marine scientist in Wellington, New Zealand, said that "live fossils" — sponges, sea snails, lace corals and sea lilies — were found by French researchers in 1985, but the nature of their discoveries was not realized until last week. Dr. Gordon then identified the first of the lace corals as a variety believed to have been made extinct when dinosaurs were wiped out 66 million years ago.[30]

Although all rocks so far identified as Cambrian have been identified as marine deposits, and the same is true of most of the Ordovician, it is notable that land plants and animals have been found in every "age" from late Ordovician and early Silurian onwards.

> It was not until the Silurian period, 400 to 450 million years ago, that plants and some animals adapted to a land environment and became well established there.[31]

> Paleobotanical studies have indicated that terrestrial floras became established between late Ordovician and mid-Silurian times. The presence of predatory arthropods on land in the late Silurian supports the idea that the main components of terrestrial ecosystems were in place substantially earlier.[32]

Not surprisingly, no transitional forms have been found between the marine plants and the terrestrial plants.

> We still lack any precise information concerning the presumed aquatic ancestors from which land plants evolved, and the search for evidence of these precursors continues.[33]

The same absence of transitions applies to the land invertebrates.

---

[30] See London *Daily Telegraph*, News section (December 8, 1989).

[31] Patricia G. Gensel and Henry N. Andrews, "The Evolution of Early Land Plants," *American Scientist*, vol. 75 (September/October 1987), p. 478.

[32] Andrew J. Jeram, Paul A. Selden and Dianne Edwards, "Land Animals in the Silurian: Arachnids and Myriapods from Shropshire England," *Science*, vol. 250 (November 2, 1990), p. 660.

[33] Gensel and Andrews, "Evolution of Early Land Plants," p. 481.

The basal Pridoli arthropods described here now constitute the earliest known terrestrial fauna. Moreover, like the Devonian faunas, this assemblage is dominated by predators, suggesting that the arthropod occupiers of lower trophic layers remain to be discovered.[34]

Now consider also the remarkable case of the insects. Once again there are no transitional forms leading up to them.

We are in the dark concerning the origin of insects.[35]

The flying insects are especially noteworthy. Their wings are not like the wings of birds, bats, or flying reptiles. Each type of wing is supposed by evolutionists to have *evolved independently* of the others. (Seriously, what are the "chances" of this?)

Insects include some of the most versatile of all flying machines . . . some insects — through a combination of low mass, sophisticated neurosensory systems and complex musculature — display astonishing aerobatic feats.[36]

It staggers the mind how evolutionists can believe that such amazing structures could be so beautifully designed without a designer.

Houseflies, for example, can decelerate from fast flight, hover, turn in their own length, fly upside down, loop roll and land on a ceiling — all in a fraction of a second.[37]

Insect wings are far more subtly constructed than sails and distinctly more interesting. Many, for example, have lines of flexion across the wing, as already described in the fossil cicadas. They also incorporate shock absorbers, counterweights, ripstop mechanisms, and many other simple but brilliantly effective devices, all of which increase the wing's aerodynamic effectiveness.[38]

They have few if any technological parallels — yet.[39]

[34] Jeram, Selden and Edwards, "Land Animals in the Silurian," p. 660.

[35] Pierre Grassé, *Evolution of Living Organisms* (New York: Academic Press, 1977), p. 30.

[36] Robin J. Wootton, "The Mechanical Design of Insect Wings," *Scientific American*, vol. 263 (November 1990), p. 114.

[37] *Ibid.*

[38] *Ibid.*, p. 117.

[39] *Ibid.*, p. 120.

It surely would seem that such structures and mechanisms, designed far more intricately and efficiently than any structural designer or aeronautical engineer could ever hope to accomplish, clearly proclaim the existence of an intelligent Creator.

Furthermore, they are all "living fossils," with the only changes being toward diminishing size and complexity.

> Some 84 percent of the insect families alive today were alive 100 million years ago.[40]

> Insects are "slow to evolve," and "even slower to go extinct."[41]

Consider the remarkable bee, as an example of insect persistence.

> David Grimaldi, a curator at the American Museum of Natural History, NY, reported in December that the stingless bee's advanced features have changed little in the last 80 million years. . . . The oldest bee known before this find is 45 million years old. The stingless characteristics and other features of the fossilized bee indicate that bees are far older than 80 million years.[42]

Insects are not easily preserved as fossils in sedimentary rocks, of course, and most of the best finds, like the bee, are found in amber. These are usually preserved in remarkable detail, however, and nearly always are found to be practically identical with their modern counterparts. This is also true of ants, cicadas, beetles, termites, and on and on.

Somewhat different types are the arachnids and multipods, but the same persistency is found in them as well.

> Scientists digging in upstate New York have discovered 380 million year old fossils of a tiny land-dwelling animal called a pseudoscorpion. . . . Before the new finds, . . . the pseudoscorpion fossil record went back only 35 million years. . . . The first land animals appear in the fossil record at the end of the Silurian period . . . roughly 400 million years ago. But many of these earliest fossils, including the newly found pseudoscorpions, show highly

---

[40]Carl Zimmer, "Insects Ascendant," *Scientific American*, vol. 14 (November 1993), p. 30.
[41]*Ibid.*
[42]"Fossil Finds," *Geotimes*, vol. 33 (May 1988), p. 27.

evolved features, including well-developed sensory hairs.[43]

Many of the fossil insects — including, most notably, the cockroaches and dragon-flies, among others — are much larger than their present-day descendants, but are otherwise much the same.

Another evidence of continuity worth noting is the symbiotic relation between insects and flowering plants.

> So intricate and so mutually adapted are the features of both flower and insect in many cases — special colors and odors to attract the insects, exquisitely fashioned mouth parts to extract the nectar, for example — that this pairing has become our classic example of co-evolution, or promotion of adaptation and diversity by interaction among organisms during their evolution.[44]

Co-evolution, indeed! This neologistic word game merely compounds the problem of finding the eternally elusive mechanisms of evolution. Neither the plant nor its insect pollinator could have survived at all without the symbiotic relationship being in place *from the start.* These phenomena are far better evidence of creation, than of "co-evolution."

When we consider the vertebrates (fish, amphibians, reptiles, birds, and mammals), once again we find an abundance of living fossils. Among the fish, fossil beds of sharks, herring, catfish, lungfish, and others — as well as whales, dolphins, and other marine mammals — not to mention the famous coelacanth, are abundant. The same is true of land vertebrates. A great many modern mammals seem to have considerably larger counterparts in the fossils (e.g., elephants, bears, tigers, sloths, beavers, etc.).

They are certainly similar to extant animals in the same families, at least. Of course, many animals have apparently become extinct that once were on the earth (e.g., titanotheres, pterosaurs, therapsids, etc.), but remember that *extinction is not evolution* — in fact, it is the polar opposite of evolution! In any case, most *living* land vertebrates are also found as fossils.

> Of the 329 living families of terrestrial vertebrates, 261 or 79.1 percent have been found as fossils and, when

---

[43] R. Monastersky, "Old Pseudoscorpion Has Modern Features," *Science News*, vol. 136 (October 21, 1989), p. 263.

[44] Stephen Jay Gould, "In the Mind of the Beholder," *Natural History*, vol. 103 (February 1994), p. 18.

birds (which are poorly fossilized) are excluded, the percentage rises to 87.8 percent.[45]

One might suspect that even more living plants and animals will be found in fossil form through further exploration. Also, there is the misleading and egotistic habit paleontologists have in more or less masking the true affinity of their fossil finds by giving them different names from those of their surviving relatives.

> There just is no rationale, no purpose to be served in giving different names to such virtually identical creatures just because they are separated by 3 million years of time. Yet that is the natural propensity of paleontologists: collections of otherwise similar, if not completely identical, fossils tend to get different names for no reason other than their supposedly significant age differences.[46]

Dinosaurs and Dragons

A possible candidate for recognition as a special type of living fossil is the great dinosaur, normally considered to have become extinct at the end of the Cretaceous period about seventy million years ago. The intriguing possibility exists, however, that the dinosaurs themselves were relegated to the distant past by the very device deplored by Dr. Eldredge: that of giving them "a different name for no reason other than their supposedly significant age difference."

There is considerable reason to suppose that many dinosaurs were animals well known to earlier nations by the name of *dragons*. When the first dinosaur (or dragon) bones were discovered early in the 19th century, however, the living animals had evidently been extinct for several hundred years and nearly forgotten, except in ancient tales that had become almost legendary by then. These huge animals seem to have bones and teeth similar to those of iguanas and other lizards, so they were named, simply, "terrible lizards," or *dinosaurs*, the prefix coming from the Greek *dunamis* ("power").

But the dragons also had looked like huge lizards, and they apparently existed in great variety. Some were described as giant serpents, some were said to have powerful legs and tails, some even had wings. Some dwelt in the ocean, some in swamps, some in deserts,

---

[45] Michael Denton, *Evolution: A Theory in Crisis* (London: Burnett Books, Ltd., 1985), p. 189.

[46] Niles Eldredge, *Time Frames* (New York: Simon and Schuster, 1985), p. 21.

some in caves or other places. Their sizes also varied considerably according to the tales. Mythological embellishments apparently equipped some with more than one head, and some were said to breathe out fire.

Tales about dragons have come down from many nations all over the world, and it is simply impossible that these various peoples were all inventing the same imaginary animals. There must have been a basis of fact in their tales, and it is not surprising that such fearsome animals would have inspired stories that soon became encrusted with mythical and magical accretions.

For some strange reason, however, modern evolutionists have vigorously and emotionally resisted any suggestion that dinosaurs might have lived contemporaneously with human beings. But this idea should not be any more shocking to evolutionists than the discovery of the living coelacanth fish, which was supposed to have been extinct since the dinosaur age, or that of New Zealand's living tuatara reptile, also presumed to have died out with the dinosaurs.

In patterns analogous to the various dragon stories, dinosaur bones and footprints have also been found all over the world on every continent, even Antarctica. There are numerous accounts, even by modern sailors, of great sea serpents, that seem to correlate well with the ancient tales of ocean-dwelling dragons, and also with the fossil remains of such dinosaur-like marine reptiles as the plesiosaurs.

There is the American Indian folklore of the "thunder-bird," a huge flying creature whose description sounds like the fearsome pterosaur. Also, there are pictographs of dinosaur-like animals that have been found on canyon walls in Arizona and Utah, and on cave walls in Siberia and South Africa. There are even reports of a large, living, lake-dwelling dinosaur-like animal in an almost inaccessible swamp area in the central African rain forest, reports brought out by the pygmies and other natives of the region. And what about the Loch Ness Monster and other plesiosaur-like creatures reported in various seas and deep lakes around the world?

Much circumstantial evidence exists, therefore, that even the dinosaurs could be included among the living — or recently living — fossils. Although modern geologists dogmatically reject such a notion, many authorities on dragon lore do recognize the undeniable resemblances. The writer in a standard encyclopedia put it this way:

> The belief in dragons seems to have arisen without
> the slightest knowledge on the part of the ancients of the

gigantic and astonishingly dragon-like extinct reptiles of past ages.[47]

The dinosaurs were, thus, admittedly "astonishingly dragon-like." Another encyclopedia also acknowledges the similarity as follows:

> The dragons of legend are strangely like actual crea-
> tures that have lived in the past. They are much like the
> great reptiles which inhabited the earth long before man is
> supposed to have appeared on earth.[48]

Interestingly, modern paleontologists, committed as they are to evolutionism, refuse to recognize the strong resemblance of dinosaurs to dragons, whereas specialists in myth and legend, as well as in heraldry and ancient literature, do see clearly the resemblance of dragons to dinosaurs — even though they also, for the most part, believe in evolution.

From the point of view of the creationist, of course, there is no valid reason that dinosaurs (or dragons) could not have been contemporaneous with man, just as a great number of other living fossils have been contemporaneous with man. Perhaps it is an "image" problem with evolutionists. Dinosaurs have been so glamorized as denizens of the long-ago, prehistoric past that they have almost become synonymous with evolutionism in the public mind — and evolutionists feel emotionally attached to them, afraid that if they yield on this point, the whole evolutionary structure will crumble.

At any rate, with or without dinosaurs on the list of living fossils, it seems evident that the ancient world preserved in the fossil record was much like the present world, with the same general array of plants and animals. The one difference is that the present world is "zoologically impoverished," as an early geologist put it. There is nothing new in the present world, but the old world was vibrant with many creatures that are now gone.

Finally, it would seem that we are well justified in wondering whether these multi-billion year ages ever existed at all. Not only are most living kinds of plants and animals very little different from fossils of like kinds supposedly living millions of years ago, but it is beginning to seem that some actual living organisms may have been alive individually through all those ages.

[47] Walter A. Philips, "Dragon," Article in *Encyclopedia Britannica*, vol. 7 (1949), p. 569, 570.

[48] "Dragons," Article in *World Book Encyclopedia*, 1965 Edition.

From bees entombed in amber for up to 40 million years, U.S. scientists have extracted bacterial spores and brought them back to life.[49]

The scientists who accomplished this feat insist that "the lightly controlled conditions of isolation and growth, and the DNA analysis should convince any skeptics that the bug is genuinely ancient."[50]

The same scientists claim to have revived 135 million-year-old DNA from other insects preserved in amber. There seems no valid reason to dispute their claims, as extreme precautions were taken against contamination. However, there is surely good reason to reject the millions of years alleged. Surely no organism could ever stay "alive" that long. Possibly a few thousand years could be acceptable, but not 40 million!

---

[49] Roger Lewin, "They Cam from 40 Million B.C.," *New Scientist*, vol. 146 (May 27, 1995), p. 18.
[50] *Ibid.*

Chapter 6

Evolution Is Not Even Possible

We have shown evidence in some detail, with documentation from evolutionists themselves, that no macroevolution is taking place today and that none ever occurred in the past. On the other hand, all the real scientific evidence conforms elegantly and unmistakably to natural predictions from the creation model. In this chapter we shall see that the reason *why* evolution does not happen is that it is precluded by the very laws of science.

The Law of Cause and Effect

One very fundamental law of science is the principle of cause and effect: no effect can be greater than its cause. It should be intuitively obvious to everyone that our very complex universe of stars and planets, and animals and people, must have been caused by a great First Cause capable of producing stars and planets and animals and people.

Since, however, this foundational principle leads us back naturally to an omnipotent Creator, our modern evolutionary cosmologists have tried to develop a mathematical system that can do away with the very idea of a cause for the universe. A typical statement of this remarkable and illogical conclusion is as follows:

> Let me start by saying that many people believe that everything in nature has to have a causal explanation. Although this may be true at the macroscopic level, it is not necessarily the case at the microscopic level, as quantum physics has demonstrated. Transitions, decays, and nuclear reactions do sometimes occur spontaneously without

apparent cause. Similarly, the universe itself does not require a cause.[1]

Modern cosmologists are mostly now advocating the Big Bang theory as explaining the origin of the universe. This concept will be discussed critically in chapter 8, but one of our objections to it is that the laws of science cannot be applied to this primordial explosion. It is said to be a "singularity" in which the laws themselves were somehow originated. Therefore, causal reasoning, which is applicable everywhere in the real world of human experience, does not work here (if it were used, the whole Big Bang scenario would vanish). Hence, the universe had a beginning without a cause, so say our cosmophysical philosophers:

> Thus we reach a general conclusion: there is no *philosophy of big bang cosmology* that makes it reasonable to reject the fundamental thesis of *big bang cosmology*; that the universe began to exist without a cause.[2]

Presumably, therefore, one must choose between believing the mathematical speculations of the theoretical physicists, which seem to allow a purely accidental and causeless universe, *or else* the universally proven law of cause-and-effect, which is known to apply without exception to all phenomena and systems in the real world of experience.

If one chooses to believe the latter, then the universe must have a First Cause, and that Cause must be capable of producing all the observable "effects" in the universe. Not only has the First Cause generated the space-mass-time cosmos itself, but also all the phenomena of force, motion, and energy, as well as life, intelligence, volition, morality, beauty, and emotion. By cause-and-effect reasoning, therefore, the First Cause must be an eternal, omniscient, omnipotent, living, volitional, moral, aesthetic, emotional being!

Furthermore, there are two other basic and universal laws of science that seem to tell us that evolution is impossible. These laws make it clear why it is that no one in human history has ever observed real *macroevolution* happening in the present, and why the records of the rocks and bones show that it never happened in the past.

---

[1] Richard A. Crowe, "Is Quantum Cosmology Science?" *Skeptical Inquirer* (March/April 1995), p. 54. Professor Crowe is chairman of the Department of Physics and Astronomy at the University of Hawaii.

[2] Quentin Smith, "Did the Big Bang Have a Cause?" *British Journal of Philosophy of Science*, vol. 45 (1994), p. 666. Italics are his.

The Laws of Thermodynamics Versus Evolution

The Law of Increasing Entropy is an impenetrable barrier that no evolutionary mechanism yet suggested has ever been able to overcome. Evolution and entropy are opposing and mutually exclusive concepts. If the entropy principle is really a universal law, then evolution *must be impossible*.

The very terms themselves express contradictory concepts. The word "evolution" is, of course, derived from a Latin word meaning "out-rolling." The picture is of an outward-progressing spiral, an unrolling from an infinitesimal beginning through ever-broadening circles, until finally all reality is embraced within.

"Entropy," on the other hand, means literally "in-turning." It is derived from the two Greek words *en* (meaning "in") and *trope* (meaning "turning"). The concept is of something spiraling inward upon itself, exactly the opposite concept to that of "evolution." Evolution is change outward and upward; entropy is change inward and downward.

That the principles of evolution and entropy are both believed to be universal principles and yet are mutually contradictory is seen from the following authoritative definitions.

> [There is a] general natural tendency of all observed systems to go from order to disorder, reflecting dissipation of energy available for future transformation — the law of increasing entropy.[3]

> This law states that all natural processes generate entropy, a measure of disorder.[4]

> Entropy, in short, is the measurement of molecular disorder. The law of the irreversible increase in entropy is a law of progressive disorganization, of the complete disappearance of the initial conditions.[5]

It can hardly be questioned that evolution is at least superficially contradicted by entropy. The obvious prediction from the evolution model that there must be a universal principle that *increases* order is

[3] R. B. Lindsay, "Physics — To What Extent Is It Deterministic?" *American Scientist*, vol. 56 (Summer 1968), p. 100.

[4] David Layzer, "The Arrow of Time," *Scientific American*, vol. 223 (December 1975), p. 56. Dr. Layzer is professor of astronomy at Harvard.

[5] Ilya Prigogine, "Can Thermodynamics Explain Biological Order?" *Impact of Science on Society*, vol. 23, no. 3 (1973), p. 162. Dr. Prigogine is professor in the Faculty of Sciences at the University Libre de Belgique and is one of the world's leading thermodynamicists.

confronted by the scientific fact of a universal principle that *decreases* order. Nevertheless evolutionists retain the faith that, somehow, evolution and entropy can co-exist, even though they do not know how.

> In the complex course of its evolution, life exhibits a remarkable contrast to the tendency expressed in the Second Law of Thermodynamics. Where the Second Law expresses an irreversible progression toward increased entropy and disorder, life evolves continually higher levels of order. The still more remarkable fact is that this evolutionary drive to greater and greater order also is irreversible. Evolution does not go backward.[6]

> Back of the spontaneous generation of life under other conditions than now obtained upon this planet, there occurred a spontaneous generation of elements of the kind that still goes on in the stars; and back of that I suppose a spontaneous generation of elementary particles under circumstances still to be fathomed, that ended in giving them the properties that alone make possible the universe we know.[7]

> Life might be described as an unexpected force that somehow organizes inanimate matter into a living system that perceives, reacts to, and evolves to cope with changes to the physical environment that threatens to destroy its organization.[8]

The most comprehensive statement on evolution as a process is the classic definition of Sir Julian Huxley, as follows:

> Evolution in the extended sense can be defined as a directional and essentially irreversible process occurring in time, which in its course gives rise to an increase of variety and an increasingly high level of organization in its products. Our present knowledge indeed forces us to the view that the whole of reality *is* evolution — a single process of self-transformation.[9]

[6] J. H. Rush, *The Dawn of Life* (New York, NY: Signet, 1962), p. 35.

[7] George Wald, "Fitness in the Universe," *Origins of Life*, vol. 5 (1974), p. 26.

[8] National Aeronautics and Space Administration, *Mars and Earth*, NF-61 (Washington, DC: GPO, August 1975), p. 5.

[9] Julian Huxley, "Evolution and Genetics," in *What is Man?*, ed. J. R. Newman (New York, NY: Simon and Schuster, 1955), p. 278.

Thus, in the *one* instance, "all observed systems . . . go from order to disorder"; and in the *other*, "the whole of reality . . . gives rise to an increasingly high level of organization in its products." It seems obvious that either evolution or entropy has been vastly overrated, or else that something is wrong with the English language!

The entropy principle, however, is nothing less than the Second Law of Thermodynamics, which is as universal and certain a law as exists in science. First, however, before discussing the Second Law, we should define the First Law and, for that matter, thermodynamics itself.

Thermodynamics is a compound of two Greek words, *therme* ("heat") and *dunamis* ("power"). It is the science that treats of the power of energy contained in heat, and its conversion to other forms of energy. The term "energy" is itself derived from the Greek word *energeia* ("working"), and is normally defined as "the capacity to do work." In modern scientific terminology, "energy" and "work" are considered equivalent, each measured as the product of a force times the distance through which it acts (foot-pounds, in the English system of dimensions). Something that has "energy" has the "capacity to do work;" that is, the "capacity to exert a force through a distance."

The concept of "power" is closely related to that of "energy," except that the time factor must also be taken into account. Power is the work done, or the energy expended to do the work per unit of time — measured in foot-pounds per second, for example.

Thus the science of thermodynamics began as the study of the conversion of heat power into mechanical power, like the use of steam to turn the wheels and move the load. The invention of the steam engine, and the development of the theoretical equations of thermodynamics by which to design it, led to the great Industrial Revolution and our modern age of technology. The golden age of science and the greatest scientists of all — Newton, Maxwell, Kelvin, and others — produced the discipline and the Laws of Thermodynamics.

Not long after the discovery of the "mechanical equivalent of heat" by Joule and others, it was realized that there were also other forms of energy (electrical energy, chemical energy, light, heat, sound, etc.), and that all of them were comprehended within these same Laws of Thermodynamics. The advent of the atomic age made it evident that even matter itself was merely another form of energy, and that it also could be brought under the broad umbrella of thermodynamics.

Therefore, the modern scientist has come to recognize that the science of thermodynamics is exceedingly broad. It provides the basic framework for all energy-conversion processes, whereby heat, electricity, or any other form of energy can be converted into any other form. In the twentieth century, it also includes the processes of mass-energy interchanges.

Since all processes are fundamentally energy-conversion processes, and since everything that happens in the physical universe is a "process" of some kind, it is obvious why the Two Laws of Thermodynamics are recognized as the most universal and fundamental of all scientific laws. Everything that *exists* in the universe is some form of energy, and everything that *happens* is some form of energy conversion. Thus, the Laws that govern energy and energy conversion are of paramount importance in understanding the world in which we live.

It should be underlined that these Laws are empirical laws. That is, like all other laws of science, they are accepted on the basis of experience and testing, not because of some deterministic mathematical proof. However, they are based on better and more varied evidence than any other scientific principle whatever!

Isaac Asimov defines the First Law as follows:

> To express all this, we can say: "Energy can be transferred from one place to another, or transformed from one form to another, but it can be neither created nor destroyed." Or we can put it another way: "The total quantity of energy in the universe is constant." When the total quantity of something does not change, we say that it is conserved. The two statements given above, then, are two ways of expressing "the law of conservation of energy." This law is considered the most powerful and most fundamental generalization about the universe that scientists have ever been able to make.[10]

As long as nuclear reactions are not involved, the Law of Conservation of Matter also applies. However, matter can be converted into energy and energy into matter, and in either case, the sum total of matter and energy remains the same. Similarly, as long as the process involves only changes in kinetic energy (that is, energy of motion), then the Law of Conservation of Momentum applies. However, the most comprehensive of all the conservation laws is the Law of Conservation of Mass-Energy, and this is the First Law of Thermodynamics.

The First Law is itself a strong witness against evolution, since it implies a basic condition of stability in the universe. The fundamental

---

[10] Isaac Asimov, "In the Game of Energy and Thermodynamics You Can't Even Break Even," *Smithsonian Institute Journal* (June 1970), p. 6.

structure of the cosmos is one of conservation, not innovation. However, this fact in itself is not impressive to the evolutionist, as he merely assumes that the process of evolution takes place within the framework of energy conservation, never stopping to wonder how it came to pass that the total energy was constant from the beginning at the supposed Big Bang.

But it is the Second Law that wipes out the theory of evolution. There *is* a universal process of change, and it *is* a directional change, but it is *not* an upward change.

This entropy law appears in three main forms, corresponding to 1) classical thermodynamics, 2) statistical thermodynamics, and 3) informational thermodynamics. Each of these corresponds to a different, though equivalent, concept of entropy.

In so-called classical thermodynamics, the Second Law, like the First, is formulated in terms of energy:

> It is in the transformation process that Nature appears to exact a penalty and this is where the second principle makes its appearance. For every naturally occurring transformation of energy is accompanied, somewhere, by a loss in the *availability* of energy for the future performance of work.[11]

In this instance, entropy can be expressed mathematically in terms of the total irreversible flow of heat. It expresses quantitatively the amount of energy in an energy conversion process that becomes unavailable for further work. In order for work to be done, the available energy has to "flow" from a higher level to a lower level. When it reaches the lower level, the energy is still in existence, but no longer capable of doing work. Heat will naturally flow from a hot body to a cold body, but not from a cold body to a hot body. For this reason, no process can be 100 percent efficient, with all of the available energy converted into work. Some must be deployed to overcome friction, and will be degraded to non-recoverable heat energy, which will finally be radiated into space and dispersed. For the same reason, a self-contained perpetual motion machine is an impossibility.

Since, as we have noted, everything in the physical universe is energy in some form and, since in every process some energy becomes unavailable, it is obvious that ultimately *all* energy in the universe will be unavailable energy, if present processes go on long enough. When

---

[11] R. B. Lindsay, "Entropy Consumption and Values in Physical Science," *American Scientist*, vol. 47 (September 1959), p. 378.

that happens, presumably all the various forms of energy in the universe will have been gradually converted through a multiplicity of processes into uniformly (that is, randomly) dispersed heat energy. Everything will be at the same low temperature. There will be no "differential" of energy levels, and, therefore, no "gradient" of energy to induce its flow. No more work can then be done, and the universe will reach what classical physicists used to call its ultimate "heat death."

This is a depressing outlook for the future, but it is what must come eventually, if present processes continue. The fact that the universe has not yet reached this dead condition, and, in fact, is still very much alive, with tremendous reservoirs of available energy everywhere, proves that it is *not* infinitely old. If it were of infinite antiquity, it would already be dead.

Thus, the Second Law proves, *as certainly as observable science can prove anything whatever*, that the universe had a beginning. Similarly, the First Law shows that the universe could not have begun itself. The total quantity of energy in the universe is constant, but the quantity of *available* energy is decreasing. Therefore, as we go *backward* in time, the available energy would have been progressively greater until, finally, we would reach the beginning point, where available energy equaled total energy. Time could go back no further than this. At this point both energy and time must have come into existence. Since energy could not create itself, the most scientific and logical conclusion to which we could possibly come is that the First Cause created energy (including matter), as well as time.

The evolutionist will not accept this conclusion, however. He hypothesizes that either: (1) some natural law canceling out the Second Law prevailed far back in time, or (2) some natural law canceling out the Second Law prevails far out in space.

When he makes such assumptions, however, he is denying his own theory, which says that all things can be explained in terms of presently observable laws and processes. He is really resorting to creationism, but refusing to acknowledge a Creator.

A second way of stating the entropy law is in terms of statistical thermodynamics. It is recognized today not only that all scientific laws are empirical, but also that they are statistical. A great number of individual molecules, in a gas for example, may behave in such a way that the overall aspects of that gas produce predictable patterns in the aggregate, even though individual molecules may deviate from the norm. Laws describing such behavior must be formulated statistically, or probabilistically, rather than strictly dynamically. The dynamical laws then can theoretically be deduced as limiting cases of the probabilistic statements.

In this context, entropy is a probability function related to the degree of disorder in a system. The more disordered (or disorganized) a system may be, the more highly entropic it is, and the more probable it is. A highly organized system, on the other hand, is highly improbable, and must be explained by something more than random processes.

> All real processes go with an increase of entropy. The entropy also measures the randomness, or lack of orderliness of the system; the greater the randomness, the greater the entropy.[12]

Note again the universality expressed here: *all real processes.* Isaac Asimov defined this concept interestingly as follows:

> Another way of stating the Second Law then is: "the universe is constantly getting more disorderly." Viewed that way, we can see the Second Law all about us. We have to work hard to straighten a room, but left to itself, it becomes a mess again very quickly and very easily. Even if we never enter it, it becomes dusty and musty. How difficult to maintain houses, and machinery, and our own bodies in perfect working order; how easy to let them deteriorate. In fact, all we have to do is nothing, and everything deteriorates, collapses, breaks down, wears out, all by itself — and that is what the Second Law is all about.[13]

Remember that this tendency to move from order to disorder applies to all real processes. Real processes include, of course, biological and geological processes, as well as chemical and physical processes. The interesting question is this: "How does a real biological process, which goes from order to disorder, result in evolution, which goes from disorder to order?" Perhaps the evolutionists can ultimately find an answer to this question, but at least they should not ignore it, or speculate their way around it, as most evolutionists do.

Especially is such a question vital when we are thinking of evolution as a growth process on the grand scale from particles to people. This represents an absolutely *gigantic* increase in organization and complexity, and is clearly out of place altogether in the context of the Second Law!

---

[12] Harold Blum, "Perspectives in Evolution," *American Scientist* (October 1955), p. 595.
[13] Asimov, "In the Game of Energy and Thermodynamics," p. 6.

A third and still more fascinating concept of entropy comes from the field of information theory, or what may be called communicational thermodynamics. This scientific discipline is a product of the computer age and the field of cybernetics. Informational science attempts to quantify the communication of meaningful information from sender to receiver. Communications systems include books, television sets, tape recorders, computer discs, and many other devices. Even a man or woman and his or her brain can be considered as such a system.

In information theory, entropy is considered to be a measure of the degree in which information is lost or becomes garbled in the transmission process. It measures the "noise" or "static" that tends to inhibit the perfect transmission of a message. The process of communication is surprisingly analogous to a standard energy-conversion process. Just as some energy is lost in the conversion process, so always some information is lost in the communication process. No one appropriates the teacher's complete lecture, and the recording never reproduces the orchestral rendition with perfect fidelity.

One can sense intuitively that all three concepts of entropy are similar and basically equivalent to each other. As a matter of fact, this equivalence can be demonstrated quite rigorously by mathematics, though the proof is much too complicated to try to reproduce here. The fact that entropy is really the same entity, whether defined in classical, statistical, or informational terms, is in fact one of the major discoveries of modern science.

The equivalence of entropy in the classical and statistical context is implied in the following:

> Each quantity of energy has a characteristic quality called entropy associated with it. The entropy measures the degree of disorder associated with the energy. Energy must always flow in such a direction that the entropy increases.[14]

Similarly, the equivalence of these concepts with the informational concept is recognized:

> It is certain that the conceptual connection between information and the Second Law of Thermodynamics is now firmly established.[15]

---

[14] Freeman J. Dyson, "Energy in the Universe," *Scientific American*, vol. 224 (September 1971), p. 52.

[15] Myron Tribus and Edward C. McIrvine, "Energy and Information," *Scientific American*, vol. 224 (September 1971), p. 188.

All sorts of intriguing illustrations of these relationships may be discovered. For example, the sun's energy is converted through photosynthesis into vegetables. These are eaten by a man, whose metabolic processes convert their stored chemical energy into energy-imparting molecules transmitted through the blood stream to various parts of the body, especially the brain. The blood energizes the complex brain cells and circuitry, which then generate thought and convey information.

Isaac Asimov confirms that all these different ways of looking at the Second Law are really equivalent to each other.

> That is one way [that is, decreasing availability of energy] of stating what is called the Second Law of Thermodynamics. It is one of many ways; all of them are equivalent although some very sophisticated mathematics and physics are involved in showing the equivalence.[16]

Hence, there are three basic vehicles of physical reality associated with the entropy concept. In the structure of all systems, entropy is a measure of *disorder*. In the maintenance of all processes, entropy is a measure of *wasted energy*. In the transmission of all information, entropy is a measure of *useless noise*. Each of these three concepts is basically equivalent to the other two, even though it expresses a distinct concept.

Always, furthermore, entropy tends to increase. Everywhere in the physical universe there is an inexorable downhill trend toward ultimate complete randomness, utter meaninglessness, and absolute stillness. The evolutionary delusion becomes absolute nonsense in the context of the all-comprehensive Second Law.

When confronted directly with this problem (e.g., in creation/evolution debates), evolutionists often will completely ignore it. Some will honestly admit that they do not know how to resolve the problem, but will simply express confidence that there must be a way, since otherwise one would have to believe in supernatural creation. George Wald puts it this way:

> In this strange paper I have ventured to suggest that natural selection of a sort has extended even beyond the elements, to determine the properties of protons and electrons. Curious as that seems, it is a possibility worth weighing against the only alternative I can imagine,

---

[16] Asimov, "In the Game of Energy and Thermodynamics," p. 8.

Eddington's suggestion that God is a mathematical physicist.[17]

Some evolutionists try to solve the problem by suggesting that the entropy law is only statistical and that exceptions can occur, which would allow occasional accidental increases in order. Whether this is so, however, is entirely a matter of faith. No one has ever *seen* such an exception — and science is based upon observation!

> There is thus no justification for the view, often glibly repeated, that the Second Law of Thermodynamics is only statistically true, in the sense that microscopic violations repeatedly occur, but never violations of any serious magnitude. On the contrary, no evidence has ever been presented that the Second Law breaks down under any circumstances.[18]

It is surprising, but true, that most textbooks dealing with some aspect of organic evolution never even mention the entropy problem. In creation-evolution debates, the evolutionist debater normally will ignore it altogether.

The popular syndicated columnist, Sydney Harris, once commented on the evolution-entropy conflict as follows:

> There is a factor called "entropy" in physics, indicating that the whole universe of matter is running down, and ultimately will reduce itself to uniform chaos. This follows from the Second Law of Thermodynamics, which seems about as basic and unquestionable to modern scientific minds as any truth can be.
>
> At the same time that this is happening on the physical level of existence, something quite different seems to be happening on the biological level: structure and species are becoming more complex, more sophisticated, more organized, with higher degrees of performance and consciousness.[19]

---

[17] George Wald, "Fitness in the Universe," *Origins of Life*, vol. 5 (1974), p. 26. Wald was a famous humanistic biologist at Harvard.

[18] A. B. Pippard, *Elements of Chemical Thermodynamics for Advanced Students of Physics* (Cambridge, England: Cambridge University Press, 1966), p. 100. Pippard was professor of physics at Cambridge.

[19] Sydney Harris, Field Enterprise Syndicate, *San Francisco Examiner* (January 27, 1984).

As Harris points out, the law of increasing entropy is a universal law of *decreasing* complexity, whereas evolution is supposed to be a universal law of *increasing* complexity. Creationists have been pointing out this serious contradiction for years, and it is encouraging that at least some evolutionists are beginning to be aware of this basic and irreconcilable conflict:

> How can the forces of biological development and the forces of physical degeneration be operating at cross purposes? It would take, of course, a far greater mind than mine even to attempt to penetrate this riddle. I can only pose the question because it seems to me the question most worth asking and working upon with all our intellectual and scientific resources.[20]

This, indeed, is a good question, and one for which evolutionists so far have no answer. Some have tried to imagine exceptions to the Second Law at some time or times in the past, which allowed evolution to proceed in spite of entropy, but such ideas are nothing but wishful thinking. Physicist Frank Greco says the following:

> Being a generalization of experience, the second law could only be invalidated by an actual engine. In other words, the question, "Can the second law of thermodynamics be circumvented?" is not well-worded and could be answered only if the model incorporated every feature of the real world. But the answer can readily be given to the question, "Has the second law of thermodynamics been circumvented?" Not yet.[21]

Of course, the fact that no exception to the law of increasing entropy has ever been observed does not prove that such a thing never happened. It simply shows that such ideas are outside the scope of science. Evolutionists are free to believe in such "singularities" by faith, if they wish, but they have no right to impose them on unsuspecting young minds in the name of science.

Some evolutionists take refuge in the idea that, since the universe is almost infinitely large, and we can sample only a small part of it, we don't really know that the entropy principle always applies. However, what we *do* know is that, wherever it has been tested, it always works. Whether the Second Law may hold on some hypothetical planet a

---

[20] *Ibid.*

[21] Frank Greco, *American Laboratory Practice* (October 1982), p. 88.

million light years away has no bearing on the fact that it always holds true on *this* planet, where evolution is supposed to be happening.

The Vacuous Open-System Argument

Most knowledgeable evolutionists, however, if pushed for an answer to the entropy problem, will take refuge in the "open-system" argument. Asimov asserts that:

> Life on earth has steadily grown more complex, more versatile, more elaborate, more orderly, over the billions of years of the planet's existence. . . . How could that vast increase in order (and therefore that vast decrease in entropy) have taken place? The answer is it could *not* have taken place without a tremendous source of energy constantly bathing the earth, for it is on that energy that life subsists. . . . In the billions of years that it took for the human brain to develop, the increase in entropy that took place in the sun was far greater — far, far greater than the decrease that is represented by the evolution required to develop the human brain.[22]

In other words, the earth in its geologic time setting is "open" to the sun's energy, and it is this tremendous influx of energy that powers the evolutionary process and enables it to rise and overcome the entropy law which would otherwise inhibit it. The First and Second Laws of Thermodynamics, evolutionists say, apply only to *isolated systems* — systems into which no external energy can flow — and so supposedly do not apply to the earth.

The evolutionist will also cite various examples of growth in open systems to illustrate his point, such as a seed growing up into a tree with many seeds. In like manner, he says, the sun supplies energy to the open earth-system throughout geologic time to keep evolution going, even though perhaps at some long-distant time the greater earth-sun system will finally die and evolution will stop.

Roger Lewin expresses this curious idea as follows:

> One problem biologists have faced is the apparent contradiction by evolution of the second law of thermodynamics. Systems should decay through time, giving less, not more, order.
>
> One legitimate response to this challenge is that life on earth is an open system with respect to energy and

---
[22] Asimov, "In the Game of Energy and Thermodynamics," p. 11.

therefore the process of evolution sidesteps the law's demands for increasing disorder with time.[23]

It is amazing how many anti-creationist debaters and writers try to "sidestep" this serious problem with such a simplistic cliché as the above. Creationists who cite the entropy principle against the evolutionary philosophy are, time and again, dismissed as either ignorant of thermodynamics or dishonest in their use of the Second Law. Such charges are inappropriate, to say the least.

This open-system gambit is an exceedingly naive argument, and it indicates the desperate state of evolutionary theory that leads otherwise competent scientists to resort to it. It should be self-evident that the mere existence of an open system of some kind, with access to the sun's energy, *does not of itself generate growth.* The sun's energy may bathe the site of an automobile junk yard for a million years, but it will never cause the rusted, broken parts to grow together again into a functioning automobile.

A beaker containing a fluid mixture of hydrochloric acid, water, salt, or any other combination of chemicals may lie exposed to the sun for endless years, but the chemicals will never combine into a living bacterium or any other self-replicating organism. More likely, it would destroy any organisms that might accidentally have been caught in it. Availability of energy (by the First Law of Thermodynamics) has in itself no mechanism for thwarting the basic decay principle enunciated by the Second Law of Thermodynamics. *Quantity* of energy is not the question, but *quality*!

In the first place, when evolutionists argue that the Second Law applies only to isolated systems (from which external sources of information and order are excluded), the argument is irrelevant, for there is no such thing as a real, isolated system. Yet entropy certainly increases in most systems. The earth and its biosphere are indeed open systems, with an ample supply of energy coming in from the sun to do the work of building up the complexity of these systems. Furthermore, evolutionists cite specific examples of systems in which the order increases — such as the growth of a crystal out of solution, the growth of a seed or embryo into an adult plant or animal, or the growth of a small Stone-Age population into a large complex technological culture — as proof that the Second Law does not inhibit the growth of more highly-ordered systems.

Arguments and examples such as these, however, are specious! It

---

[23] Roger Lewin, "A Downward Slope to Greater Diversity," *Science*, vol. 217 (September 24, 1982), p. 1239.

is like arguing that, since NASA was able to put men on the moon, therefore, it is reasonable to believe that cows can jump over the moon! Creationists have for many years been emphasizing that the Second Law really applies *only* to *open* systems, since there is no such thing as a truly isolated system. The great French scientist and mathematician, Emil Borel, has proved this fact mathematically, as acknowledged thus by Layzer:

> Borel showed that no finite physical system can be considered closed.[24]

Creationists have long acknowledged — in fact *emphasized* — that order can and does increase in certain special types of open systems, but this is no proof that order increases in *every* open system! The statement that "the earth is an open system" is a vacuous statement, containing no specific information, since all systems are open systems.

Secondly, the entropy principle applies at least as much to *open* systems as to *closed* systems. In an isolated system, shut off from external energy, the entropy (or disorganization) would certainly increase. In an open system (such as the earth receiving an influx of heat energy from the sun), the entropy always *tends to increase*, and, as a matter of fact, will *usually increase more rapidly* than if the system remained closed! An example would be a tornado sweeping through a decaying ghost town or a cast-iron wrecking ball imposed on an abandoned building. Anyone familiar with the actual equations of heat flow will know that a simple influx of heat energy into a system *increases* the entropy of that system; it does not decrease it, as evolution would demand. Opening a system to external energy does not resolve the entropy problem at all, but rather makes it worse! The author of one of the most respected and widely used textbooks on thermodynamics says:

> The statement in integral form, namely that the entropy in an isolated system cannot decrease, can be replaced by its corollary in differential form, which asserts that the quantity of entropy generated locally cannot be negative irrespective of whether the system is isolated or not, and irrespective of whether the process under consideration is irreversible or not.[25]

Thus, entropy (or disorganization) in an open system *always* at

---

[24]Layzer, "The Arrow of Time," *Scientific American*, vol. 223 (December 1975), p. 65.

[25] Arnold Sommerfeld, *Thermodynamics and Statistical Mechanics* (Academic Press, 1956), p. 155.

least tends to increase, no matter how much external energy may be available to it from the sun or any other source. If this tendency is to be overcome so that order in the system might be made to increase instead (as evolution would require), then the external energy must somehow be supplied to it, not as raw energy (like a bull in a china shop), but as organizing information.

If the energy of the sun is going somehow to transform the non-living molecules of the primeval soup into intricately complex, highly organized, replicating living cells, and then to evolve populations of simple organisms, like worms, into complex, thinking human beings, then that raw energy has to be converted into these evolutionary marvels through some unknown but very complex series of codes and specifically designed mechanisms. If such codes and mechanisms are not available on the earth (and no one yet has any evidence that any such things exist at all), then the incoming heat energy from the sun will simply disintegrate any organized systems that might accidentally have shown up here.

Criteria for a Growth Process

The Second Law says that all processes basically must be decay processes. Apparent superficial exceptions to this rule do indeed exist, however, especially in the phenomena of life. A seed grows up into a tree, and an embryo grows up into an adult animal. Even in the non-living world, there seem to be some exceptions; for example, the formation and growth of a crystal. And, of course, there are many artificial growth processes which can be produced. Threads can be made to "grow" into a dress and bricks can be made to "grow" into a building.

It should never be forgotten, however, that all such apparent decreases of entropy can be produced only at the expense of a still greater increase of entropy in the external environment, so that the world as a whole, or the universe as a whole, continues to run down. Furthermore, such growth processes are only temporary at best. The tree and the animal eventually die, and the crystal sooner or later disintegrates. The dress wears out, and the building crumbles. "Dust to dust" is always the victor in the end.

But we still need to consider the problem of the production of even a local, temporary growth process. What criteria have to be satisfied before such a "negentropic" (or entropy-reversing) process becomes possible, and does the supposed evolutionary process meet these criteria?

A little consideration quickly makes it evident that at least *four* criteria have to be satisfied before a growth process can be initiated and maintained. The first two of these are obvious:

1. *An Open System.* Obviously, growth cannot occur in an isolated, or closed system; the Second Law is in fact *defined* in terms of a closed system. However, this criterion is only theoretical, because in the real world closed systems do not even exist! It is evident that the Laws of Thermodynamics apply to open systems as well, since they have been tested and proved only on open systems!

2. *Available Energy.* This criterion is also actually redundant, since the energy of the sun is always available, either directly or indirectly, to all systems of any kind on the entire earth.

   Now, however, we come to the real heart of the problem. The evolutionist glibly gives entropy the brush-off because the earth is an open system bathed in the sun's energy. Such an answer is vacuous and trivial, for *all* systems are open to the sun's energy, but only a few exhibit a growth process, and even these only temporarily. What must be the remarkable *additional conditions* that can empower a worldwide evolutionary growth process in the whole biosphere for over four billion years?

   For even the local, temporary growth systems with which men have observational acquaintance (as distinct from philosophical predilection or preference), there must be at least two additional criteria satisfied:

3. *A Coded Plan.* There must always, without known exception, exist a pre-planned program, or pattern, or template, or code, if growth is to take place. Disorder will never randomly become order. Something must sift and sort and direct the environmental energy before it can "know" how to organize the unorganized components. The fact that a "need" exists for growth to take place, is of little importance to bobbing particles.

   In the case of the plant, for example, the necessary program for its growth has been written into the structure of the germ cells, including especially the *genetic code*, the amazing system of the DNA-RNA complex that somehow, by its intricately coiled template structure and "messenger" functions, directs the assimilation of the environmental chemicals into a resulting plant structure like that of its predecessor plants. A similar coding system is also present in the animal "seed."

In inorganic systems, the growth is directed by the intricate molecular structure of the crystal compound and by the chemical properties of the elements comprising it. Each crystal is directed into a predictable geometric pattern on the basis of the chemical code implicit in the periodic table of the elements and their own pre-existing structures. As a matter of fact, in the case of the crystallization process, there is an important sense in which the formation of a crystal really represents an *increase* of entropy, even in the solution from which it forms. That is, there is more "information" or "energy," for the production of work, in the liquid solution than in the stable structure that crystallizes out of it.

Artificial processes also have their "codes." The building is based on a blueprint, and the dress on a pattern.

But whence came these codes? How did the chemical elements acquire their orderly properties? What primeval DNA molecule had no previous DNA molecule to go by?

Our experience with artificial processes indicates that a code for growth requires an intelligent planner. An architect had to draw the blueprint, and a dress designer prepared the pattern. Could mindless, darting particles plan the systematic structure of the elements that they were to form? Even more unbelievably, could these elements later get together and program the genetic code, which could not only direct the formation of complex living systems of all kinds, but even enter into the replication process that would insure the continued production of new representatives of each kind? To imagine such marvels as this is to believe in magic — and magic without even a magician at that!

A code *always* requires an intelligent coder. A program requires a programmer. To say that the most fantastically complex and effective code of all — the genetic code — somehow coded itself in the first place is to abandon all pretense of science and reason in the study of the world as it is.

But the genetic code is utter chaos in comparison with the complexity of a program that might conceivably direct the evolutionary growth process from particles to people over five billion years of earth history! Where is the evidence for such a program? What structure does it have? How does it function, in order to direct elements into proteins, proteins into cells, cells into plants and invertebrates, fishes into birds, and monkeys into men?

The sun's energy is there all right, and the earth is assuredly an open system, but by what marvelous automated directional system is this energy instructed how to transmute a school of jellyfish into a colony of beavers?

Does the evolutionist imagine that mutation and natural selection could really perform the function of such an unimaginably complex program? Mutation is not a code, but only a random process which, like all random processes, *generates disorder in its products*. Natural selection is not a code, but only a sort of cybernetic device that snuffs out the disorderly effects of the mutation process. Is the evolutionist really so foolish as to think that this kind of mindless interplay could produce the human brain?

But there is still another criterion that must be satisfied, even for a local temporary growth process:

4. *An Energy-Conversion Mechanism.* It is naively simplistic merely to say: "The sun's energy sustains the evolutionary process." The question is this: "*How* does the sun's energy sustain the evolutionary process?" This type of reasoning is inexcusable for scientists, because it confuses the First Law of Thermodynamics with the Second Law. There is no doubt that there is a large enough *quantity* of energy (First Law) to support evolution, but there is nothing in the simple heat energy of the sun of sufficiently high *quality* (Second Law) to produce the infinitely-ordered products of the age-long process of evolutionary growth.

One could much more reasonably assume that the sun's energy bathing the stockpiles of bricks and lumber on a construction site will, by itself, erect an apartment building, which is an infinitely simpler structural project than the supposed products of organic evolution. There is far more than enough energy reaching the building site than is necessary to build the building, so why bother to rent equipment and hire workmen? This very "reasonable" suggestion will not work, however, even if the sun's heat beams down on those materials for a billion years.

The missing ingredient is an energy-conversion mechanism! Some mechanism has to be on hand to convert the sun's energy into the mechanical energy required to erect the structure. This is *always* true, for any growth process. The natural tendency is to decay, so that for growth to take place, some very special and effective mechanism must be superimposed to convert the simple heat energy into the complex growth system.

In the case of the seed growing up into a tree, for example, the mechanism is that of photosynthesis. This is a marvelous and intricate mechanism by which the sun's radiant energy is somehow transformed into the growing plant tissue. Photosynthesis is so complex and wonderful a mechanism that scientists even yet do not fully comprehend it,[26] involving as it does a complex combination of electrochemical reactions, bacterial agencies, and other factors.

Similarly, various metabolic mechanisms convert the chemical energy stored in the plant into the mechanical and other forms of energy which the animal that eats the plant needs in his activities. The plant's energy may also eventually be converted into coal, the burning of which may drive a boiler that produces steam for a generator to make electrical energy. The latter is available at the construction site for conversion into the mechanical energy necessary for the construction equipment as it is operated by persons to build the building.

Dr. Lewis Thomas expresses this requirement in somewhat different terminology, using the concept of the "membrane," especially regarding the earth's atmosphere-biosphere complex as such a structure.

> It takes a membrane to make sense out of disorder in biology. You have to be able to catch energy and hold it, storing precisely the needed amount and releasing it in measured shares. A cell does this, and so do the organelles inside. Each unit is poised in the flow of solar energy, tapping off energy from metabolic surrogates of the sun. To stay alive, you have to be able to hold out against equilibrium, maintain imbalance, bank against entropy. In our kind of world, you can only transact this business with membranes.[27]

But what is the source of such marvelously designed systems that thus maintain life and permit its reproduction in spite of entropy? Thomas continues as follows:

> You could say that the breathing of oxygen into the atmosphere was the result of evolution, or you could turn it around and say that evolution was the result of oxygen. You can have it either way.[28]

Which is one convenient way of avoiding hard questions! Evolution must indeed be a magnificent phenomenon if it can evolve the conditions necessary for its own origin. But that is not all, for

---

[26] R. P. Levine, "The Mechanism of Photosynthesis," *Scientific American*, vol. 221 (December 1969), p. 58-70. Levine is professor of biology at Harvard.

[27] Lewis Thomas, "The Miraculous Membrane," *Intellectual Digest*, vol. 4 (February 1974), p. 56.

[28] *Ibid.*

Thomas goes on with animation thus:

> It is another illustration of our fantastic luck that oxygen filters out the very bands of ultraviolet light that are most devastating to nucleic acids and proteins, while allowing full penetration of the visible light needed for photosynthesis. If it had not been for this semi-permeability, we could never have come along.[29]

We are, indeed, very "lucky"! Had it not been for this fantastic mechanism that "accidentally" developed, the law of entropy would never have allowed living things to exist at all.

Always, therefore, one or more energy-conversion mechanisms must be available for utilization of the sun's energy whenever there is any kind of growth process. This is in addition to the pre-programmed plan for directing the growth process that must also be available.

But the most extensive and energy-demanding growth process of all — namely, the organic evolution of the entire biosphere — has no such mechanism! Neither does it have, as we have seen, a program. How, then, can it possibly work?

The evolutionists' answer, of course, is *mutation and natural selection*. However, neither of these constitutes a coded plan. Likewise, neither of them is an energy-conversion mechanism. If neither is either, how can both be both?

A mutation is a random change in an already ordered code, and natural selection is a sort of sieve which screens out these mutants and, thereby, preserves this previous order. Neither one has the potential to convert the sun's energy (or any other kind of energy) into some other form of energy that will generate new and higher order in the species. The theory of evolution, therefore, must be suspended in an evidential vacuum, with no visible mechanism of support. It flatly contradicts the universal Second Law of Thermodynamics, and it fails completely to meet the necessary criteria for even those superficial exceptions to the Law that occur in living organisms. Evolutionists, therefore, walk by faith, not by sight!

The Second Law of Thermodynamics could well be stated as follows: "In any ordered system, open or closed, there exists a *tendency* for that system to decay to a state of disorder, which tendency can be suspended or reversed only by an external source of ordering energy directed by an informational program, and transformed through an

---

[29] Lewis Thomas, "The Miraculous Membrane," *Intellectual Digest*, vol. 4 (February 1974), p. 56.

ingestion-storage-converter mechanism into the specific work required to build up the complex structure of that system."

If either the information program or the converter mechanism is not available to that "open" system, it will *not* increase in order, no matter how much external energy surrounds it, or flows into it or through it. The system will inevitably proceed to decay in accordance with the Second Law of Thermodynamics.

To cite special cases (such as the seed, for which the genetic code and the conversion mechanism of photosynthesis *are* available) is futile as far as "evolution" is concerned, since there is neither a directing program nor conversion apparatus available to produce an imaginary evolutionary growth-in-complexity of the earth and its biosphere.

It is even more futile to refer to inorganic processes such as crystallization as evidence of evolution. Even Prigogine recognizes this as follows:

> The point is that in a non-isolated system there exists a possibility for formation of ordered, low-entropy structures at sufficiently low temperatures. This ordering principle is responsible for the appearance of ordered structures such as crystals as well as for the phenomena of phase transitions.
>
> Unfortunately this principle cannot explain the formation of biological structures. The probability that at ordinary temperatures a macroscopic number of molecules is assembled to give rise to the highly-ordered structures and to the coordinated functions characterizing living organisms is vanishingly small. The idea of spontaneous genesis of life in its present form is therefore highly improbable, even on the scale of the billions of years during which pre-biotic evolution occurred.[30]

Another scientist has also pointed out the fallacy in comparing crystallization to evolution:

> Attempts to relate the idea of "order" in a crystal with biological organization or specificity must be regarded as a play on words which cannot stand careful scrutiny.[31]

---

[30] Ilya Prigogine, Gregoire Nicolis and Agnes Babloyants, "Thermodynamics of Evolution," *Physics Today*, vol. 25 (November 1972), p. 23.

[31] Hubert P. Yockey, "A Calculation of the Probability of Spontaneous Biogenesis by Information Theory," *Journal of Theoretical Biology*, vol. 67 (1977), p. 380.

Therefore, the highly specialized conditions that enable crystals to form, and plants and animals to grow have nothing whatever to do with evolution. These special conditions themselves (that is, the marvelous process of photosynthesis, the complex information programs in the living cell, and even the electrochemical properties of the molecules in the crystal, etc.) could never arise by chance: their own complexity could never have been produced within the constraints imposed by the Second Law. But without these conditions, the crystal would not form, and the seed would never grow.

But what is the information code that tells primeval random particles how to organize themselves into stars and planets, and what is the conversion mechanism that transforms amoebas into men? These are questions that are not answered by a superficial, specious reference to the earth as an open system! And until they *are* answered, the Second Law makes evolution appear wholly impossible.

To their credit, there are a few evolutionists (though apparently *very* few) who recognize the critical nature of this problem and are trying to solve it. Prigogine has proposed an involved theory of "order through fluctuations" and "dissipative structures."[32] We shall look at this work in somewhat more detail later.

But his examples are from inorganic systems, and he acknowledges that there is a long way to go to explain how these become *living* systems by his theory.

> But let us have no illusions — our research would still leave us quite unable to grasp the extreme complexity of the simplest of organisms.[33]

Another writer who has partially recognized the seriousness of this problem is Charles J. Smith.

> The thermodynamicist immediately clarifies the latter question by pointing out that the Second Law classically refers to isolated systems which exchange neither energy nor matter with the environment; biological systems are open and enhance both energy and matter.... This explanation, however, is not completely satisfying, because it still leaves open the problem of how or why the ordering process has arisen (an apparent lowering of the

---

[32] Prigogine, Nicolis, and Babloyants, "Thermodynamics of Evolution," p. 23-28.

[33] Ilya Prigogine, "Can Thermodynamics Explain Biological Order?" *Impact of Science on Society*, vol. 23, no. 3 (1973), p. 178.

entropy), and a number of scientists have wrestled with this issue. Bertelanffy (1968) called the relation between irreversible thermodynamics and information theory one of the most fundamental unsolved problems in biology. I would go further and include the problem of meaning and value.[34]

Whether rank-and-file evolutionists know it or not, the problem that they have with entropy is "*one of the most fundamental unsolved problems in biology.*" In fact, it is more than a problem: it is a devastating denial of the evolution model itself! It will continue to be so until evolutionists can demonstrate that the vast imagined evolutionary continuum in space and time has both a *program* to guide it, and an *energy converter* to empower it. Otherwise, the Second Law precludes it.

Although it is really inconceivable, just suppose that evolutionists might eventually manage to formulate a plausible code and mechanism to explain how both entropy and evolution could co-exist. Even if they could, however, the evolution model would still not be as good as the creation model. At the most, such a suggestion would only constitute an imaginary modification of the basic evolution model. The latter could certainly never *predict* the Second Law!

The evolution model thus cannot even explain the Second Law, but the creation model *predicts* it! The creationist is not embarrassed or perplexed by entropy, since it is exactly what he expects. The creation model postulates a perfect creation of all things completed during a period of special creation in the beginning. From this model, the creationist naturally predicts *limited horizontal* changes within the created entities (e.g., variations within biologic types, enabling them to adapt to environmental changes).

If "vertical" changes occur, however, from one level of order to another, they would have to go in a downward direction, toward lower order. The Creator, both omniscient and omnipotent, made all things perfect in the beginning. No process of evolutionary change could improve them, but deteriorative changes could disorder them.

Not only does the creation model predict the entropy principle, but the entropy principle directly points to creation. That is, if all things are now running down to disorder, they must originally have been in a state of high order. Since there is no naturalistic process that could produce such an initial condition, its cause must have been supernatural. The only

---

[34] Charles J. Smith, "Problems with Entropy in Biology," *Biosystems*, vol. 1 (1975), p. 259.

adequate cause of the initial order and complexity of the universe must have been an omniscient programmer, and the cause of its boundless power an omnipotent energizer. The Second Law of Thermodynamics, with its principle of increasing entropy, both repudiates the evolution model, and strongly confirms the creation model.

Order through Chaos and Dissipation

Evolutionists hardly even considered this problem until recent years, let alone solved it. There are, to their credit, a few theorists who have at least recognized the problem and offered certain speculations as to possible directions in which to search for a solution. The one man whose speculations have received the most attention (even helping to acquire for him a Nobel Prize in 1977) is Belgian physicist Ilya Prigogine, who advanced the strange idea of "dissipative structures" as a possible source of new complexity in nature.

He postulated that when systems somehow are "perturbed" to a "far-from-equilibrium" condition, as a result of a large influx of external energy that produces an inordinate amount of internal-energy dissipation, then certain "structures" might be generated. An example would be the generation of storm cells in the earth's atmosphere by incoming solar heat.

How such "dissipative structures" could possibly produce organic evolution is completely unknown, of course, and seems quite impossible to imagine. Such systems in no way contradict the principle of entropy but rather are illustrations of entropy, working overtime! A Harvard scientist, John Ross, comments on the invulnerability of the Second Law thus:

> There are no known violations of the second law of thermodynamics. Ordinarily the Second Law is stated for isolated systems, but the second law applies equally well to open systems. . . . There is somehow associated with the field of far from equilibrium phenomena the notion that the Second Law of Thermodynamics fails for such systems. It is important to make sure that this error does not perpetuate itself.[35]

Nevertheless, the extraordinary notion of generating organization through chaos has achieved a remarkably numerous following in recent years, not only among evolutionists anxious for any solution to the entropy problem, but also among radicals desiring a scientific justifica-

---

[35] John Ross, letter to the editor, *Chemical and Engineering News* (July 7, 1980), p. 40.

tion for social revolutions, as discussed in Volume 3 of this Trilogy. For example, UNESCO scientist Ervin Laszlo, has said the following (as quoted by Wil Lepkowski):

> What I see Prigogine doing is giving legitimization to the process of evolution — self-organization under conditions of change. . . . Its analogy to social systems and evolution should be very fruitful.[36]

There is little need for extended discussion here of the many speculative applications that have been related to Prigogine's suggestion since he "gave legitimization to evolution," as Laszlo put it (thus admitting by inference that evolution was illegitimate until Prigogine came along with this unique "remedy" for entropy).

One must give Prigogine credit at least for trying to resolve this intractable problem. Here is what Prigogine and his followers have claimed:

> Our scientific heritage includes two basic questions to which until now no answer was provided. One is the relation between disorder and order. The famous law of increase of entropy describes the world as evolving from order to disorder; still biological or social evolution shows us the complex emerging from the simple.[37]

But Prigogine never even considers whether evolutionists have really *shown* this, or merely *believe* it! Prigogine noted that, in a field with a high flow-through of energy, resulting in much energy dissipation (or "chaos"), certain ephemeral structures tend to appear for a time (e.g., vortices in a turbulent flow wake behind a bridge pier, hurricane or tornado cells in the atmosphere, small whirls in a cup of hot coffee), and he thought that these "dissipative structures" might somehow support the idea of order out of chaos, or the evolution of the biosphere. He acknowledged that this question of how evolution could occur in a world governed by the entropy law had, indeed, been a vexing question, even though most biologists have ignored it.

> There is another question, which has plagued us for more than a century: What significance does the evolution

---

[36] Wil Lepkowski, "The Social Thermodynamics of Ilya Prigogine," *Chemical and Engineering News* (April 16, 1979), p. 30.

[37] Ilya Prigogine and Isabelle Stengers, *Order Out of Chaos* (New York, NY: Bantam Books, 1984), p. xxix.

of a living being have in the world described by thermodynamics, a world of ever-increasing disorder?[38]

Prigogine then argues that the problem is essentially solved through his dissipative structures, since they constitute a sort of order generated in a chaotic milieu:

> We now know that far from equilibrium, new types of structures may originate spontaneously. In far-from-equilibrium conditions, we may have transformation from disorder, from thermal chaos, into order. New dynamic states of matter may originate, states that reflect the interaction of a given system with its surroundings. We have called these new structures dissipative structures to emphasize the constructive role of dissipative processes in their formation.[39]

Just how excessive "dissipation" can be "constructive" remains a mystery. No real evidence is ever given that these "new structures" are stable and, therefore, able to serve as a future base for still higher degrees of order, such as any evolutionary process would require. In the real world, any "structures" so generated seem always to disappear quickly.

For example, large vortices generated in a turbulent wake behind an obstruction in a stream are very soon broken up into smaller and smaller vortices farther downstream, and their energy is quickly dissipated through friction, and lost to any further utility. One of the present writers (H. Morris) did his Ph.D. dissertation on such dissipation of energy structures more than 45 years ago,[40] and this was certainly the result in water flows at least. An old poetic cliché among hydraulicians goes something like this: "Big whirls make little whirls that feed on their velocity; little whirls make tiny whirls, and so on to viscosity."

Nevertheless, although he still expresses some hesitation, Prigogine seems confident that he really has hit on the key to the puzzle.

> We come to one of our main conclusions: At all levels, be it the level of macroscopic physics, the level of fluctuations, or the microscopic level, *non-equilibrium is the source of order. Non-equilibrium brings "order out of*

---

[38] Ilya Prigogine and Isabelle Stengers, *Order Out of Chaos* (New York, NY: Bantam Books, 1984), p. 129.

[39] *Ibid.*, p. 12.

[40] Henry M. Morris, *A New Concept of Flow in Rough Conduits* (Minneapolis, MN: University of Minnesota, 1950), 151 p.

chaos." But as we have already mentioned, the concept of order (or disorder) is more complex than was thought.[41]

Especially would this difficulty become a problem with respect to how to preserve and use this "order" that emerges out of chaos. It is significant that Prigogine's studies were all mathematical and philosophical, not experimental. He can present no real observational *proof* that the generation of fluctuations, or perturbations, or far-from-equilibrium conditions, or dissipative structures, or whatever terms he may use to describe chaos, will ever enable evolution to overcome entropy.

Among the very few evolutionists who have seriously tried to work out a harmony between evolution and entropy, not simply dismissing the issue with an irrelevant "open-system" cop-out, probably the most ambitious were D. R. Brooks and E. O. Wiley, who wrote a book several years ago actually attempting to *equate* evolution and entropy! Unfortunately, they relied heavily on Prigogine's analysis.

> Our theory suggests that evolution is a phenomenon involving systems (species) far from equilibrium. The hierarchy results from speciation, which we will try to show exhibits dynamics *analogous* to "ordering through fluctuations" (Prigogine, Nicholis, and Babloyantz, 1972). It is important to understand that this is an analogy. Ordering through fluctuations in strictly thermodynamic systems is a direct by-product of energy flows. Ordering through fluctuations in evolution is a direct by-product of information and cohesion and not, we submit, energy flows.[42]

Building a theory on an analogy with another very dubious theory in a different field would not seem to bear great promise, but Brooks and Wiley attempt it anyway. Here is their reasoning:

> Why is there order and not chaos in the living world? Because living systems, organisms and species, are individualized dissipative structures (1) exhibiting finite information and cohesion, (2) maintaining themselves through irreversible dissipation of matter and energy, and (3) existing in an open energy system.[43]

---

[41] Prigogine and Stengers, *Order Out of Chaos*, p. 286. Emphasis is theirs.

[42] Daniel R. Brooks and Edward O. Wiley, *Evolution as Entropy* (Chicago, IL: University of Chicago Press, 1985), p. 43. Emphasis is theirs.

[43] *Ibid.*, p. 70.

Whereas this statement may be meaningful in explaining how an organism maintains itself as an orderly system, it says nothing about how the species became thus organized in the first place.

> While the structural complexity of living organisms as little violates the second law of thermodynamics (or any other law of physics) as does that of a television set or a jet engine, we need to look elsewhere for a detailed understanding of the origin of this complexity during development and evolution.[44]

There is probably nothing wrong with calling living organisms "dissipative structures," if such a term is deemed useful for some reason. They are, indeed, extremely complex structures; they are certainly "open systems;" and they do dissipate much matter and energy irreversibly as they maintain their structure. Like Prigogine's vortices, however, they eventually are dissipated themselves. As individuals they finally die; as species they may atrophy and become extinct. But, as we have seen in earlier chapters, they never evolve into some more complex species. Here, Brooks and Wiley must continue to rely on mutations, but, as Charlesworth says, they provide no evidence that mutations ever accomplish evolution!

> There is nothing in evolutionary or developmental biology that justifies their assumptions that a successful mutation (which seems merely to mean a selectively neutral one in their model) is always associated with an increase in some global measure of phenotype. Nor is there anything to support the assumption that new species arise as the result of single gene mutations and are initially genetically uniform. If these assumptions are removed, the whole edifice collapses.[45]

Although Brooks and Wiley call their book *Evolution as Entropy*, they don't quite mean that. They realize that entropy will eventually win out in the end:

> Evolution is a process that slows down the entropy decay of lineages, minimizing their entropy increases. This

---

[44] Brian Charlesworth, "Entropy: The Great Illusion," Review of *Evolution as Entropy*, by Brooks and Wiley (Chicago, IL, 1985), appearing in *Evolution*, vol. 40, no. 4 (1986), p. 880.

[45] *Ibid.*

suggests that, as the interplay of information and cohesion, biological evolution should exhibit an intrinsic tendency toward efficiency or parsimony, which in turn should relate to the principle of minimum entropy production.[46]

Perhaps, in the terminology of Gould and Eldredge, dissipative-structure theory might explain why such long periods of stasis precede extinction, but there still is no explanation of how the *chaos of extinction* will generate the *higher complexity* required by vertical evolution.

Another reviewer compliments their intentions, but remains unsatisfied by their concept:

> I was disappointed by Brooks and Wiley's discussion of entropy and evolution because it did not seem to me that they present a theory at all. It is not that their theory is wrong; it seems to be vacuous instead.[47]

> Brooks and Wiley have not produced a new evolutionary theory, or even a very useful re-description of existing theories, but I cannot fault them for trying. They see the importance of the task, and here they are right and my fellow population geneticists are both wrong and wrongheaded.[48]

At least Brooks and Wiley realize that they cannot eliminate the entropy problem by the trivial and irrelevant open-system argument to which most biologists and other evolutionists resort. Their courage in attempting to harmonize evolution with entropy is perhaps commendable, but their task is impossible! The law of entropy makes evolution impossible, and there is really no way around it, except to assume that the entropy law somehow was suspended while evolution was occurring.

They also admit that, as with other suggested evolutionary mechanisms, Prigogine's approach may be able to "retrodict" evolutionary events with just-so-stories, but it cannot *predict* any.

> These states are historically emergent and can be discerned retrospectively, but cannot be predicted from initial conditions.[49]

---

[46] Brooks and Wiley, *Evolution as Entropy*, p. 74.

[47] Joseph Felsenstein, "Waiting for Post-Neo-Darwin," *Evolution*, vol. 40, no. 4 (1986), p. 887.

[48] *Ibid.*, p. 888.

[49] Brooks and Wiley, *Evolution as Entropy*, p. 72.

Even Prigogine has expressed doubts about their analysis, though he still believes that his own approach does, somehow, hold the key to evolution.

> "I see how you can do this with molecules," he told Brooks, "but I don't see how you can do it with species. I don't understand the extrapolation."[50]

In short, despite all the acclaim that Prigogine has received for his work (even getting the Nobel Prize for it!), he really contributed nothing to resolving the basic conflict of evolution with the Second Law of Thermodynamics. And, despite their noble attempt to extrapolate Prigogine's analysis by analogy, into a harmony of entropy and evolutionary biology, neither do Brooks and Wiley. Charlesworth summarizes their failure thus:

> Their work suffers, however, from the usual faults of half-baked theorizing in biology. The worst of these is the lack of any convincing derivation of the supposed laws of change from known principles, in contrast to the program of statistical mechanics which provides the background for their ideas.[51]

To our knowledge, the work of Prigogine plus that of Brooks and Wiley represent the most serious and extensive attempts to correlate entropy and evolution. Their efforts failed.

Nevertheless, many other writers, and evolutionists in general, continue blithely along on the assumption that the Second Law of Thermodynamics poses no problem for evolution! Typically, they smugly accuse creationists of ignorance of thermodynamics for even thinking that this is an issue. Usually they shrug it off with a nonchalant reference to closed and open systems, or else a with patronizing mini-lecture on Prigogine and his "illumination" of how it all works.

Then there are the "new-age" evolutionists, who place even more reliance on Prigogine and his revelation of "order through chaos," as well as on Gould and his "punctuated equilibria," maintaining that certain mysterious forces in the cosmos, or even the conscious cosmos itself, intermittently brings higher orders, out of lower orders through traumatic episodes of catastrophe and extinction, followed by spurts of creative integration or something.

---

[50]Cited by Roger Lewin, "A Downward Slope to Greater Diversity," *Science* (1982), p. 1239. Lewin himself called their speculations mere "heuristic formulations."
[51] Charlesworth, "Entropy, the Great Illusion," p. 879.

All such evolutionary notions, if scrutinized seriously, fail when they confront the mountain of hard scientific data — in fact, *all real factual data* — verifying the universal control of the laws of thermodynamics over all natural processes. No matter what sort of semantic circumlocution is formulated to get around it, the fact is that evolution is *supposed to be* a universal law that generates greater organization and complexity, whereas the Second Law of Thermodynamics is *known to be* a universal law that tends to produce lower organization and complexity. Each is presented as a universal law of change — one of *upward* change, the other of *downward* change.

How, if language has any logic, could both be valid? The Second Law is known to be valid in all real processes, with no known exception, whenever those processes are observable and measurable. Evolution, on the other hand, has never been observed to occur in the present, and, to all appearances in the fossil record, never occurred in the past! It seems that if one wants to be *scientific* in choosing which to believe, he should go with the *law* that fits all the scientific evidence, and therefore he should repudiate all faith in the *theory* of evolution.

Now, despite the fact that neither Prigogine nor anyone else has solved the irreconcilable problem between evolution and entropy, many evolutionists are blithely assuming today — as did Brooks and Wiley — that Prigogine *has* solved it with his "dissipative structures," and much of the new theories about "order out of chaos" are built on this assumption. Carl Sagan, for example, in a recent book refers indirectly to Prigogine when he says:

> We repeatedly discover that natural processes — collisional selection of worlds, say, or natural selection of gene pools, or even the convection pattern in a pot of boiling water — can extract order out of chaos, and deceive us into deducing purpose where there is none.[52]

Even more recently, a review article by a professor of the philosophy of science at Tel Aviv University in Israel has summarized all these notions and insists that a law of total evolution (particles to people) should be built up on the assumed "equivalence" of evolutionary progress with the principles of thermodynamics.

> The recently suggested re-formulation of Darwinian evolutionary theory, based on the thermodynamics of self-organizing processes, has strong philosophical implications.

---

[52] Carl Sagan, *A Pale Blue Dot* (New York, NY: Random House, 1993), p. 57.

> My claim is that the main philosophic merit of the thermo-
> dynamic approach . . . is its insistence on the law-governed
> continuous nature of evolution.[53]

All these anomalous concepts do, indeed, have "strong philosophical implications," but their scientific foundation is based strictly on
wishful thinking, not evidence.

The Ubiquitous Entropy Principle

As a sort of appendix to the foregoing discussion, it is instructive
to note the universality of the entropy principle. Many other illustrations
of the decay principle abound throughout the world of nature and of life.
A few of these are mentioned briefly below:

1. *Frictional resistance to motion.* Everything happening in
   our space-time universe involves motion, and every motion
   requires a force to initiate it against inertia and sustain it
   against the retarding force of friction. There is always some
   friction resisting the movement, and some of the energy
   maintaining it must be used to overcome the friction, being
   converted thereby into non-recoverable heat energy. Thus
   all processes tend eventually to slow down and cease. Perpetual motion is impossible, and no process can be operated
   at 100 percent efficiency.

2. *Aging and death of individuals.* Individual organisms of all
   kinds eventually die, no matter how much energy may be
   available to them in the environment. Body cells deteriorate,
   complex protein molecules break down into simpler compounds, and eventually some vital organ or process ceases to
   function and death ensues. The causes of the aging process
   are not yet well understood, but there seems no basic reason
   why it could not be slowed down considerably, with resulting increased longevity. The Second Law does not specify
   the rate, but only the fact, of decay.

3. *Decay and extinction of species.* Just as individuals die, so do
   species. The real testimony of the fossil record is not the slow
   development of species, but rather the sudden extinction of
   species. Similarly, there may be such things as *vestigial*
   organs in both extinct and living kinds of animals, but no one

---

[53] Iris Frey, "Evolution in Thermodynamic Perspective: A Historical and Philosophical
Angle," *Zygon*, vol. 30 (June 1995), p. 227.

is able to point to any *nascent* (that is, beginning to evolve into something useful) organs.

4. *Wear*. Another result of friction is that of wear. Not only does friction convert useful energy into useless heat, but also useful material into dust.

    > The inexorable loss of material from surfaces in sliding contact eventually destroys the usefulness of most things.[54]

5. *Disease*. Both plants and animals are subject to still another kind of deterioration, namely, disease.

    > Long before man began to evolve about one million years ago, the earth was inhabited at least half a billion years ago by numerous other animals: the fishes, the reptiles, and eventually the mammals, many of which are now extinct. These prehistoric animals, scientists say, often were afflicted with disease.[55]

6. *Decay of environment*. Not only do both individual organisms and even entire species decay and die, but also the very environment of life tends to decay. People have become especially aware of this factor in connection with pollutional problems in recent years, but actually the environment is continually decaying even apart from man-made pollution. Soil erosion, for example, continually contributes to stream and ocean dissolved chemicals, quite independently of the artificial contamination thereof. Climatic factors are constantly changing also.

7. *Decay of nations, cultures, and languages*. Although it might be difficult to demonstrate a formal connection with thermodynamics, there is a marked analogy between the birth, growth, and death of an individual, and the rise and fall of nations and cultures. Languages also typically become decadent and simple (losing complexity) in their old age.

8. *Breakdown of morals and religion*. Similarly, societies commonly experience a period of strong religious faith and strict

---

[54] Ernest Rabinowicz, "Wear," *Scientific American*, vol. 206 (February 1962), p. 127.

[55] James A. Tobey, "Disease is Older than Man," *Science Digest* (April 1958), p. 53.

moral standards in the early days of their development, only to be gradually affected by an apparently inevitable decline in faith and morals as they become older.

9. *Personal disintegration*. Finally, a universal fact of experience is that one's moral behavior is under constant pressure to drop down to lower levels. If one simply "lets himself go," he inevitably goes down, degenerates, morally and spiritually. He does not automatically get better.

In summary of this chapter, it seems that, if science proves anything at all, biological evolution has not only *never* occurred in the past or present, but also will *never occur* at all in the future. In fact, evolution is against the law: the law of ever-increasing entropy!

However, there are two other vital components of evolutionary theory that have not been discussed in this chapter because we wish to treat them each in a separate chapter of their own. One is that of nonbiological, or inorganic evolution, the origin of matter and of the physical universe. The other is the evolution of inorganic materials into replicating chemicals, or the origin of life.

Both of these are also negated by the Second Law of Thermodynamics, as well as by all other scientific evidence, as we shall see in the next two chapters.

Chapter 7

The Probability of Life Is Zero

We have been discussing the general subject of the origin of the various species of plants and animals, and have shown that the creation model of origins fits the actual scientific data (from genetics, paleontology, thermodynamics, etc.) far better than the evolution model. As predicted from the creation model, there is *no* evidence at all that the transmutation of any species into a more complex species has ever occurred in the past, is occurring now, or could ever occur in the future.

We have not yet considered, however, the origin of the very first species: the species from which, according to the evolution model, all other species have developed by natural processes. Did the very first one-celled organism evolve naturalistically from non-living chemical molecules, or was life created supernaturally? Even if the first form of life was simply a replicating protein molecule or something of the sort, could *this* somehow have developed by chance, even from complex organic chemicals?

Creationists would answer "no," of course; life, even at the very simplest imaginary level, could never have arisen by any random, unguided combination of non-living substances. Most evolutionists, however, are "total" evolutionists. They argue that it is not scientific to allow a Creator to interfere anywhere in the processes of nature, and this includes the beginning of life:

> This survival-of-the-fittest scenario takes place even at the level of molecules. On primordial earth, chemicals with slight individual variations must have replicated themselves

and competed with one another, scientists believe. The successful ones gave rise to the complex biological molecules that serve living organisms today.[1]

Most evolutionists believe this, but they do so by blind faith! This process is not occurring today, and it seems altogether impossible to understand how it could ever have happened in the past. One of the world's leading evolutionary biochemists, a man who has written extensively on this difficult subject, recognizes this fact as follows:

> It is extremely improbable that proteins and nucleic acids, both of which are structurally complex, arose spontaneously in the same place at the same time. Yet it also seems impossible to have one without the other. And so, at first glance, one might have to conclude that life could never, in fact, have originated by chemical means.[2]

Nevertheless, the author of this very sensible conclusion still believes in "abiogenesis," the origin of life by natural evolutionary processes without benefit of a Creator. In the past, Dr. Orgel has proposed that life on earth came through seeding by aliens from some distant planet, "directed panspermia." More recently, he has tried to develop the idea that it arose through the prior evolution of "pre-biotic RNA." Both ideas are born of desperation, are incapable of proof, and are merely illustrative of the deep dedication of many scientists to the religion of atheism.

The Probability Barrier

Before discussing the various ideas and experiments that have been devoted to this elusive search, it would be well to look at the overwhelming odds against its success. With no intelligence to direct the assembly of elementary particles into complex chemicals or to guide the transformation of such chemicals into chemical substances able to reproduce themselves, we must rely strictly on chance to do it all. What is the chance, or probability, that such particles could somehow evolve themselves into replicating systems?

Many evolutionary scientists have analyzed this very concept in terms of the laws of probability, hoping to show that chance processes, if operating long enough, can accidentally, as it were, generate systems

---

[1] Karen A. Schmidt, "Evolution in a Test Tube," *Science News*, vol. 144 (August 7, 1993), p. 90.
[2] Leslie E. Orgel, "The Origin of Life on the Earth," *Scientific American*, vol. 271 (October 1994), p. 78.

that might appear to have been the product of intelligent design. This is the thesis, for example, of Richard Dawkin's famous and very influential book, *The Blind Watchmaker.*

The argument from design has always been considered a most powerful evidence for the existence of God. A watch requires a watchmaker; then, what about the far more intricate and precise atomic and sidereal clocks? A water-supply system requires the efforts of a great many skilled engineers and builders; then, what about the marvelous reservoir, pumping, purification, and distribution system involved in the hydrologic cycle, which supplies water to the earth's inhabitants? A great building presupposes a trained architect; but the infinitely more complex structure of the human body cannot even be analyzed, let alone designed, by man. The greatest digital computers are absurdly simple in comparison to the complex circuitry of the human brain and nervous system.

The idea that a complex structure or system can somehow be formed by chance is a persistent delusion accepted by evolutionists. Typical naturalistic reasoning supposes that anything can happen if enough time is available. Monkeys pawing away blindly at typewriter keys are bound eventually to hit on Shakespeare's *Hamlet*, so the thinking goes.

But this idea is preposterous! To illustrate, consider an ordered structure of, say, 200 parts. This is not a large number; the very simplest one-celled organism, for example, contains more than 200 separate inter-related components, all aligned together into a perfectly integrated functioning whole. There are innumerable systems in the world far more complicated than this.

Consider the possible number of different ways 200 parts could be aligned together. A system of one part could be lined up in only one way; one of two parts could be lined up in two ways (1 x 2); one of three parts in six ways 1 x 2 x 3); one of four parts in 24 ways (1 x 2 x 3 x 4); and so on. Thus, a system of 200 parts could be aligned in a stupendous number of different ways, equal to 1 x 2 x 3 x 4 x 5 x 6 . . . x . . . x 200. This number is called "200 factorial" and is written "200"!

Now that is a tremendously large number. It can be shown to be approximately 10^{375}, that is, a number written as "one" followed by 375 "zeros." Therefore, the *correct* alignment of the 200 parts has only one chance out of 10^{375} of being selected on the first trial.

Suppose a new trial can be made every second. In all of the supposed astronomic time (say, 20 billion years), there have only been 10^{18} seconds, so the chance that the correct alignment might be obtained once in the 10 billions years would be only one out of $10^{(375-18)}$, or 1 in 10^{337}. This is still practically zero!

Suppose that we try to improve the chances by arranging to have a large number of sets of the 200 parts, all being tried simultaneously. Suppose that each part is only the size of an electron, which is essentially the smallest particle definitely known to exist in the universe. Then, let us fill the entire universe (of radius, say, 5 billion light-years) with solidly packed sets of electrons. It can be shown that the whole universe could only contain, at the most, 10^{130} such sets of 200 solidly-packed electrons. Therefore, we now are trying to visualize 10^{130} sets of 200 parts each, and trying to arrange *only one* set into the correct alignment by chance, just *once* in twenty billion years, anywhere in the universe.

Suppose also that we invent a machine capable of making not one trial per second, but a billion-billion different trials every second, on every one of the 10^{130} sets. Surely, this is the maximum number of possible trials that anyone could possibly conceive as ever being made on this type of situation. This would permit a total of $(10^{130})(10^{18})(10^{18})$, or 10^{166}, trials to be made.

Still, after all this, the chance that one of these 10^{166} trials would give the right result and make the system work is only one out of $10^{(375-166)}$, or 1 in 10^{209}. In other words, the idea that a system of 200 parts could be arranged by *chance* into the correct order is *absolutely absurd*!

Most systems, of course, including all living organisms, are far more complex than a mere 200 parts. The cerebral cortex in the human brain, for example, contains over 10 billion cells, all arranged in proper order, and each of these cells is itself infinitely complex!

The obvious conclusion is that complex, ordered structures of any kind (and the world is full of them) simply *could never have happened by chance*. Disorder never spontaneously turns into order. Organization requires an organizer. The infinite array of complex effects seen in the universe *must* have been produced by an adequate cause. An adequate cause is God, the Creator, and nothing less!

The modern Darwinian evolutionist thinks that he has a naturalistic explanation for all this, of course. The magic formula that transforms electrons into living cells, and frogs into princes, is "random mutation and natural selection," and the magic wand that makes it work is "billions of years."

For example, leading geneticist Francisco J. Ayala has insisted on this perspective as follows:

> Darwin substituted a scientific teleology for a theo-
> logical one. The teleology of nature could now be ex-

plained, at least in principle, as the result of natural laws manifested in natural processes, without recourse to an external Creator or to spiritual or non-material forces.[3]

As we have seen, however, Darwinism is not really a "scientific teleology" at all. Random mutations necessarily generate disorder, not order, and natural selection at best constitutes a screening mechanism for sieving out the disorganized misfits produced by mutational pressures, and, therewith, a means for conserving the original complex systems already present. Furthermore, the longer the period of time available for such pressures to operate, the more likely it is that they will tend to overcome the selection process and drag the entire biosphere downhill to lower levels of order!

The tenet of neo-Darwinism — that random mutation combined with natural selection eliminates the need for God — is premature, to say the least. It has been shown that complex ordered structures could never be produced by "random selection" of their parts. Nevertheless, evolutionists insist that "selection" can somehow affect the "random" nature of the process. Even though genetic mutation is a random process, they feel that natural selection can so efficiently strain out the "good" mutations that its randomness is gradually converted into increased order, even without an intelligent organizer to control it.

But this is asking far too much of such an impersonal, unintelligent, static phenomenon as natural selection. At the very best, natural selection cannot produce the mutations; it does not energize or organize anything itself. All it can do is "decide" whether a combination of parts presented to it by the *random* mutation process is more ordered or less ordered than its non-mutated predecessor combination; and we have already seen that a *random* process could never produce an ordered structure for selection to "select" — even such a relatively simple structure as one containing only 200 components.

At this point, the evolutionist might object that he is being misunderstood. He does not propose that an ordered structure should be suddenly organized from its 200 separate parts all simultaneously. Rather, the process works gradually, part upon part, slowly, over long ages. Only one part is added at a time.

However, a little consideration will show that this only makes matters worse! The same selection process has to take place over and over again, and each time against greater odds than the time before.

---

[3] Francisco J. Ayala, "Teleological Explanations in Evolutionary Biology," *Philosophy of Science*, vol. 37 (March 1970), p. 2.

That is, when the structure advances from one to two parts, it has two "choices" as to alignment, and therefore a 1 in 2 chance of success. When it goes from two to three parts, it has six choices, and therefore a 1 in 6 chance, and so on. If it goes all the way to 200 parts, its final advance has, as calculated earlier, only a 1 in 10^{375} chance. Each step in the chain has to keep "trying" until it hits on the right combination at each step before it can go on to the next one.

Therefore, the probability of developing an ordered structure of 200 parts, using this step-by-step mutation-selection technique, is only about 1 out of the number represented by the series $2! + 3! + 4! + \ldots + 199! + 200!$ This number is obviously far larger than an all-at-once selection. The evolutionist should have left well enough alone!

Now, admittedly, the above analysis assumes that each successive step must, in effect, "start from scratch," and this isn't really fair. The evolutionist does not visualize all parts being completely reshuffled at each step. On the other hand, it must also be remembered that in every living organized system there is an intricate inter-dependence of all parts upon each other. The elevation of an nth-degree ordered system to an $(n + 1)^{th}$ degree ordered system is certainly far more involved than a mere linking of the new part on to the previous structure unchanged.

And there is also the question of where the new part comes from in the first place! A mutation may cause a change in an *existing* part, but how does it create a *new* part to add to the system? Furthermore, if there is to be a change, what is to prevent the system from going downhill to less order, instead of uphill to higher order?

As a matter of fact, if mutations constitute the mechanism for producing this supposed increasing complexity, it is far more likely that the system will become *less ordered* with each change in order, instead of *more ordered*. All evolutionary geneticists agree that the great majority of mutations (if not all) are harmful.

However, let us give the evolutionary process the maximum possible benefit of the doubt and assume that each successive step has a 50:50 chance of success. That is, for a given structure, the probability that the next change will be an *addition of order* is assumed to be exactly the same as that it will be a *decrease of order*. The probability of success at each step is 1 out of 2.

There are 200 steps, of course, to be made to arrive at an integrated 200-component system. If any *one* of these steps fails (that is, produces a "lethal" or otherwise "harmful" mutation), then, of course, the evolutionary process in that particular system either stops altogether or goes backward.

All 200 steps must succeed, and the probability of success at each step is 1/2. Elementary statistical theory shows that the probability of success of the whole chain of steps is the product of the probabilities for each step. That is, the probability that a 200-step evolutionary chain can succeed is only one out of $(1/2)^{200}$, or 1 in 2^{200}, even assuming that beneficial mutations are as frequent as harmful mutations.

This number is equal to one represented by 1 with 60 zeros, or 10^{60}, or a quadrillion quadrillion quadrillion quadrillion. Not a very likely sequence!

Therefore, even this very simple evolutionary sequence of 200 steps is for all practical purposes impossible. An ordered system, by any means mathematically conceivable, *can never* arise by a random process from non-ordered components, even if a screening mechanism such as natural selection is available to conserve its acceptable products.

The evolutionist may still offer one faint objection, saying that even though one given system has only a 1 in 10^{60} chance of evolutionary success, there must be at least *some* systems in the world that make the grade.

So, let's go this one more mile with him. The surface area of the earth contains about 5.5×10^{15} sq. ft. Assume that each part of our hypothetical system is actually a living cell, and the entire surface of the earth is covered with living cells stacked one foot deep. Assuming there are about 10^{13} cells per cubic foot of living substance, there would be about 10^{13} cells then piled on top of each square foot, and the earth's surface would hold about 5.5×10^{28} such cells. If all of these are operative in this evolutionary process simultaneously, there would be, therefore, about systems of 200 parts each available on the entire earth. Since each of them has one chance in 10^{60} of evolutionary success, the chance that one out of all the 2.8×10^{26} sets would succeed is thereby reduced to about 1 in 10^{34}. This is still an impossibly large number!

However, as each set fails, then let a fresh set come in and try again. Suppose that each step takes one-half second, so that the 200 steps in each set would take 100 seconds. Then, in the 10^{18} seconds of astronomic time, each of the sets could have 10^{16} tries. Thus, a total of 2.8×10^{42} attempts could be made in all time, in all the world, to evolve a structure of 200 parts. The probability that one of them would ever succeed anywhere is still only 1 in 10^{18}, or one chance out of a billion billion.

And this is only one very simple structure! The world is full of vast numbers of far more complicated structures and systems than this.

We conclude that evolution by any kind of chance process, even with natural selection operating, is *mathematical* and *scientific nonsense*.

The argument from design, therefore, has not at all been refuted by natural selection theory, but is actually stronger than ever. The innumerable and marvelous structures and systems of the cosmos, and their intricate adaptations to each other constitute a vast complex of intelligible order for which creative forethought and design can be the only rational explanation. It is pointless to give examples because literally every system of any kind in the whole cosmos is itself a prodigious model of intricate structure and complex planning.

The great Designer who created this wonderful world can be none other than an omnipotent, omnipresent, omniscient, holy — yet also personal, loving, and gracious Creator. The Cause of all the phenomena of the universe must encompass at least all their own characteristics.

Zero Probability

As another example, consider a series of ten flash cards, numbered from one to ten. If these are thoroughly and randomly mixed, and then laid out successively in a linear array upon the table, it would be extremely unlikely that the numbers would fall out in order from one to ten. Actually, there are 3,628,800 different ways in which these numbers could be arranged, so that the "probability" of this particular ordered arrangement (one to ten) is only one in 3,628,800. (This number is "ten factorial," written as 10!, calculated simply by multiplying together all the numbers from one to ten.)

Obviously, the probability of such a numerically ordered arrangement decreases rapidly as the number of components increases. For any linear system of 100 components in specified order, the probability is one in 100!, or one chance in 10^{158} (a number represented by "one followed by 158 zeroes").

A system requiring such a high degree of order could never happen by chance. This follows from the fact that probability theory applies only to systems with a finite possibility of occurring at least once in the universe, and it would be inconceivable that 10^{158} different trials could ever be made in our entire space-time universe.

Astrophysicists estimate that there are no more than 10^{80} infinitesimal "particles" in the universe, and that the age of the universe in its present form is no greater than 10^{18} seconds (30 billion years). Assuming that each particle can participate in a thousand billion (10^{12}) different events every second (this is impossibly high, of course), then the greatest number of events that could ever happen (or trials that could ever be made) *in all the universe throughout its entire history* is only 10^{80} x 10^{18} x 10^{12}, or 10^{110} (most mathematicians/astrophysicists would make this figure much lower, about 10^{50}). Any event with a probability significantly lower than one chance in 10^{110}, therefore, cannot occur. Its probability becomes zero, at least in our known universe.

This conclusion is intuitively obvious, but it has also been demonstrated mathematically by a great French mathematician, Emil Borel, who called it "the sole law of chance," the law that is the basis of all other laws of probability.

A French scientist, drawing on Borel's work, has defined this law as follows:

> A phenomenon whose probability is sufficiently weak
> — that is, below a certain threshold — will never occur,
> "never" meaning here within the limits of space and time
> at our disposal, that is to say within the limits within which
> it is possible to repeat the trials, for as long as a world, all
> of whose known dimensions are finite, allows.[4]

It should be observed, also, that we have been considering only the probability of a certain arrangement of a very specialized class of events: that is, the ordered linear alignment of 100 pre-specified components. There are also, of course, an unending series of altogether different other classes of events that might occur in space and time, each of which could be specified and studied probabilistically.

All events of all categories and arrangements must be counted among the 10^{110} *possible* events. To say that a certain event in one given class of events has a probability in that class of only one in 10^{110} is to say that its probability is still *infinitely lower* when innumerably other classes of events also have to be crowded into the available space and time.

Therefore, the above-suggested ordered arrangement of 100 components has a zero probability. It could *never* happen by chance. Since every single living cell is infinitely more complex and ordered than this, it is impossible that even the simplest form of life could ever have originated by chance. Even the simplest conceivable replicating protein molecule that could be imagined has been shown by Golay[5] to have a probability of one in 10^{450}. Salisbury[6] calculates the probability of a typical DNA chain to be one in 10^{600}.

---

[4] Georges Salet, *Evolution in the Light of Modern Biology*, reviewed by Louis Lafont in *Permanences*, vol. 94 (November 1972). trans. Geoffrey Lawman, in *Approaches Supplement*, p. 7.

[5] Marcel Golay, "Reflections of a Communications Engineer," *Analytical Chemistry*, vol. 33 (June 1961), p. 23.

[6] Frank B. Salisbury, "Doubts about the Modern Synthetic Theory of Evolution," *American Biology Teacher* (September 1971), p. 336.

The Improbability of Any Kind of Order

However, when creationists use this evidence from probability while lecturing or debating on the creation/evolution question, evolutionists often dismiss the evidence as irrelevant, using the clever and confusing argument that no arrangement is more or less probable than any other arrangement, and *some* arrangement *must* exist!

For example, suppose the ten flash cards showed up as follows:

Figure 1

(a)

This arrangement obviously is *unordered* in comparison with the *ordered* arrangement below:

(b)

Nevertheless, the evolutionist will say that the unordered arrangement has the same probability (one in 3,628,800, or 10!) as the ordered arrangement. Consequently, since some arrangement is necessary, and any arrangement is just as probable as any other, there is no reason to see any particular significance in the arrangement that happens to occur. Hence, any argument for design based on probability, says the evolutionist, is meaningless.

Superficially, this assertion may seem logical, even though we immediately sense that something is wrong with it. We know intuitively, as well as experimentally, that *ordered* arrangements are much less probable than *unordered* arrangements. Random arrangements of boulders on a hillside, for example, are "natural," whereas the same boulders arranged in a circle would require explanation.

Closer consideration, of course, does quickly reveal that such evolutionary reasoning is specious. If arrangement (a) had, for some reason, been specified before hand, then its actual occurrence in the shuffle would indeed have been surprising. It could then no longer be considered an unordered arrangement, since it had been "ordered" externally! But it was *not* specified ahead of time — it was just the "luck of the draw." Arrangement (b), however, has intrinsic order, and its actual occurrence, therefore, would almost certainly not have been by chance.

This type of evolutionary equivocation appears in various guises. One debater responded to the creationist's probability argument by calling attention to the particular combination of people in the audience. With all the persons in the state, he noted, the probability that this specific group, rather than some other group, would come together by chance was extremely small, yet there they were! The answer, of course, was that the group had not come together by chance at all: each person had come by direct intent. Nor had the individuals in the group been pre-specified, as would have been the case in a designed system, where each component had to occupy a specific position in order for the system to function.

Occasionally, the objection is a little more subtle. The fact that a certain ordered structure, functioning in a specific way, seems to have an infinitesimal probability of origin by chance is side-stepped by asserting that if some other chance assemblage had come together, it may have functioned in some other way. Evolution might then have taken a different direction. The present functioning system, it is argued, is merely the natural development from the components that happened to come together, and this is no less probable than any other assemblage that might have evolved differently.

But this tenuous argument implicitly assumes that *any* chance aggregation of particles will contain some amount of "information" and, therefore, will have some kind of evolutionary potential. Such a belief is gratuitous and naive, to say the least, when all *real* experience indicates the exact opposite! That is, it is far easier and more common to generate something disordered and useless, than something organized and functioning.

One cannot simply pull a working system out of a hat full of random particles. The system must possess the requisite "information" before it can get anywhere or do anything constructive. It must be organized in some kind of pattern, and patterns do not usually appear spontaneously. They are not inevitable, as the above evolutionary argument implies, but *extremely rare*.

For example, although one could arrange the ten flash cards in a number of possible "ordered" patterns, the number is quite limited. There seems to be a certain amount of "information" in each of the arrangements shown below (See Figure 2), but it is obvious that arrangements **(b)** and **(c)** are more "ordered," containing more information than any of the others. Arrangement **(a)**, as noted earlier, contains *no* real order or information: it is strictly "random." No doubt a few other arrangements could be devised with a small amount of order to them, but only a few.

Figure 2

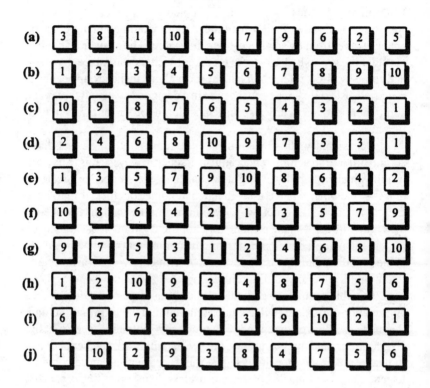

To be generous, however, let us assume that as many as 100 patterns could be devised for the ten cards that would contain some modicum of order. Each of these would have some amount of "information" and, therefore, might theoretically be able to specify some sort of wobbly function. This is entirely speculative, of course, since the only one that is *known* to be functional is the ideal pattern, as defined in arrangement **(b)**.

Even at best, however, there would be only 100 possible functional arrangements, leaving 3,628,700 completely unordered, and, therefore, non-functional arrangements, a ratio of over 36,000 to one. That is, the odds are at least 36,000 to one against any random assemblage of ten components in a meaningful system, one that could possibly serve as a base or pattern for anything.

This simple examination merely confirms what is intuitively

obvious anyhow, namely, that disorder in a system is tremendously more probable than *any kind* of order in that system — not only one specific pattern, but *any* kind of pattern! Furthermore, this improbability increases as the number of components in the system increases.

Number of Components	Number of Arrangements			Ratio of Disordered to Ordered Arrangements
	Possible	Ordered	Disordered	
2	2	2	0	0
3	6	2	4	2:1
4	24	6	18	3:1
5	120	10	110	11:1
10	3,628,800	100	3,628,700	36,287:1

The number of ordered arrangements shown in the table is somewhat arbitrary, of course, but certainly generous. In any event, it is very clear that the probability of the *chance* occurrence of any kind of "information" in a system is exceedingly small, and that this probability rapidly diminishes as the complexity of the system increases.

This means that, whenever one sees any kind of real ordered complexity in nature, particularly as found in living systems, he can be sure that such complexity was *designed*.

> One must conclude that, contrary to the established and current wisdom, a scenario describing the genesis of life on earth by chance and natural causes which can be accepted on the basis of fact and not faith has not yet been written.[7]

> I believe we developed this practice (i.e., of postulating pre-biological natural selection) to avoid facing the conclusion that the probability of a self-replicating state is zero. . . . When for practical purposes the concept of infinite time and matter has to be invoked, that concept of probability is annulled.[8]

---

[7] Hubert P. Yockey, "A Calculation of the Probability of Spontaneous Biogenesis by Information Theory," *Journal of Theoretical Biology*, vol. 67 (1977), p. 398.

[8] Peter T. Mora, "The Folly of Probability," in *The Origins of Prebiological Systems*, ed. Sydney Fox (New York: Academic Press, 1965), p. 45.

There is still the other evolutionary equivocation of natural selection, however. What chance cannot accomplish, evolutionists glibly attribute to natural selection.

> So natural selection as a process is okay. We are also pretty sure that it goes on in nature although good examples are surprisingly rare. The best evidence comes from the many cases where it can be shown that biological structures have been optimized — that is, structures that represent optimal engineering solutions to the problems that an animal has of feeding or escaping predators or generally functioning in its environment. . . . The presence of these optimal structures does not, of course, prove that they developed through natural selection, but it does provide strong circumstantial argument.[9]

This is a rather typical example of the way evolutionists evade even the strongest evidences for design. Dr. Raup, with a doctorate from Harvard, is a highly competent geologist, serving as curator of geology at Chicago's great Field Museum, and professor of geology at the University of Chicago. He has candidly acknowledged the complete absence of transitional forms in the fossil record and the complete absence of evidence for observable progressive evolution.

> Instead of finding the gradual unfolding of life, what geologists of Darwin's time, and geologists of the present day actually find is a highly uneven or jerky record; that is, species appear in the sequence very suddenly, show little or no change during their existence in the record, then abruptly go out of the record. And it is not always clear, in fact it's rarely clear, that the descendants were actually better adapted than their predecessors. In other words, biological improvement is hard to find.[10]

Thus, in spite of the utter lack of evidence in either living populations or the fossil record that natural selection ever generates higher orders of complexity (or "biological improvement," or "better adaptation"), the mere existence of "optimal structures" is taken by evolutionists as confirmation of the remarkable power of natural

---

[9] David M. Raup, "Conflicts Between Darwin and Paleontology," *Bulletin of the Field Museum of Natural History*, vol. 50 (January 1979), p. 25-26.
[10] *Ibid.*, p. 23.

selection! As a matter of fact, we have already shown the utter inability of the mutation-selection process to generate complex functioning systems.

And, of course, such a process as natural selection does not even *exist* at the pre-biological level! Whatever effect selection may possibly have had on random processes in later biological reproduction, it is clear beyond any rational argument that chance processes could never have produced even the simplest forms of life in the first place. Without a living God to create life, the laws of probability and complexity prove *beyond doubt* that life could never come into existence at all. Life, at the very simplest level conceivable, has absolutely no possibility of having been generated by any other means than special creation by a living Creator.

Life and the Second Law

Basically, the argument against evolution in terms of probability theory is merely another way of looking at the argument based on entropy, or the Second Law of Thermodynamics. Statistical thermodynamics, in fact, is essentially a probability statement, indicating that disorganized systems are more probable than organized systems. Systems, left to themselves, tend to go from complexity to simplicity, from organization to randomness, from improbable states to more probable states, from low entropy to high entropy.

Dr. V. F. Weisskopf, former president of the American Academy of Arts and Sciences, has pointed up the problem in the following words:

> The evolutionary history of the world from the "big bang" to the present universe is a series of gradual steps from the simple to the complicated, from the unordered to the organized, from the formless gas of elementary particles to the morphic atoms and molecules and further to the still more structured liquids and solids, and finally to the sophisticated living organisms. There is an obvious tendency of nature from disorder to order and organization. Is this tendency in contradiction to the famous second law of thermodynamics, which says that disorder must increase in nature? The law says that entropy, the measure of disorder, must grow in any natural system.[11]

---

[11] Victor F. Weisskopf, "The Frontiers and Limits of Science," *American Scientist*, vol. 65 (July/August 1977), p. 409.

The "obvious tendency of nature from disorder to order and organization" is, of course, only a religious (humanistic) assumption of evolutionists. The real tendency in the natural world, as expressed by the Second Law of Thermodynamics, is from order and organization to disorder. This very obvious problem is commonly bypassed by evolutionists (including Weisskopf) with the naive statement that the earth is a system open to the energy of the sun, and that there *may be* organizing processes *somewhere*, and that this resolves the problem!

Creationists, in turn, have reminded them that while an open system and available energy constitute *necessary* conditions before a growth in order (or information) can take place, they are not *sufficient* conditions. In addition, there must be a pre-coded program containing the necessary information to direct the growth of the system, and one or more conversion mechanisms to convert the external energy into the highly specific work of internal growth. Since the vast system of the hypothetically evolving biosphere as a space-time continuum seems to lack both a program and a mechanism, other than Prigogine's irrelevant "dissipative structures," it is clearly and decisively precluded by the Second Law.

It has been especially difficult to imagine ways to get life started in the first place. How can unordered non-living chemical elements be combined naturalistically into the extremely sophisticated ordered information in a replicating system? The common belief that this problem has been practically solved by modern biochemists is certainly premature, to say the least. Freeman Dyson said the following more than two decades ago:

> We are still at the very beginning of the quest for understanding of the origin of life. We do not yet have even a rough picture of the nature of the obstacles that prebiotic evolution has had to overcome. We do not have a well-defined set of criteria by which to judge whether any given theory of the origin of life is adequate.[12]

And evolutionists are *still* at the very beginning of their futile quest!

The nature of the problem in trying to account for the origin of a replicating system was well expressed by Angrist and Hepler:

---

[12] Freeman Dyson, "Honoring Dirac," *Science*, vol. 185 (September 27, 1974), p. 1161. Dyson is at Princeton's Institute for Advanced Study.

Life, the temporary reversal of a universal trend toward maximum disorder, was brought about by the production of information mechanisms. In order for such mechanisms to first arise it was necessary to have matter capable of forming itself into a self-reproducing structure that could extract energy from the environment for its first self-assembly. Directions for the reproduction of plans, for the extraction of energy and chemicals from the environment, for the growth sequence and the mechanism for translating instructions into growth all had to be simultaneously present at that moment. This combination of events has seemed an incredibly unlikely happenstance and often divine intervention is prescribed as the only way it could have come about.[13]

Small wonder! In the real world, every effect must have an adequate cause, but the usual laws of science do not seem to intimidate evolutionists. In the strange wonderland of evolutionary credulity, impossible things may happen: plans draw themselves, mechanisms design themselves, order generates itself from chaos, and life creates itself! Yet evolutionists call creationists unscientific because they postulate an adequate cause (divine intervention) to account for the marvelous effect called life.

In creation-evolution debates, creationists commonly place great emphasis on the Second Law of Thermodynamics as an overwhelming evidence against evolution. Although there have been over 300 such debates held within the period 1972-95 with leading evolutionist professors on major college and university campuses, the latter have never yet been able to come up with an answer of any consequence to the entropy-disorder problem. Even more amazingly, most of them do not even seem to understand the problem, either dismissing it as irrelevant or else making some vacuous reference to ice crystals or open systems or dissipative structures!

Apparently, only a few evolutionists realize the magnitude of the problem and have been trying to find a solution. By far the most important of these efforts was the suggestion of Ilya Prigogine, as noted in chapter 6. Prigogine was a widely-known chemist and thermodynamicist, with faculty appointments at both the University Libre de Bruxelles and the University of Texas at Austin. An indication of the strategic

---

[13] Stanley W. Angrist and Loren G. Hepler, *Order and Chaos* (New York: Basic Books, Inc., 1967), p. 203-204.

significance of Prigogine's ideas is that they have won for him the Nobel Prize in chemistry. Judging from the popular announcements, the main reason for this award may well have been the ray of hope Prigogine has given evolutionists in their presumptuous and foredoomed battle with entropy!

According to *Newsweek*, for example, the significance of Prigogine's work is as follows:

> Scientists who have sought to explain the origin of life as the result of chemical interactions have been confounded by the second law of thermodynamics: energy tends to dissipate and organized systems drift inevitably toward entropy, or chaos.... Prigogine's insights will give biologists new grounds for learning how the first random molecules organized themselves into life forms. . . . Prigogine thinks the Nobel committee recognized that his work is building a bridge between the physical and human sciences.[14]

According to an interview in a professional chemical journal, Prigogine himself was "really surprised" at the decision of the Nobel committee. He also said: "The fact that the Nobel committee has chosen this one subject is a great encouragement."[15]

If, indeed, Prigogine had shown that the inconceivably tremendous amount of information necessary for molecular self-replication can be produced naturalistically despite the entropy law, his achievement would be well worth the Nobel Prize! It would be all the more remarkable in view of the fact that Prigogine himself has "not actually worked in a chemistry lab for decades."[16]

At best, however, he offered only a theoretical speculation, not an experimental demonstration. It is hard to avoid the suspicion that the Nobel award in this case resulted less from the scientific value of Prigogine's achievement, than from the urgent need of the evolutionary establishment for some kind of answer, no matter how superficial, to the entropy problem.

Just how has Dr. Prigogine proposed to harmonize molecular evolution with the Second Law? Here it is, in his own words:

> In all these phenomena, a new ordering mechanism

---

[14] "Chemistry: The Flow of Life," *Newsweek* (October 24, 1977), p. 87.
[15] *Chemical and Engineering News* (October 17, 1977), p. 4.
[16] "Chemistry: The Flow of Life," p. 87.

... appears. For reasons to be explained later, we shall refer to this principle as *order through fluctuations*. The structures are created by the continuous flow of energy and matter from the outside world; their maintenance requires a critical distance from equilibrium, that is, a minimum level of dissipation. For all these reasons we have called them dissipative structures.[17]

These "dissipative structures" are supposed to exhibit a higher degree of structure, or order, than they possessed before being subjected to a large influx of outside energy, while at the same time their generation is accompanied by a large dissipation of energy in the form of heat. These structures are, however, very unstable and easily destroyed.

Moreover, dissipative structures could hardly serve as a substrate for still *higher* order, since they themselves require an abnormally large input of energy just to maintain their own structures. Prigogine himself says that, as far as chemical or biological reactions are concerned, the generation of dissipative structures is apparently limited to "auto-catalytic" processes. But catalytic processes, like fluid vortices, do not generate higher order: they merely speed up reactions that themselves are already going downhill thermodynamically in the first place. And any imaginary "auto-catalytic" processes would certainly *require* already-living systems for their own generation, so they can hardly explain the *generation* of living systems!

Although Prigogine wistfully expresses the hope that his speculations may someday lead to an understanding of how life may have evolved from non-life, he is at least more cautious than those of his fellow evolutionists who are currently exuberating over it. He warns:

> It would be too simple to say that the concepts of life and dissipative structures are intermingled. ... But it is not just one instability that makes it possible to cross the threshold between life and non-life; it is, rather, a succession of instabilities of which we are only now beginning to identify certain stages.[18]

In a later section of his essay, he again suggests caution:

> But let us have no illusions. If today we look into the

---

[17] Ilya Prigogine, Gregoire Nicolis, and Agnes Babloyants, "Thermodynamics of Evolution," *Physics Today*, vol. 25 (November 1972), p. 25.

[18] Ilya Prigogine, "Can Thermodynamics Explain Biological Order?" *Impact of Science on Society*, vol. 23, no. 3 (1973), p. 169.

situation where the analogy with the life sciences is the most striking — even if we discovered within biological systems some operations distant from the state of equilibrium — our research would still leave us quite unable to grasp the extreme complexity of the simplest of organisms.[19]

One thing is clear. Whatever of scientific value may be deduced from Prigogine's analysis, he has *not* solved the problem of harmonizing entropy with evolution, and he certainly has *not* shown that life can evolve from non-living chemicals! His dissipative structures do not constitute either the required program or the required mechanism to enable any kind of permanently increased order to be produced in an open system. However, he should perhaps be commended for trying. Maybe next someone can work on a perpetual-motion machine!

The problem of the origin of life can really be resolved only by recognition of the omnipotent Creator. The only alternative to belief in special creation is *credulous faith in impotent chance.*

> We are faced with the idea that genesis was a statistically unlikely event. We are also faced with the certainty that it occurred. Was there a temporary repeal of the second law that permitted a "fortuitous concourse of atoms?" If so, study of the Repealer and Genesis is a subject properly left to theologians. Or we may hold with the more traditional scientific attitude that the origin of life is beclouded merely because we don't know enough about the composition of the atmosphere and other conditions on the earth many eons ago.[20]

Yes, not knowing how life could be formed would indeed becloud the understanding of the origin of life! The problem is why this should be called the *scientific* attitude when all the *scientific evidence* continues to support special creation.

Returning to the quotation from V. F. Weisskopf with which this section began, Dr. Weisskopf in no way intended to repudiate evolution because of its apparent conflict with the Second Law of Thermodynamics. However, he, like Prigogine, recognized that there is an apparent problem, and he felt that he should at least

---

[19] *Ibid.*, p. 178.
[20] Angrist and Hepler, *Order and Chaos*, p. 205.

contribute a suggestion as to how it might be resolved. His attempted harmonization, depressingly (for evolutionism), is even less viable than that of Prigogine.

Dr. Weisskopf, indeed, assumed evolution to be so certain that its continual energizing by the sun could be elevated to the status of a *fourth law of thermodynamics*.[21] He suggested that "order" on earth continually increases as the earth cools from its primeval molten state, and that the continual influx of solar radiation provides the necessary energy for evolutionary work. Dr. Weisskopf also noted that since the cooling of dissolved substances promotes crystalliza- tion (and thus increased order), the cooling of the earth's primeval soupy sea would encourage the analogous "crystallization" of highly ordered organic molecules.

If anyone thinks that the writers have somehow misrepresented these exotic suggestions, he should read the paper firsthand. Further, there is no need to comment on them here, since Dr. George P. Stravropoulos has already done so very effectively in a subsequent issue of the same journal.[22] Speaking of Dr. Weisskopf's ingenious suggestion about crystals and the first living molecules, Dr. Stravropoulos makes the following observation:

> He makes it appear as though crystals and highly ordered organic molecules belong in the same class, when in fact they do not. When a crystal is broken up, the smaller crystals are physically and chemically identical to the original. This is never observed with (organic) molecules; when the original molecule is split up, lesser molecules appear, and part of the original information is lost. To ignore such fundamental differences in an effort to arrive at some general overview or law is to create a false over- view, a pseudo-law.[23]

To which criticism might be added the observation that such dead- end crystals actually contain less "information" than the solution out of which they crystallize. Rather than providing an exception to the Second Law, they illustrate it!

Dr. Weisskopf's premature suggestion to make evolution a "fourth

---

[21] The Third Law describes zero entropy, or perfect order, as occurring at a temperature of absolute zero.

[22] George P. Stravropoulos, Letters Section, *American Scientist*, vol. 65 (November/ December 1977), p. 675-676.

[23] *Ibid.*, p. 675.

law" of thermodynamics is rightly and unequivocally dismissed by Dr. Stravropoulos as follows:

> To say that "there is an obvious tendency of nature from disorder to order and organization" and to advance this idea to a "fourth law" is to misunderstand completely and to compromise all of thermodynamics.[24]

Thermodynamics is highly quantitative, and its laws are as fully confirmed as any laws of science can be confirmed; but the notion of the sun's energy driving the evolutionary process is about as fully *unconfirmed* as any process ever concocted by human speculation.
Dr. Stravropoulous continues thus:

> Under ordinary conditions, no complex organic molecule can ever form spontaneously but will rather disintegrate, in agreement with the second law. Indeed, the more complex it is, the more unstable it is, and the more assured, sooner or later, is its disintegration. Photosynthesis and all life processes, and life itself, despite confused or deliberately confusing language, cannot yet be understood in terms of thermodynamics or any other exact science.[25]

The *coup de grace* to the facile notion that solar energy produces terrestrial evolution is administered when it is pointed out that the influx of raw heat energy to an open system *increases* (not decreases!) the *entropy* (disorder) of that system. This is a fundamental principle of thermodynamics. That is, unmodified, undirected solar energy impacting on the earth would cause internal disintegration, not evolution! Listen again to Dr. Stravropoulos in summary:

> The thrust of Dr. Weisskopf's argument that order appears in a cooling body — runs against his statement that the flow of heat from the sun to the Earth resulted in photosynthesis and the development of "highly hierarchical" forms of organic matter on earth. For one thing, why only Earth? Why has Mars failed the test? And for another, the sun cools and Earth necessarily warms up (if we consider only the "sun-Earth system") and therefore it is

---

[24] George P. Stravropoulos, Letters Section, *American Scientist*, vol. 65 (November/December 1977), p. 675.
[25] *Ibid.*, p. 676.

the sun that should be drawing toward order, Earth toward disorder.[26]

The writers hope, too optimistically perhaps, that the discussion in this and the preceding chapter will permanently dispel the evolutionary misconception that the "open-system" argument somehow harmonizes entropy and evolution. An open system is, indeed, a *necessary* condition for a decrease of entropy in that system, but it is far from being a *sufficient* condition!

Some writers use the term "negentropy," and talk about negentropy entering a system to increase its complexity. Since there is no such thing as "negentropy," this idea is also fruitless.

> Certain old untenable ideas have served only to confuse the solution of the problem. Negentropy is not a concept because entropy cannot be negative. The role that negentropy has played in previous discussions is replaced by "complexity" as defined in information theory.[27]

Complexity and information do not flow into a system by chance, of course. Once again, there must be both a control system of some complex form and a storage-conversion mechanism of some kind before this can happen. Since evolution has *neither* a control system, *nor* a conversion mechanism, evolution will not happen.

> An uninvited guest at any discussion of the origin of life and of evolution from the materialistic reductionist point of view is the role of thermodynamic entropy and the "heat death" of the universe which it predicts.[28]

As far as the naturalistic evolution of life from non-living chemicals is concerned, therefore, neither Weisskopf nor Prigogine nor anyone else has provided the slightest evidence of any mechanism for overcoming the impregnable entropy barrier. Yockey's evaluation of this whole idea is a fitting conclusion:

> The "warm little pond" scenario was invented *ad hoc* to serve as a materialistic reductionist explanation of the origin of life. It is unsupported by any other evidence, and it will remain *ad hoc* until such evidence is found. . . . One

---

[26] *Ibid.*

[27] Hubert P. Yockey, "A Calculation of the Probability of Spontaneous Biogenesis by Information Theory," *Journal of Theoretical Biology*, vol. 67 (1977), p. 377.

[28] *Ibid.*, p. 380.

must conclude that, contrary to the established and current wisdom, a scenario describing the genesis of life on earth by chance and natural causes which can be accepted on the basis of fact and not faith has not yet been written.[29]

Complexity and Cosmic Bootstraps

No matter what the laws of probability or the laws of thermodynamics imply, however, evolutionists are insistent that somehow life has evolved from non-life and order has arisen out of chaos, all without benefit of a Creator or of intelligent design.

> In their more public pronouncements, researchers interested in the origin of life sometimes behave a bit like the creationist opponents they so despise — glossing over the great mysteries that remain unsolved and pretending they have firm answers that they have not really got.... We still know very little about how our genesis came about, and to provide a more satisfactory account than we have at present remains one of science's great challenges.[30]

The overwhelming difficulties involved in breaching this entropy and probability barrier are not appreciated adequately by evolutionists. Even if they choose to ignore these fundamental scientific laws, they yet will find it impossible to devise a biochemical explanation for the origin of life that doesn't require some unknown process which, in terms of known science, at least, would amount to a miracle. One writer uses the bootstrap figure, though he himself is a committed evolutionist, possibly of "new age" leanings.

> A natural and fundamental question to ask on learning of these incredibly interlocking pieces of software and hardware is: "How did they ever get started in the first place?" It is truly a baffling thing. One has to imagine some sort of bootstrap process occurring, somewhat like that which is used in the development of new computer languages — but a bootstrap from simple molecules to entire cells is almost beyond one's power to imagine. There are various theories on the origin of life. They all run aground on this most central of all central questions: "How did the Genetic Code, along with the mechanisms for its translation (ribosomes and RNA

---

[29] Hubert P. Yockey, "A Calculation of the Probability of Spontaneous Biogenesis by Information Theory," *Journal of Theoretical Biology*, vol. 67 (1977), p. 398.

[30] Andrew Scott, "Update on Genesis," *New Scientist*, vol. 106 (May 2, 1985), p. 32.

molecules), originate?" For the moment, we will have to content ourselves with a sense of wonder and awe, rather than with an answer.[31]

A similar admission was made by Leslie Orgel, certainly one of the most distinguished scientists working in this field:

> We do not yet understand even the general features of the origin of the genetic code. . . . The origin of the genetic code is the most baffling aspect of the problem of the origins of life, and a major conceptual or experimental breakthrough may be needed before we can make any substantial progress.[32]

As a matter of fact, nothing less than a miracle would be required to create life from non-living chemicals. Creationists have long insisted that the Second Law of Thermodynamics constitutes an impregnable natural barrier against any such event's ever occurring by chance. In response, evolutionists have simply, and monotonously, continued to berate creationists for misrepresenting the Second Law.

Thermodynamics applies only to isolated systems, they say (although no thermodynamics textbook says any such thing), and creationists don't realize that the earth is an open system (but creationists do realize this, and have always developed their arguments in the context of open-system thermodynamics). Evolutionists seem to have a strange mental block at this point. If they *really* understood the legitimate implications of the Second Law in origin-of-life problems, of course, they would have to repudiate *either* evolution or the Second Law.

One of the few evolutionary biochemists who have seriously addressed this problem is Germany's Manfred Eigen, and he rather arrogantly glosses over the problems encountered in his efforts. Note the following statements excerpted from an article that attempts to imagine this process.

> It was therefore necessary for the first organizing principle to be highly selective from the start. It had to tolerate an enormous overburden of small molecules that

---

[31] Douglas R. Hofstadter, *Godel, Escher, Bach: An Eternal Golden Braid* (New York: Vintage Books, 1980), p. 548.

[32] Leslie Orgel, "Darwinism at the Very Beginning of Life," *New Scientist*, vol. 94 (April 15, 1982), p. 151.

were biologically "wrong" but chemically possible. . . . The primitive soup did face an energy crisis, early life forms needed somehow to extract chemical energy from the molecules in the soup. For the story we have to tell here it is not important how they did so; some system of energy storage and delivery based on phosphates can be assumed.[33]

This requirement of an energy storage and delivery system is exactly what creationists have always insisted is necessary to drive a system upward toward higher complexity against its innate tendency (as expressed in the Second Law of Thermodynamics) to go downward. Note, however, that Eigen did not *describe* such a system — he merely *assumed* it! Further, he assumed that it was somehow based on "phosphates," which are, indeed, important energy storage-and-delivery systems in already living-and-replicating organisms. But, these marvelous "batteries" are themselves produced by the metabolism of the living systems that they energize. Eigen also glides over this problem:

> Non-metabolic replenishment of the phosphate energy reservoir . . . had to last until a mechanism evolved for fermenting some otherwise unneeded components of the soup.[34]

Ah, here is another unknown *mechanism* that must be *assumed* in order to reverse the downhill direction otherwise specified by the Second Law. But that is not all. Eigen continues as follows:

> One can safely assume that primordial routes of synthesis and differentiation provided minute concentrations of short sequences of nucleotides that would be recognized as "correct" by the standards of today's biochemistry. . . . The primitive RNA strands that happened to have the right backbone and the right nucleotides had a second and crucial advantage. They alone were capable of stable self-replication.[35]

Exactly what these "primordial routes of synthesis and differentiation" may have been, we, of course, do not know; but we may,

---

[33] Manfred Eigen et al., "The Origin of Genetic Information," *Scientific American*, vol. 244 (April 1981), p. 88.

[34] *Ibid.*

[35] *Ibid.*, p. 91.

nevertheless, "safely assume them!" And although many incorrect sequences of nucleotides, no doubt, were assembled in the unknown processes of this scenario, those which happened to be correct were able to reproduce themselves and so managed to survive, so the script goes.

This imaginative scenario is offered to us in all seriousness as an explanation of how life could have evolved from non-life, despite the negative pressures imposed by the Second Law. Eigen and his associates have dressed these statements of faith in impressive mathematical and biochemical verbiage, and have even claimed experimental confirmation of one or two steps in the long process, so that some evolutionary biologists now merely refer to Eigen when confronted with the Second-Law argument against evolution.

Nevertheless, the basic problem is still completely unsolved. Eigen, *et al.*, did not even attempt to deal with the barrier of stereo-chemistry (the universal prevalence of "left-handed" amino acids in the protein structure of living systems, as against the uniform distribution of left-handed and right-handed molecules in non-living systems), nor did they deal with the evolution of nucleic acids into proteins, nor with many other key problems in the origin of life. Furthermore, they could not solve the all-important "chicken-egg" problem:

> Which came first, function or information? As we shall show, neither one could precede the other; they had to evolve together.[36]

Despite the high claims and reputation of their advocates, such speculations are pointless.

No creationist has ever denied that the earth is an open system (although evolutionist after evolutionist keeps repeating this false-hood), nor that it has always had an abundance of solar energy accessible to its processes. Solar energy sustains the earth's atmospheric circulation and its hydrologic cycle, but it does not generate life in an organic soup. Solar energy produces tornadoes, but tornadoes do not fabricate airplanes. Solar energy perpetually bathes the building materials resting on a construction site, and these constitute a patently open system, but it would never in a billion, billion years organize these components into a building.

How can evolutionists remain so stubbornly blind to the fact that, thermodynamically, an energy field imposed on a complexly organized

---

[36] *Ibid.*

open system will cause the system to become *less* organized, not *more* organized, *unless* that open system also has, intrinsic to its structure, a pre-programmed information system (e.g., the genetic code), and a pre-packaged storage-conversion-delivery system for the incoming energy (e.g., photosynthesis) to direct and energize its growth in complexity?

The thermodynamic barrier to the naturalistic synthesis of life has often, and alternatively, been expressed in terms of probabilities. But evolutionary biologists have been confronted with this probabilistic argument many times before, and they respond merely (and wisely?) by ignoring it. The only alternative to a naturalistic origin of life is the creation of life, and this they consider to be unthinkable. No matter how improbable it may be, life must have arisen *by chance* somehow, because here we are! . . . so the "reasoning" goes.

Many evolutionists have sought to escape the probability argument by appealing to the great expanse of geological time. Any impossible thing becomes possible if there is enough time, they hope.

There is really not that much time, however, *even if* the geological ages have been correctly identified and dated by the accepted methods of geochronometry. The problem is that life originated almost as soon as the primeval earth became cool enough to permit life to survive. The earth *is said* to be 4.6 billion years old, but the oldest dated rocks are assigned a 3.8 billion-year date, and the oldest life forms (fossil prokaryotes in South Africa) are dated at more than 3.4 billion years. Stephen Jay Gould acknowledges the time problem thus:

> We are left with very little time between the development of suitable conditions for life on the earth's surface and the origin of life. . . . Life apparently arose about as soon as the earth became cool enough to support it.[37]

But Gould, instead of acknowledging creation, has instead used the sudden origin of life on earth as an argument supporting his own approach to evolution, the so-called "punctuated-equilibrium" mechanism:

> Gradualism . . . was primarily a prejudice of nineteenth-century liberalism facing a world in revolution. But it continues to color our supposedly objective reading of life's history. . . . The history of life, as I read it, is a series of long stable states, punctuated at rare intervals by major

---

[37] Stephen Jay Gould, "An Early Start," *Natural History*, vol. 87 (February 1978), p. 10, 24.

events that occur with great rapidity and set up the next stable era. . . . My favorite metaphor is a world of occasional pulses, driving recalcitrant systems from one stable state to the next.[38]

So Gould takes the position that life arose explosively, just as did all later evolutionary advances in the history of life. The particular reaction — or series of reactions — which thus quickly transmuted chemicals into living cells remains yet to be discovered (or imagined, or invented), of course.

Sir Fred Hoyle, on the other hand, says that it is inconceivable thermodynamically that life could have arisen by chance here on the earth at all, even in five billion years! Instead of concluding that it must have been created on the earth, however, Sir Fred says that life must therefore be a cosmic phenomenon, translated to earth somehow from outer space.

Some have dismissed his ideas rather smugly, since he is not a biochemist.[39] However, the "directed panspermia" theory of Leslie Orgel and Francis Crick (co-discoverer of DNA) is not very much different from Hoyle's speculations, and these two men are among the world's top biochemists. They have argued that "life-seeds" have been directed through space by advanced civilizations in other galaxies, hence the term *directed panspermia*. Hoyle speaks of a "life cloud" permeating space. But all agree that life could not have evolved on the earth by chance.

Hoyle and his colleague, Chandra Wickramasinghe, have gone even further. The same type of probability calculation that they applied to geologic time on earth was also applied, with only slightly modified numbers, to cosmic time in the whole universe. Thus, they concluded finally that life in space must be the product of intelligent creation, and they are even willing to speak of God.

> Once we see that the probability of life originating at random is so utterly minuscule as to make it absurd, it becomes sensible to think that the favourable properties of physics, on which life depends, are in every respect *deliberate*. It is

---

[38] *Ibid.*, p. 24.

[39] Sir Fred Hoyle is best known as the originator of the Steady-State Theory of cosmogony, but he has written extensively on many important scientific themes. For many years he was University Lecturer in Mathematics at Cambridge University. He later was an honorary research professor at Manchester University and University College, Cardiff. By any reckoning, he has been one of the most original thinkers among modern scientists.

almost inevitable that our own measure of intelligence must reflect higher intelligence — even to the limit of God.[40]

These two very distinguished scientists have thus in recent years become converts (of a sort) to creationism (of a sort) and have suffered much rejection and ridicule by their erstwhile colleagues. Dr. Wickramasinghe has testified that he was previously a consistent atheistic Buddhist, but he has reluctantly been forced to a creationist position by the scientific facts. He was even willing to testify for the creationist side at the creation law trial in Arkansas in 1981.

The most interesting aspect of their conversion to creationism was that the Bible had nothing to do with it. Evolutionists have continually insisted that creationists are creationists because of their belief in the Bible, so the Hoyle-Wickramasinghe conversion was a particular embarrassment. These two scientists do not believe in either the biblical record of creation or even in the God of the Bible. Nevertheless, they insist that solid scientific considerations compel them, reluctantly, to conclude that life can only be the product of some cosmic intelligence, not of any kind of naturalistic evolutionary process, and they are even willing to call it God.

Evolutionists, therefore, still have no factual evidence, or even a workable model, to account for this very first stage in organic evolution. If there is any kind of evolutionary family tree, it is a tree without roots! The infinitely complex structures, symbiotic relationships, and informational programs found in all living cells are separated by an unbridgeable thermodynamic and probabilistic gulf from all non-living systems, and more and more *careful* and *consistent* scientists are recognizing this fact today.

An important evolutionary biochemist who has made similar probability calculations on the origin of life is Dr. Hubert P. Yockey. In an article entitled "Self-Organization Origin of Life Scenarios and Information Theory," he acknowledges the following:

> The calculations presented in this paper show that the origin of a rather accurate genetic code, not necessarily the modern one, is a *pons asinorum* which must be crossed over the abyss which separates crystallography, high polymer chemistry and physics from biology. The information

---

[40] Fred Hoyle and Chandra Wickramasinghe, *Evolution from Space* (London: Dent, 1981). Wickamasinghe is Professor of Astronomy and Applied Mathematics at University College, Cardiff.

content of amino acid sequences cannot increase until a genetic code with an adapter function has appeared. Nothing which even vaguely resembles a code exists in the physico-chemical world. One must conclude that no valid scientific explanation of the origin of life exists at present.[41]

For those unfamiliar with Latin, *pons asinorum* means "bridge of asses," a colorful metaphor for an exceedingly difficult bridge to negotiate. If the rest of the jargon in the quotation is troublesome, the last sentence is clear enough, and that is the crucial admission!

But when this or similar probability arguments are used in creation-evolution debates, as discussed before, the evolutionists' shamefully weak response is usually something like this: "Yes, but every individual combination of factors has exactly the same probability; the one that specified life is no more improbable than any other, so the argument from probability is meaningless."

Yockey's response to such a naive reply is kind, but pointed and helpful:

A practical man will not believe a scenario which appears to him to have a very small probability. . . . If a tossed coin is observed to fall heads ten times consecutively, a practical man will believe it to be two-headed *without examining it*, even though the sequence of all heads is exactly as probable as any other sequence.[42]

One can easily calculate that the number of possible sequences in a ten-sequence coin toss is 1,024 (or 2^{10}), so the probability of a sequence of heads ten times in a row is 1 out of 1,024. Even though no "practical" gambler would bet on a thousand-to-one shot, this probability is really an extremely high probability compared to the extremely low probability of a chance assemblage of chemical molecules into a meaningful and functioning genetic code of any kind whatever. As Hoyle has shown (along with many others), the universe is neither big enough nor old enough for it ever to have happened *even once* by chance. Life *must* have been specially created.

Conditions in the Primeval Soup

Apart from the question of complexity and probability, there would also have to be just the right environmental conditions for any

---

[41] Hubert P. Yockey, "Self-Organization Origin of Life Scenarios and Information Theory," *Journal of Theoretical Biology*, vol. 91 (1981), p. 26.

[42] *Ibid.*, p. 27.

imaginary simple-life form to evolve from non-life, and then to survive and reproduce on the primitive earth. The speculations associated with this scenario — especially in view of the fact that the "spontaneous generation" of bacterial life in the present world was completely disproved by Louis Pasteur a hundred years ago — have been wildly imaginative, to say the least.

For more than 25 years, school children have been taught the imaginary drama of life's beginning on the primeval earth perhaps 3 billion years ago. The scenario has assumed an ancient atmosphere containing no oxygen, since an oxidizing environment would have destroyed any supposed molecules on the verge of evolving into living systems. Stanley Miller's famous laboratory apparatus, by which he synthesized certain amino acids in a gaseous mixture simulating this hypothetical atmosphere, has appeared on the pages of innumerable classroom textbooks; and the book *Origin of Life on Earth* by the Russian Communist Oparin, has been taught as dogma almost everywhere.

Now, however, like so many other evolutionary fables, the primeval "reducing" atmosphere is being dissipated by the hard facts of science. For more than a decade now, various scientists have been developing a wide range of evidences that the earth's atmosphere was rich in oxygen right from the beginning! In an important study,[43] two British geologists have accumulated a mass of geological evidence that the ancient earth never had a reducing atmosphere at all. They conclude thus:

> The existence of early red beds, sea and groundwater sulphate, oxidized terrestrial and sea-floor weathering crusts, and the distribution of ferric iron in sedimentary rocks are geological observations and inferences compatible with the biological and planetary predictions. It is suggested that from the time of the earliest dated rocks at 3.7 b.y. ago, Earth had an oxygenic atmosphere.[44]

This fact means, of course, that life could never have evolved from non-life, at least by this method, and that all the textbooks need to be rewritten. But since belief in evolution is really religious rather than scientific, atheistic scientists do not intend to become creationists. Rather, they merely search for another evolutionary scenario. The one that they suggest currently is that life evolved somewhere *else* in the

---

[43] H. Clemmey and N. Badham, *Geology*, vol. 10 (March 1982), p. 141-146.
[44] *Ibid.*, p. 141.

universe and was transported to earth!

An interesting recent confirmation of an oxygen-abundant atmosphere in the primordial earth has come from Australia.

> The oldest plant life ever found has been discovered in the Western Australian outback. Resembling seaweed, it grew about 1,100 million years ago, compared with an age of 540 million years for the previously oldest-known plants.
>
> This discovery has thrown into confusion the history of how the Earth's atmosphere evolved.[45]

The reason for such confusion is that plants require an oxygenized atmosphere, not the "reducing atmosphere" long assumed by A. I. Oparin, Stanley Miller, and other conjecturing "authorities" whose names have been eulogized in countless high-school textbooks as the men who presumably "proved" that life evolved abiogenetically.

The famous experiment of Miller, who was able to produce certain amino acids in his laboratory under conditions supposedly simulating conditions on the primitive earth, has frequently been cited as of importance almost equal to the work of Charles Darwin. His experiment was entirely artificial, of course, and came nowhere near to producing life in the laboratory, as many of the credulous have been led to believe. Miller's conclusion has been completely negated now by the rapidly growing knowledge that the primeval earth did not have the required reducing atmosphere at all.

This refutation has not shaken Miller's faith in abiogenesis, however. In a review article on the current status of origin-of-life theory, John Horgan comments as follows:

> Miller, who after almost four decades is still in hard pursuit of life's biggest secret, agrees that the field needs a dramatic finding to constrain the rampant speculation. . . . Does he ever entertain the possibility that genesis was a miracle not reproducible by mere humans? Not at all, Miller replies. "I think we just haven't learned the right tricks yet."[46]

Rampant Speculation
Stanley Miller spoke disparagingly of the "rampant speculation"

---

[45] Adiran Berry, "Oldest Plants Breathe Chaos into Life Theory," *London Daily Telegraph,* June 2, 1990.

[46] John Horgan, "In the Beginning," *Scientific American*, vol. 264 (February 1991), p. 125.

that is plaguing origin-of-life studies — just as if his own widely publicized scenario had been sober science! Horgan reviewed some of these speculations, and got Miller's opinion concerning them, noting that they were all being put forth by credentialed biochemists:

> That bothers Miller, who is known as both a rigorous experimentalist and a bit of a curmudgeon. . . . He calls the organic-matter-from-space concept "a loser," the vent hypothesis "garbage" and the pyrite theory "paper chemistry." Such work, he grumbles, perpetuates the reputation of the origin-of-life field as being on the fringe of science and not worthy of serious pursuit.[47]

And how does Stanley Miller, the "rigorous experimentalist," now think life began?

> The current version of genesis held by Miller and others is also couched in Darwinian terms. Life began, they say, when some compound or class of compounds developed the ability to copy itself in such a way that it occasionally made heritable "mistakes." These mistakes sometimes produced generations of molecules that could replicate more efficiently than their predecessors. Voila: evolution, and so life.[48]

Isn't Darwinism magnificent? It offers us natural selection not only to explain the origin of species, but also the origin of life! This amazing concept is tendered without one iota of experimental evidence, rigorous or otherwise! Didn't Miller say something about "rampant speculation"?

Furthermore, Darwinian selection is supposed not only to account for the origin of life and the origin of new species. Somehow, in between these two end-points of the selection spectrum, it supposedly also produces the evolution of cells:

> What is life? No one would accuse the new breed of mathematical biologists of setting their sights too low. . . . The accepted theory of cell evolution says that each of the various cell types in the human body evolved through the rigors of Darwinian natural selection; that is, by conveying

---

[47] John Horgan, "In the Beginning," *Scientific American*, vol. 264 (February 1991), p. 118.
[48] *Ibid.*

some competitive advantage on those of our evolutionary ancestors who had it. . . . The human genome may be a self-organizing system, like his computer model: it may produce the range of human cell types on its own.[49]

It is all so simple, on paper. Everything organizes itself and, if it's good, natural selection preserves it!

One cannot prove a universal negative, of course, and we do not have access to a time machine. Who knows what magical events Mother Nature might have generated a billion years ago? We *do* know such things do not happen now, however.

As of now, all life is built around the marvelous DNA molecule, and there is no clue as to how DNA was first formed.

DNA cannot do its work, including forming more DNA, without the help of catalytic proteins, or enzymes. In short, proteins cannot form without DNA, but neither can DNA form without proteins.[50]

There is that old chicken-and-egg conundrum again. Perhaps the proteins — if they could not be formed by DNA (deoxyribose nucleic acid) — could be dependent on some other nucleic acid. But it's still the same problem:

We are grappling with a classic "chicken and egg" dilemma. Nucleic acids are required to make proteins, whereas proteins are needed to make nucleic acids and also to allow them to direct the process of protein manufacture itself.[51]

The emergence of the gene-protein link, an absolutely vital stage on the way up from lifeless atoms to ourselves, is still shrouded in almost complete mystery.[52]

To the creationist, of course, the origin of life is no mystery at all!

Dr. Leslie Orgel, to whom we have referred before as one of the leading researchers in this field, is a colleague of Dr. Stanley Miller (of amino-acid-synthesis fame) at the University of California at San Diego. He was also associated with Sir Francis Crick (famous as the co-discoverer of DNA) in the development of their notorious "directed

---

[49] Gary Taubes, "The Body Chaotic," *Discover*, vol. 10 (May 1989), p. 67.

[50] John Horgan, "In the Beginning," p. 119.

[51] Andrew Scott, "Update on Genesis," *New Scientist*, vol. 106 (May 2, 1985), p. 31.

[52] *Ibid.*, p. 33.

panspermia" theory, which proposed the following:

> That the seeds of life were sent to the earth in a spaceship by intelligent beings living on another planet. Orgel says the proposal, which is known as directed panspermia, was "sort of a joke." But he notes that it had a serious intent: to point out the inadequacy of all explanations of terrestrial genesis. As Crick once wrote: "The origin of life appears to be almost a miracle, so many are the conditions which would have had to be satisfied to get it going."[53]

Presumably Orgel has now abandoned this idea, which his U.C.S.D. colleague, Stanley Miller, called a "loser," but many other scientists are still actively promoting some form of extra-terrestrial origin of life on earth. This was one of the main topics discussed at a recent conference on "chirality," the "handedness" of amino acids in stereoptical activity within cells.[54]

Orgel commented on this phenomenon thus over a decade ago:

> Since the time of Louis Pasteur, the origin of optical activity in biological systems has attracted a great deal of attention. Two very different questions must be answered. First, why do all amino acids in proteins or all nucleotides in nucleic acids have the same handedness? Secondly, why are the amino acids all left-handed (L–) and the nucleotides all right-handed (D–)?[55]

The answer to this extremely critical question was not obtained at the conference, however, although the discussion was quite heated. Miller and others merely "rolled their eyes" at the theory that the phenomenon had an extra-terrestrial source, but advocates of the latter kept pointing out that all terrestrial-source theories had proved sterile. The problem, of course, stems from the fact that amino acids in living organisms are all "left-handed," whereas in non-living systems they are

---

[53] John Horgan, "In the Beginning," p. 125.

[54] The conference on "The Origin of Homochirality" was held in February 1995 in Santa Monica. The participants argued vigorously about its origin, but all agreed that: "Homochirality . . . is necessary for present-day life because the cellular machinery that has evolved to keep organisms alive and replicating, from microorganisms to humans, is built around the fact that genetic material veers right and amino acids veer left." (*Science*, vol. 267, March 3, 1995), p. 1265.

[55] Leslie Orgel, "Darwinism at the Very Beginning of Life," *New Scientist*, vol. 94 (April 15, 1982), p. 151.

"racemized" — that is, with evenly mixed left-handed and right-handed molecules. One of the fatal flaws in Stanley Miller's famous experiment, of course, was that the amino acids generated in his apparatus were racemized, and so could not have been potential precursors of life, despite Miller's claim.

Anyway, Orgel has apparently given up on directed panspermia and, along with others, is now promoting the idea that the answer is in RNA, instead of DNA.

> We proposed that RNA might well have come first and established what is now called the RNA world.[56]

Orgel and his followers have worked out a sort of scenario by which this *might* have happened. However, there are major problems:

> This scenario could have occurred, we noted, if pre-biotic RNA had two properties not evident today: a capacity to replicate without the help of proteins and an ability to catalyze every step of protein synthesis.[57]

Orgel writes as though these "ifs" were just trivial problems! Indeed such properties are *not* evident today, and there is not a bit of evidence that they *ever* could have existed in the past. If RNA, or any other molecule, could replicate itself unaided, *that* would be *life*, not a stage in the development of life. But that's the very problem! It is like saying that we could explain the origin of life if only we could explain the origin of life.

> But as researchers continue to examine the RNA world concept closely, more problems emerge. How did RNA arise initially? RNA and its components are difficult to synthesize in a laboratory under the best of conditions, much less under plausible prebiotic ones. For example, the process by which one creates the sugar ribose, a key ingredient of RNA, also yields a host of other sugars that would inhibit RNA synthesis. Moreover, no one has yet come up with a satisfactory explanation of how phosphorus, which is a relatively rare substance in nature, became such a crucial ingredient in RNA (and DNA).[58]

---

[56] Leslie E. Orgel, "The Origin of Life on the Earth," *Scientific American*, vol. 271 (October 1994), p. 78.

[57] *Ibid.*

[58] John Horgan, "In the Beginning," p. 119.

Orgel himself is aware of the problems, but he remains stubbornly optimistic.

> The precise events giving rise to the RNA world remain unclear. As we have seen, investigators have proposed many hypotheses, but evidence in favor of each of them is fragmentary at best. The full details of how the RNA world, and life, emerged may not be revealed in the near future.[59]

The evidence is indeed "fragmentary" — more like non-existent!

Stanley Miller has recently joined his UCSD colleague, Jeffrey Bada, in a new rampant speculation. They propose that the surface of the primeval earth was an ocean of ice covering a liquid ocean of prebiotic soup in which primitive replicating molecules could form. The ice shell, several hundred meters thick, was then cracked upon by collision with a wandering planetesimal, which led to the melting of the entire shell, the evolution of the present ocean, and the evolution of life.[60] We anxiously await the next speculation!

Professor Dr. Klaus Dose, director of the Institute for Biochemistry in the Johannes Gutenberg University in Germany, probably knows as much about this type of study and speculation as anyone. In a 1988 review, while considering how chirality could originate in RNA or DNA or in any other living substance, he said this:

> In spite of many attempts, there have been no breakthroughs during the past 30 years to help to explain the origin of chirality in living cells.[61]

The 1994 chirality conference didn't solve the problem either.

The review by Klaus Dose covers much more than this strange phenomenon of mono-chirality, however.

> More than 30 years of experimentation on the origin of life in the fields of chemical and molecular evolution have led to a better perception of the immensity of the problem of the origin of life on earth, rather than to its solution. At present all discussions on principal theories

---

[59] Leslie Orgel, "Origin of Life on Earth," p. 83.

[60] Jeffrey L. Bada, "Cold Start," *The Sciences*, vol. 35 (May/June 1995), p. 21-25.

[61] Klaus Dose, "The Origin of Life: More Questions than Answers," *Interdisciplinary Science Reviews*, vol. 13, no. 4 (1988), p. 352.

and experiments in the field either end in stalemate or in a confession of ignorance.[62]

Professor Dose goes on to describe some of the problems involved:

> The problem is that the principal evolutionary processes from prebiotic molecules to progenotes have not been proven by experimentation and that the environmental conditions under which these processes occurred are not known. Moreover we do not actually know where the genetic information of all living cells originates, how the first replicable polynucleotides (nucleic acids) evolved, or how the extremely complex structure-function relationships in modern cells came into existence.[63]

Dose could almost have said that, after half a century of intense searching for a naturalistic explanation of life's origin, we now know nothing whatever about it, and we should accept the obvious fact that life was created by an omnipotent living Creator. He could not say that, of course, because he is an evolutionist. If he *had* tried to say that, his article would not have been published and he probably would have been asked to resign his position. He did, however, dare to draw the following conclusion:

> It appears that the field has now reached a stage of stalemate, a stage in which hypothetical arguments often dominate over facts based on experimentation or observation.[64]

In other words, pronouncements on the origin of life are based either on philosophy or religion, or on sheer prejudicial speculation. The conclusion of Paul Erbich is similar:

> Why then does the scientific theory of evolution hold on to the concept of chance to the degree it does? I suspect it is the fact that there is no alternative whatsoever that could explain the fact of universal evolution at least in principle, and be formulated within the framework of natural science. If no alternative should be forthcoming, if chance remains overtaxed, then the conclusion seems inevitable that evolution and therefore living beings cannot

---

[62] *Ibid.*, p. 348.
[63] *Ibid.*
[64] *Ibid.*, p. 349.

be grasped by natural science to the same extent as non-living things — not because organisms are so complex, but because the explaining mechanism is fundamentally inadequate.[65]

More than 25 years ago, the president of the Carnegie Institute of Washington wrote a significant summary of the state of origin-of-life knowledge as it existed at that time. His comments are as relevant and incisive today as then:

> But the most sweeping evolutionary questions at the level of biochemical genetics are still unanswered. How the genetic code first appeared and then evolved and, earlier even that that, how life itself originated on earth remain for the future to resolve, though dim and narrow pencils of illumination already play over them. The fact that in all organisms living today the processes both of replication of the DNA and of the effective translation of its code require highly precise enzymes and that, at the same time, the molecular structures of those same enzymes are precisely specified by the DNA itself, poses a remarkable evolutionary mystery.[66]

The DNA molecule and the enzymes are *both* extremely complex systems, and each is necessary for the other. There is no known way that they could both have evolved from simpler chemicals. Dr. Haskins continues with the following surprising comment on this thermodynamic mystery:

> Did the code and the means of translating it appear simultaneously in evolution? It seems almost incredible that any such coincidence could have occurred, given the extraordinary complexities of both sides and the requirement that they be coordinated accurately for survival. By a pre-Darwinian (or a skeptic of evolution after Darwin) this puzzle would surely have been interpreted as the most powerful sort of evidence for special creation.[67]

Creation indeed seems to be the only logical explanation for the

---

[65] Paul Erbich, "On the Probability of the Emergence of a Protein with a Particular Function," *Acta Biotheoretica*, vol. 34 (1985), p. 53.

[66] Carl P. Haskins, "Advances and Challenges in Science in 1970," *American Scientist*, vol. 59 (May/June 1971), p. 298.

[67] *Ibid.*

marvelous complexity of the simplest forms of living matter. Nothing less than the Creator could supply the astronomic gain in order, represented by the simplest protein molecule.

Despite the intense prejudice against creationism (possibly, in many cases, an unrecognized but intense emotional desire to escape any possibility of human responsibility to one's Creator) and against creationist scientists, regardless of their qualifications, the fact still remains that the creation model is the only model of origins that explains and correlates the scientific data relative to the origin of life. If this entails any personal responsibility to the Creator, so be it. The honest and true scientist should accept the testimony of clear and evidential factuality *even if* it makes him emotionally — or spiritually — uncomfortable.

Chapter 8

The Heavens Don't Evolve, Either

The thoroughgoing evolutionist is not content with trying to explain the origin of the species, or the origin of life. He must also encompass, if he can, the origin of the universe itself, and of the very elements of matter, within his theory of naturalistic evolution. As a total evolutionist, he would, if possible, eliminate God as Creator completely from any relation to the universe at all. Consequently, he has developed complex (and continually changing) models of cosmic evolution, stellar evolution, galactic evolution, planetary evolution, and even chemical evolution, in seeking to find explanations for *everything* without God.

Every such model, however, will be found to have fatal flaws, and that is why evolutionists are continually debating and changing their models. These cosmological "theories" seem to have great popular appeal. Both the popular press and the journals of general science regularly pour out eulogizing articles on every new speculation in cosmology that is suggested by the astronomers and cosmophysicists. Therefore, it is necessary to devote a chapter to this rather esoteric subject.

Creation and the Cosmos

First, we should note how perfectly all the physical evidence *confirms* the obvious predictions of the creation model, whereas the evolution model *fails* every test. We should remember that the basic predictions of the creation model are those of conservation and decay. That, of course, is exactly what we see in the heavens, everywhere and always. No one ever *sees* any evolution taking place in the physical cosmos at all. Evolutionary concepts in this realm are *entirely* mathematical and philosophical, *not* experimental and observational.

The creation model stipulates that God created all things perfect and complete in a short period of special creation in the beginning. This means that any changes since the creation could not be "creative" or innovative changes, but only deteriorative changes. The Creator, being both omniscient and omnipotent, knew perfectly what to do, and was able to do it, creating every system — whether stars or planets or animals or people — perfect and complete, and functioning to begin with.

Although this stipulation does not preclude future changes in the created systems of the cosmos, it does require that any such changes be in the direction of deterioration of the primeval perfection. Since the Creator is not the "de-creator," the creation itself would continue undiminished in scope, but nothing new would be added: no new stars or planets or basic types of living organisms. On the other hand, by the corollary principle of disintegration, stars and planets may break up, species may atrophy or even become extinct, and people may die, but the universe and life go on.

As we have seen in chapter 6, these two stipulations of the creation model — that is, conservation in quantity, and decay in quality — are explicitly fulfilled in the two most certain and invariable laws of science, the First and Second Laws of Thermodynamics. The First Law says that, although matter and energy can be changed in form, the total quantity of mass/energy is always "conserved": this is the law of conservation of matter and energy. The Second Law functions in various ways: energy becomes less available, systems become disorganized, information becomes garbled, matter disintegrates, organisms become extinct, environments decay, stars explode, comets disintegrate, and people get old and die.

Nowhere in the universe is anything getting bigger and better in and of itself. In all human history, no one has ever observed one kind of plant or animal evolve into a higher type. Furthermore, despite all the elaborate theories of stellar evolution, no one has ever observed a star evolve out of interstellar dust, nor one type of star evolve into a different type.

To the human eye, even through a telescope, all stars look simply like points of light, nothing else. Yet astronomers have identified many different kinds of stars; in fact, every single star will apparently plot at a different point on what is called the H-R diagram, on which the star's brightness is plotted versus-its absolute temperature. Yet they all look alike, and they keep looking the same, with their differences determined solely by their light spectra. The eminent theoretical astrophysicist

Stephen W. Hawking has noted:

> Stars are so far away that they appear to us to be just pinpoints of light. We cannot see their size or shape. So how can we tell different types of stars apart? For the vast majority of stars, there is only one characteristic feature that we can observe — the color of their light.[1]

Evolutionary astronomers have developed involved mathematical theories about how stars form and how they evolve into various kinds of stars, but such theories are, in the very nature of things, impossible even to test. Astronomers have been observing and studying the stars for thousands of years, but they each and all look exactly the same as they did four thousand years ago. Furthermore, they always maintain the same positions relative to one another. Yet astronomers write about stellar evolution just as confidently as though they had observed it happening!

Nothing has been observed to change in the heavens, with one exception. Occasionally, a nova, or even a supernova, appears, making a particular star much brighter than before, for a while. Indications are that each of these represents a stellar explosion, with massive break-up and scattering of the star's contents.

Assuming that that is what they are, such explosions could hardly be called "evolution." Rather, they are specifically in accord with the Second Law and the creation model. Explosions do not generate order! The same applies to the disintegration of comets and the breakup of asteroids and meteorites. These are changes, but they are *not* evolution.

The same principle applies to the elements of matter also. That is, none of the basic elements evolve naturally into higher elements. Once again, any changes in the chemical elements are downward changes: for example, radioactive decay (e.g., uranium and thorium disintegrating into helium and lead).

In sum, everything that we can actually *observe* in the physical world — whether at the level of giant stars or at the level of the microscopic atom — either stays at the same level of complexity or deteriorates to a lower level. Evolution to a higher level is *never observed to occur anywhere*. In today's world, all present processes and systems explicitly support the predictions of the creation model, whereas they explicitly negate the predictions of the evolution model.

All of this does not, of course, *prove* that the creation model of the

---

[1] Stephen W. Hawking, *A Brief History of Time* (New York: Bantam Books, 1988), p. 37.

universe is true and the evolution model is false. What we can say, however, is that if a person *wants* to believe that the universe and all its complexity of systems were supernaturally created, he or she can do so in full confidence that all the *real* data of scientific observation are compatible with that belief.

The Supposed Evolutionary Big Bang

The evolutionary model of cosmic origins, on the other hand, encounters numerous problems. There have been various theories in the past — especially the "steady-state theory" advocated by Fred Hoyle and others — but most of these are currently out of style.

The generally accepted evolutionary explanation for the origin of the universe for some time now has been the so-called "big-bang theory," which postulates that a primeval atom exploded about 10 to 20 billion years ago, and that molecules, stars, galaxies, and planets all gradually evolved from the expanding gases of this ancient explosion. Furthermore, the complex molecules that developed from the original exploding particles are said to have slowly evolved into living cells and, finally, into human beings!

This "miracle of the big bang," as British astronomer P.C.W. Davies has called it (though he does not believe in the biblical God, of course), contradicts at least two basic laws of science:

1. The Second Law of Thermodynamics states that "*disorder*" in a closed system must increase with time; the "big-bang" idea, on the other hand, states that the primeval explosion (which would certainly have been the *ultimate* in disorder!) has somehow increased the "*order*" of the whole universe with time.

2. The Law of Conservation of Angular Momentum states that pure radial motion (in the primeval explosion, all products would move radially outward from its center) cannot give rise to orbital motion; yet planets, stars, and galaxies somehow all managed to start to rotate in vast orbits around different centers throughout the universe.

In spite of these fundamental contradictions, this theory has been accepted by most astronomers and cosmogonists, primarily on the basis of the supposed universal background radiation. This cosmic microwave low temperature radiation was assumed to be uniform in all directions and, therefore, to represent the remnants of the big bang. In addition, the expanding universe theory seems to support the big-bang idea.

Despite its wide acceptance as the standard model of evolutionary cosmogony, however, some of the best astronomers have remained unconvinced. Several of their views will be discussed later. There are many unresolved problems with this "standard model," as it has been called.

Evolutionists have frequently criticized creationism as unscientific because of its basic commitment to the doctrine of creation *ex nihilo* — that is, "creation out of nothing." The idea that God simply called the universe into existence by His own power, without using any pre-existing materials, is rejected out of hand by evolutionists, since this would involve supernatural action, which is unscientific by definition (that is, by *their* definition).

Yet now we hear many evolutionary astrophysicists maintaining that the universe "*evolved*" itself out of nothing! Creationists at least assume an adequate Cause to produce the universe: that is, an infinite, omnipotent, omniscient transcendent self-existing personal Creator God. For those who believe in God, creation *ex nihilo* is understandable and reasonable. But even if some people refuse to acknowledge a real Creator, they should realize that a universe evolving out of nothing contradicts the law of cause-and-effect, the principle of conservation of mass/energy, the law of increasing entropy, and the very nature of reason itself. How can they believe such things?

Yet, listen, for example, to Edward P. Tryon, Professor of Physics at the City University of New York, one of the first to propound this idea:

> In 1973, I proposed that our Universe had been created spontaneously from nothing (*ex nihilo*), as a result of established principles of physics. This proposal variously struck people as preposterous, enchanting, or both.[2]

Naturally it would! But a decade later it had become semi-official "scientific" doctrine, and cosmogonists are taking it quite seriously.

For many years, the accepted evolutionary cosmogony has been the big-bang theory. However, there have always been many difficulties with that concept, one of which is to explain how the primeval explosion could be the cause of the complexity and organization of the vast cosmos, and another of which is to explain how a *uniform* explosion could generate such a *non-uniform* universe. Creationists have been emphasizing these problems for years, but now the evolutionists

---

[2] Edward P. Tryon, "What Made the World?" *New Scientist*, vol. 101 (March 8, 1984), p. 14.

themselves are beginning to recognize them:

> There is no mechanism known as yet that would allow the universe to begin in an arbitrary state and then evolve to its present highly-ordered state.[3]

> The cosmological question arises from cosmologists' habit of assuming that the universe is homogeneous. Homogeneity is known to be violated on the small scale by such things as galaxies and ordinary clusters, but cosmologists held out for a large-scale over-all homogeneity. Now if a super cluster can extend halfway around the sky, there doesn't seem too much room left to look for homogeneity.[4]

There are many other difficulties with the big-bang model, but evolutionary theorists have had nothing better to offer, especially since the abandonment of the rival steady-state theory.

Sir Fred Hoyle, outstanding astronomer and cosmologist, who finally gave up the steady-state theory that he had originated and long promoted, has also shown that the big-bang theory should be abandoned for still other reasons:

> As a result of all this, the main efforts of investigators have been in papering over holes in the big bang theory, to build up an idea that has become ever more complex and cumbersome. . . . I have little hesitation in saying that a sickly pall now hangs over the big-bang theory. When a pattern of facts becomes set against a theory, experience shows that the theory rarely recovers.[5]

The Inflationary Universe

In a new attempt to overcome some of the difficulties of the big-bang theory, an amazing concept has been promoted, a concept known as the "inflationary universe," associated especially with the name of Alan Guth. This is strictly a mathematical construct, impossible even to visualize, let alone test, but its advocates argue that it can resolve the problems posed by the initial stages of the big bang. Its essentials are outlined in the following inventive scenario:

---

[3] Don H. Page, "Inflation Does Not Explain Time Asymmetry," *Nature*, vol. 304 (July 7, 1983), p. 40.

[4] D. E. Thomsen, "Hyper-superduper Galaxy Cluster," *Science News*, vol. 122 (December 18/25, 1982), p. 391.

[5] Fred Hoyle, "The Big Bang under Attack," *Science Digest*, vol. 92 (May 1984), p. 84.

Our present understanding now leads us to the belief that sometime around 10^{-35} second the rate of expansion underwent a dramatic, albeit temporary, increase, to which we apply the term *inflation*. The physical processes that took place during the unification of the strong force with the others caused the universe to expand from a size much smaller than a single proton to something approximately the size of a grapefruit in about 10^{-35} second.[6]

Now 10^{-35} second is one hundred-millionth of a billionth of a billionth of a billionth of a second, whatever that can possibly mean. The inflationary cosmogonists are telling us that, at the beginning, the entire universe (of space, time, and matter) was concentrated as an infinitesimal particle, about the size of an electron, with all force systems (gravity, electro-magnetic, nuclear and weak forces) unified as a single type of force.

This "universe" somehow went through an inconceivably rapid inflationary stage, reaching grapefruit size in 10^{-35} second, by which time the four forces had become separate forces, the heterogeneities had been generated that would eventually become expressed in the heterogeneous nature of the expanded universe, and the universe was ready to enter the "normal" phase of its big bang. Thus, as Tryon says, "In this scenario, the 'hot big bang' was preceded by a 'cold big whoosh.'"[7]

To comprehend the arguments behind this inflationary model of the early cosmos, one would require a background in advanced mathematical physics, and not even those who have such a background all accept the model. As the very title of Page's previously cited article states, inflation does not explain time asymmetry. That is, it still contradicts the principle of increasing entropy, or disorder.

The time asymmetry of the universe is expressed by the second law of thermodynamics, that entropy increases with time as order is transformed into disorder. The mystery is not that an ordered state should become disordered but that the early universe was in a highly ordered state.[8]

Many scientists, of course, have speculated that the universe as a whole has been eternally oscillating back and forth, so that the inferred point-sized beginning of the expanding universe was merely the

---

[6] James Trefil, "The Accidental Universe," *Science Digest*, vol. 92 (June 1984), p. 54.
[7] Tryon, "What Made the World?", p. 16.
[8] Page, "Inflation Does Not Explain Time Asymmetry," p. 39.

hypothetical end result of a previously contracting universe. But this strange notion is clearly not a solution to the entropy problem.

> We now appreciate that, because of the huge entropy generated in our Universe, far from oscillating, a closed universe can only go through one cycle of expansion and contraction. Whether closed or open, reversing or monotonically expanding, the severely irreversible phase transitions transpiring give the universe a definite beginning, middle and end.[9]

In fact, Bludman, who is in the Department of Physics at the University of Pennsylvania, also makes the following fascinating comment:

> Finally, we show that if space is closed and the Universe began with low entropy, then it had to begin, not with a hot big bang, but with a non-singular tepid little bang.[10]

If the universe is "open," then its inferred expansion should go on forever; but if it is closed, and eventually begins to fold back in on itself, then it could never bounce back again. It would end in a "final crunch," says Bludman.

Which brings our discussion back again to the extraordinary beginning assumed by the inflationary model. Where did the initial "point-universe" come from? This amazing point-sized particle that somehow contained the entire universe (including time, as well as space) and, in principle, all its future galaxies, planets, and people — how do we account for *it*? Now, if one thinks that the scenario up to this point has been "enchantingly preposterous," he will surely think the rest of it is simply a creationist plot to make evolutionists look ridiculous! Readers should certainly check this out for themselves.

How did it all come to pass? Edward Tryon, who started many of these metaphysical exercises back in 1973, says:

> So I conjectured that our universe had its physical origin as a quantum fluctuation of some pre-existing true vacuum, or state of nothingness.[11]

---

[9] S. A. Bludman, "Thermodynamics and the End of a Closed Universe," *Nature*, vol. 308 (March 22, 1984), p. 322.

[10] *Ibid.*, p. 319.

[11] Tryon, "What Made the World?" p. 15.

So our vast, complex cosmos began as a conjectural point of something or other that evolved as a fluctuation from a state of nothingness!

> In this picture, the universe came into existence as a fluctuation in the quantum-mechanical vacuum. Such a hypothesis leads to a view of creation in which the entire universe is an accident. In Tryon's words, "Our universe is simply one of those things which happen from time to time."[12]

Lest any readers begin to wonder, this discussion is not intended as a satire. It is a straightforward recital of what modern astrophysical cosmogonists are proposing as the beginning of our universe. Guth and Steinhardt, two of the most active and ingenious workers in this field, say the following:

> From a historical point of view probably the most revolutionary aspect of the inflationary model is the notion that all the matter and energy in the observable universe may have emerged from almost nothing. . . . The inflationary model of the universe provides a possible mechanism by which the observed universe could have evolved from an infinitesimal region. It is then tempting to go one step further and speculate that the entire universe evolved from literally nothing.[13]

Regardless of the sophisticated mathematical calculations leading the inflationary-universe astronomers to their remarkable and fantastic statement of faith in the omnipotence of nothingness, there will continue to be many realists who prefer the creationist alternative.

Problems with the Big Bang
One would gather from reading the articles and books of the current cosmological establishment that all astronomers and cosmologists now accept the big-bang model as essentially proved and indisputable. That is not the case, however.

> The standard, hot big bang has many rivals: plasma cosmology, a steady-state universe, a cold big bang, chronometric theory, a universe modeled on fractal geometry.

[12] Trefil, "The Accidental Universe," p. 101.
[13] Alan H. Guth and Paul J. Steinhardt, "The Inflationary Universe," *Scientific American*, vol. 250 (May 1984), p. 128.

But none of these has inspired the degree of support now accorded the big bang.[14]

None of these rival cosmogonies are creationist cosmologies, of course, and they all have serious problems. It is not necessary to discuss them in detail here, since all are evolutionary cosmogonies anyhow. Our contention is that creationism is far superior to any evolutionary sub-model of cosmic origins. The point of referring to them at all is that their advocates are outstanding astronomers themselves, and they have raised serious scientific objections to the dominant big-bang theory.

> The big-bang cosmological model has several serious problems, and the inflation hypothesis, which I mentioned before, was brought in to rescue it. When the original inflation model ran into contradictions, it was replaced by a modification called the "new inflation." When further problems arose, theorists postulated yet another version called "extended inflation." Some have even advocated adding a second inflationary period — "double inflation."[15]

> In all respects save that of convenience, this view of the origin of the Universe is thoroughly unsatisfactory.[16]

> Big-bang cosmology is probably as widely believed as has been any theory of the universe in the history of Western civilization. It rests, however, on many untested, and in some cases, untestable, assumptions. Indeed, big-bang cosmology has become a bandwagon of thought that reflects faith as much as objective truth. . . . This situation is particularly worrisome because there are good reasons to think the big-bang model is seriously flawed.[17]

Such opinions — all by physicists and astronomers very well qualified to express them — could be greatly augmented if necessary. Although they do represent a more or less repressed minority view, there is a significant number of excellent scientists who find the big

[14] Ivars Peterson, "State of the Universe: If Not with a Big Bang, Then What?" *Science News*, vol. 139 (April 13, 1991), p. 235.

[15] Robert Oldershaw, "What's Wrong with the New Physics?" *New Scientist*, vol. 128 (December 22/29, 1990), p. 58.

[16] John Maddox, "Down with the Big Bang," *Nature*, vol. 340 (August 10, 1989), p. 425.

[17] Geoffrey Burbidge, "Why Only One Big Bang?" *Scientific American*, vol. 262 (February 1992), p. 120.

bang model scientifically untenable.

Only three evidences of significance are commonly offered in defense of the big-bang concept. One is the supposedly expanding universe, another is the background radiation, the third is the ability of the big bang to account for the origin of hydrogen and helium in the universe. None of these are compelling proofs, however, and all can have alternate explanations.

The expanding universe, for example, implies a primeval particle of space-time from which the expansion presumably began. An expanding universe (even if the concept is valid) in no way eliminates the possibility that the universe could have been *created* in a state of expansion, beginning with any arbitrary size already existing at the instant of creation.

However, it is not at all certain that the universe is really expanding. The evidence for expansion is the famous "red shift," the shift to the red end of the light spectra from distant galaxies. Some very competent astronomers have argued that the red shift may be caused by other phenomena than receding galaxies.

> The central figure in the Red Shift Controversy is Halton Arp, one of the world's finest astronomical observers, who was a staff astronomer at Palomar Observatory for many years and president of the Astronomical Society of the Pacific in the early 1980's. . . . It is the quality of thought embodied in work like his that is necessary to overturn the abomination of the big-bang theory.[18]

The critique of Arp and others had to do with the assumption that the amount of red-shift correlates with distance, since the velocity of recession (or expansion) is supposed to be greater for distant galaxies than for those nearby. Galaxies with greater velocities should have retreated to greater distances than those with smaller velocities.

One serious problem with this interpretation of red shifts is that Arp's observations, especially of quasars (quasi-stellar-objects, or QSO's), disagree with it.

> Arp says he has observed many objects with red shifts that do not conform to the Hubble relation. He maintains that quasars, for example, whose large red shifts suggest

---

[18] David Cherry, "Redshifts and the Spirit of Scientific Inquiry," *21st Century* (May/June 1989), p. 35.

they are the most distant objects in the universe, are actually no more distant than galaxies and are probably offshoots of them.[19]

That is, quasars are often found so near certain galaxies that they seem to be connected; yet their red shifts are vastly different:

If quasars and the nearby galaxies are connected, the two objects could not be moving at greatly different speeds; more likely their red shifts — and possibly all red shifts — result from something other than a rapid retreat from the earth.[20]

That being true, then there is no real evidence that the universe is expanding, and, therefore, no evidence that the universe began at the big bang. Still further evidence against the big bang is found in the variable brightness of quasars with the same red shift.

For QSO's however, the diagram shows a wide scatter in apparent brightness at every red shift. In fact, there is little correlation of brightness to red shift at all! Either QSO's come in an extremely wide range of intrinsic luminosities, as most people believe, or their red shifts do not indicate distance.[21]

It is a significant commentary on the American cosmological establishment that Dr. Arp felt himself forced to move to Europe several years ago because he was no longer given access to any suitable telescope for his observations, despite his reputation as an outstanding astronomical observer.

In Europe he has continued to amass impressive evidence against the use of red shifts as an indicator of distance. For example, he was able to show, via six independent lines of evidence, that two galaxies were interacting with each other, and thus bound to be at the same distance,

---

[19] John Horgan, "Big-Bang Bashers," *Scientific American*, vol. 257 (September 1987), p. 22.

[20] Anthony L. Peratt, "Not With a Bang," *The Sciences* (January/February 1990), p. 31.

[21] Geoffrey Burbidge and Adelaide Hewith, "A Catalog of Quasars Near and Far," *Sky and Telescope* (December 1994), p. 32. Very recently, Margaret Burbidge (like husband Geoffrey, an astronomer at UCSD) reported to the 1995 meeting of the American Astronomical Society at Pittsburgh that she had discovered two "nearby" quasars, likewise with large redshifts that supposedly should indicate very high velocities and very great distances. The conclusion that redshifts do *not* indicate recession velocities is thereby strengthened, and the big-bang theory further refuted (reported by *San Diego Union Tribune*, June 12, 1995).

yet one red shift was six times as great as the other's.[22]

In another article, he showed that in our own Milky Way galaxy hot young stars have excessive red shifts and seem to be moving rapidly away in all directions.[23]

Both sets of observations, as well as many others published by Dr. Arp over the years, are *completely incompatible* with the expanding-universe idea. Whatever these red shifts mean, they apparently do *not* indicate recession velocities in an expanding universe.

It was for just such indications that Arp became *persona non grata* in American observatories. Nevertheless, he is surely one of the world's most competent astronomers, and his many data *do* seem to negate the whole concept of the expanding universe.

Equally important to the big-bang theory is the uniform background radiation, supposedly a remnant from the big-bang explosion. Again, however, there are other explanations possible. Jayant Narlikar, the leading astronomer in India, objects.

> Secondly, the microwave background is believed to be the strongest evidence for the big bang. Yet such a fundamental feature as its temperature cannot be deduced from any calculations of the early universe. Its value is assumed.[24]

Big-bangers claim that basic relativity theory predicts the background radiation. However, the actual very low-level temperature of this radiation (about 3 degrees Kelvin above absolute zero) evidently *cannot* be derived from the theory. Narlikar maintains that an alternate theory, a theory which he and his colleagues are calling the "quasi-steady-state" cosmology, *does* predict it.

> In this framework, . . . we can estimate correctly the present temperature of the microwave background.[25]

The great Swedish astronomer Hannes Alfven, originator of the "plasma theory" of cosmology, has made an extensive study of this radiation, showing that the plasma theory also could account for the

---

[22] M. Moles, Halton Arp, et al., "Testing for Interaction between the Galaxies NGC450 and UGC807," *Astrophysical Journal*, vol. 432 (1994), p. 135.

[23] Halton Arp, "Companion Galaxies: A Test of the Assumption that Velocities can be Inferred from Redshifts," *Astrophysical Journal*, vol. 430 (1994), p. 74. Both articles are cited in *Science Frontiers*, no. 98 (March/April 1995), p. 2.

[24] Jayant Narlikar, "Challenge for the Big Bang," *New Scientist*, vol. 138 (June 19, 1993), p. 28.

[25] *Ibid.*, p. 29.

temperature of the background radiation, and concludes:

> The claim that this radiation lends strong support to hot big cosmologies is without foundation.[26]

Dartmouth's Robert Oldershaw adds the following information:

> The deviations from a single black-body spectrum, the indications of anisotropy, and the fact that the energy density of the microwave background is suspiciously close to that of other non-cosmological phenomena (such as the energy densities of starlight, cosmic ray particles and galactic magnetic fields) all serve to strengthen the hypothesis that this radiation also has a non-primordial astrophysical origin.[27]

Therefore both the red shift argument and the background-radiation argument are weak arguments, even though they constitute the main arguments for the big bang. The third argument is even weaker. Many years ago, Fred Hoyle and Geoffrey Burbidge (both of whom now reject the big-bang theory) showed that the intense energies of the postulated primordial atom could have generated the hydrogen and helium that are now so abundant in the stellar universe. But Narlikar cautions:

> Big-bang cosmology is supposed to explain the origin of most light nuclei. But although it can with some success explain the formation of helium and deuterium, it runs into problems with other nuclei such as lithium, beryllium and boron. Even with deuterium it places such stringent upper limits on how much baryonic matter ("ordinary" matter, in the form of neutrons and protons) is allowed in the Universe that it forces astronomers to suggest that the "dark" matter thought to make up most of the mass is in some exotic form.[28]

Note also the sharp critique of this "evidence" in a paper co-authored by five eminent astronomers.

> It is commonly supposed that the so-called primor-

[26] Hannes Alfven and Asoka Mendis, "Interpretation of Observed Cosmic Microwave Background Radiation," *Nature*, vol. 266 (April 21, 1977), p. 698.

[27] Robert L. Oldershaw, "The Continuing Case for a Hierarchical Cosmology," *Astrophysics and Space*, vol. 92 (1983), p. 356.

[28] Narlikar, "Challenge for the Big Bang," p. 28.

dial abundance of D, ^{3}He, He, and ^{7}Li provide strong evidence for big-bang cosmology. But a particular value for the baryon-to-photon ratio needs to be assumed *ad hoc* to obtain the required abundances. A theory in which results are obtained only through *ad hoc* assumptions can hardly be considered to acquire much merit thereby.[29]

Therefore, all three primary evidences supposedly "proving" the big-bang theory are badly flawed. Oldershaw says it this way:

> In the light of all these problems, it is astounding that the big-bang hypothesis is the only cosmological model that physicists have taken seriously.[30]

But there are other even more serious problems confronting the big-bang theory. These are very *serious* difficulties, in contrast to the feeble evidences offered to support it.

We have already pointed out its flagrant contradiction with the two laws of thermodynamics, not to mention the law of cause and effect. Cosmologists excuse this conflict merely by reference to the indeterminacy involved in quantum physics, even using this dodge to justify the assumption that our amazing universe just evolved itself out of nothing! Here is yet another commentary on this remarkable statement of faith.

> And now to the biggest question of all, where did the universe come from? Or, in modern terminology, what started the big bang? Could quantum fluctuations of empty space have something to do with this as well? Edward Tryon of the City University of New York thought so in 1973 when he proposed that our universe may have originated as a fluctuation of the vacuum on a large scale, as "simply one of those things which happen from time to time." The idea was later refined and updated within the context of inflationary cosmology by Alexander Vilenkin of Tufts University, who proposed that the universe is created by quantum tunneling from literally nothing into the something we call the Universe. Although highly speculative, these models indicate that physicists find themselves turning again to the void and

---

[29] Halton C. Arp, Geoffrey Burbidge, Fred Hoyle, Jayant V. Narlikar, and Nandra C. Wickramasinghe, "The Extra-Galactive Universe — an Alternative View," *Nature*, vol. 346 (August 30, 1990), p. 811.

[30] Oldershaw, "Continuing Case for Hierarchical Cosmology," p. 59.

fluctuations therein for their answers.[31]

Theoretical physics must be a captivating profession. Its practitioners need no laboratory, nor any instruments except a computer. They must have great ability in advanced mathematics, of course, and evidently a very unusual outlook on things. They find it impossible to believe in a Creator who could create the universe out of nothing, but have no difficulty in believing in a universe that can evolve *itself* out of nothing!

At any rate, one serious problem encountered by the big-bang concept is the "lumpiness" of the universe, with a very heterogeneous distribution of galaxies in space. Theoretically, the distribution of energy in the big bang and its initial inflationary phase should have been perfectly "smooth" and homogeneous. This fact seemed to have been confirmed by the homogeneity of the background radiation, but as more and more galaxies are discovered, their distribution seems to be less and less uniform. Something is obviously wrong with the theory.

> A pressing challenge now is to reconcile the apparent uniformity of the early universe with the lumpy distribution of galaxies in the present universe. Astronomers know that the density of the early universe did not vary by much, because they observe only slight irregularities in the cosmic background radiation.[32]

> In the past few years astronomers have discovered still larger clumps: huge aggregates of matter that span a billion light years or more, stretching across a substantial fraction of the observable universe. These observations conflict with all current versions of the big bang theory, which do not explain how a smooth explosion could have produced clumps of such size.[33]

> The discovery of the largest known structure in the Universe could plunge cosmology into crisis. Theorists are going to find it extremely difficult to explain how a long band of quasars stretching hundreds of millions of light

---

[31] Harold Puthoff, "Everything for Nothing," *New Scientist*, vol. 127 (July 28, 1990), p. 55. Puthoff is a theoretical physicist at the Institute for Advanced Studies in Austin, Texas.

[32] P. J. E. Peebles et al., "The Evolution of the Universe," *Scientific American*, vol. 271 (October 1994), p. 57.

[33] Eric J. Lerner, "The Big Bang Never Happened," *Discover*, vol. 9 (June 1988), p. 72.

years across space could have formed so early in the life of the universe.[34]

West German and American astronomers recently discovered a super super-cluster nearly two and a half billion light years long; to grow to such a scale under the force of gravity alone would have taken more than 100 billion years, five times longer than our big bang model allows. Furthermore, if the universe turns out to be clumpy on this scale, where is the large-scale uniformity presumed by the big bang?[35]

In a patch of sky centered roughly on the Southern Cross, astronomers are finding increasing evidence for a "Great Attractor," an enormous accumulation of mass that is perturbing the motion of galaxies for hundreds of millions of light years in every direction. . . . The theorists have been having enough trouble trying to explain the formation of clusters and super clusters of galaxies. The existence of structure on the scale of the Great Attractor may only make the challenge that much tougher.[36]

It certainly appears that the big bang is in serious trouble. It contradicts the basic laws of science, and it cannot account for the structure of the cosmos that it is presumed to have produced. And now it appears that the evidences traditionally offered in support of the big bang are dissipating, as Peratt points out:

If the red shift is no longer a reliable demonstration of an expanding universe, the big bang model is left without the phenomenon it was invented to explain.[37]

Also, our five eminent astronomers ironically note:

The commonsense inference . . . from the smoothness of the background is that, so far as microwaves are concerned, we are living in a fog and that the fog is relatively local. A man who falls asleep on the top of a mountain and

---

[34] Marcus Chown, "Giant Structure Spells Trouble for Cosmology," *New Scientist*, vol. 129 (February 23, 1991), p. 24.

[35] Anthony L. Peratt, "Not with a Bang," *The Sciences* (January/February 1990), p. 27.

[36] M. Mitchell Waldrop, "Are We All in the Grip of a Great Attractor?" *Science*, vol. 237 (September 11, 1987), p. 237, 238.

[37] Peratt, "Not with a Bang," p. 26.

who wakes in a fog does not think he is looking at the origin of the Universe. He thinks he is in a fog.[38]

Cosmic Fantasies

The field of evolutionary cosmology seems to lead its practitioners into ever-deeper excursions into fantasyland, all in the name of science, so-called. Although there is obviously no way that they can actually perform laboratory experiments on cosmic evolution or travel backwards in time to observe it, they still *imagine* that they are using the scientific method.

In science we adopt the plodding route: we accept only what is tested by experiment or observation.[39]

So they say, writing as if they could actually observe or conduct an experiment on the supposed evolution of the universe!

The lead author of that assertion, Professor Peebles, is also author of a large textbook on all aspects of physical cosmology strongly supporting and expounding the big-bang theory, called by him and others the "standard model." Yet these authors have to acknowledge:

We do not know why there was a big bang or what may have existed before.[40]

As we have seen, the inflation theory was developed to try to salvage the big-bang theory. That, in turn, has gone through several modifications. In order to escape from causality and thermodynamics, the statistical uncertainties of quantum physics have been called on to justify the fantastically incredible notion that energy and matter, as well as the laws that govern them, somehow evolved in a quantum fluctuation from nothingness!

Then, to keep the universe evolving toward higher and higher states of complexity, various other marvelous new mathematical constructs are invoked. The Australo-British theoretical astrophysicist Paul Davies philosophizes as follows:

As more and more attention is devoted to the study of self-organization and complexity in nature, so it is becoming clear that there must be new general principles —

---

[38] Arp et al., "The Extra-Galactic Universe," p. 810. It is interesting that only Burbidge is working in America.

[39] Peebles et al., "The Evolution of the Universe," p. 53.

[40] *Ibid.*, p. 57.

organizing principles over and above the known laws of physics — which have yet to be discovered. We seem to be on the verge of discovering not only wholly new laws of nature, but ways of thinking about nature that depart radically from traditional science.[41]

Very interesting! What about that "plodding route" by which "we accept only what is tested by experiment or observation"? Davies, who has authored more than 20 books, mostly on cosmology, seems to be skirting around some "new-age" concept of cosmic consciousness or something similar. Although he does not believe in the Bible, or in the God of the Bible, he received the 1995 million-dollar Templeton Prize for "Progress in Religion."

Although he has served many years as professor of theoretical physics at the University of Newcastle-on-Tyne in England and then at the University of Adelaide in Australia, he seems to eschew physics experiments to test his theories.

Logical principles governing organization can be expected to come from the study of fractals, cellular automata, games theory, network theory, complexity theory, catastrophe theory and other computational models of complexity and information. These principles will be in the form of logical rules and theorems that are required on mathematical grounds. They will not refer to specific physical mechanisms for their proof. Consequently they will augment the laws of physics in helping us to describe organizational complexity.[42]

Another brilliant theoretical cosmologist is Stephen Hawking, professor of theoretical physics at Oxford University, holding the chair once held by Isaac Newton. Severe physical disabilities prevent him from experimental or observational studies, but they have not inhibited his theorizing. In his million-copy best-selling book, he admits:

I was again fortunate in that I chose theoretical physics, because that is all in the mind. So my disability has not been a serious handicap.[43]

Mind games may be stimulating, but there seems to be no way of

---

[41] Paul Davies, *The Cosmic Blueprint* (New York: Simon and Schuster, 1988), p. 142.
[42] *Ibid.*, p. 151.
[43] Hawking, *Brief History of Time*, p. vi.

verifying them in the highly esoteric field of cosmogony. Hawking, in fact, develops an intricate argument to show that the cosmos is completely self-contained. His conclusion is this:

> But if the universe is really completely self-contained, having no boundary or edge, it would have neither beginning nor end: it would simply be. What place, then, for a creator?[44]

Although Hawking's universe has no boundary in either space or time, he does deduce somehow that "space-time" is "finite." Admittedly, the mind of engineering scientists such as the writers' boggles at the concept of finite space without boundaries, and finite time without beginning or end. Relativistic quantum physics seems to be a marvelous mathematical country with only a few citizens.

One of the peculiar aspects of that country is that its inhabitants can postulate the existence of "cold dark matter" which cannot be seen or heard or sensed in any way. It is postulated because it is needed to keep the big-bang model viable. The known universe contains perhaps 10^{25} stars, plus many other measurable entities of matter and energy. But this is not enough to explain the formation of galaxies and galactic clusters, as well as the general clumpiness of the universe. A much greater source of gravitational force is needed, so, therefore, "cold dark matter" is invented.

This invisible stuff is needed to solve various other puzzling aspects of the universe as well. A great deal of it is needed, actually. A commonly cited figure of 90 percent (recently some are saying 99 percent) of the "matter" in the universe must be in the form of "dark matter," to keep the big-bang theory from collapsing.

The problem here is that, despite much searching and theorizing, such matter cannot be found — at least not yet.

> To save the basic gravitational mechanism of the big bang itself, astronomers have postulated a variety of exotic but invisible subatomic particles that could fill the interstellar and intergalactic voids with dark but massive amounts of matter.[45]

This "exotic" matter, whatever it is (assuming that it even exists at all, which is extremely doubtful), probably would be insufficient to salvage the big bang.

---

[44] Hawking, *Brief History of Time*, p. 140.
[45] Peratt, "Not with a Bang," p. 26.

Even this *ad hoc* dark matter, however, cannot account for the enormous super clusters of galaxies astronomers have charted in recent years.[46]

Cold dark matter seems unable to explain the structures astronomers observe on the largest scales in the Universe. Hot dark matter, the alternative, has already been ruled out by astronomers.[47]

Most big-bang astronomers also want the universe to be "flat," as they call it: neither expanding forever, nor destined eventually to collapse back in on itself. But for that, they need more dark matter than is reasonable to hope for.

The universe probably has only a fraction of the mass needed to halt and reverse its expansion, say two astronomers in the U.S. Their finding strikes a blow at the popular inflation theory, which holds that the universe will neither collapse nor expand forever, but instead lies poised on the knife edge between the two.[48]

These astronomers conclude that "no successful MDM (mixed dark matter) can or will be found."

If so, the universe has less mass than inflation theory predicts, and the theory is wrong.[49]

One writer even speaks of the long band of quasars mentioned earlier as "another nail in the coffin of cold dark matter."[50]

Other difficulties exist with the big-bang theory, but the point has been made. Far from being a proved fact of science, as many allege, it is probably in its death throes. Various other farfetched theories have been proposed that try to help out, but these are even more speculative.

The inflationary theory has already been mentioned, along with some of its derivatives. One deserves special mention in this section on cosmic fantasies. That is the idea of multiple universes. In a review article, the author notes that certain cosmologists "suggest that spontaneous quantum dynamics may be doing what technology cannot; creat-

---

[46] *Ibid.*, p. 27. Peratt is a physicist at the Los Alamos National Laboratory in New Mexico.
[47] Marcus Chown, "Giant Structure Spells Trouble for Cosmology," *New Scientist*, vol. 129 (February 23, 1991), p. 24.
[48] Peter Croswell, "Popular Theory of Cosmology is in Trouble," *New Scientist*, vol. 142 (April 1994), p. 18.
[49] *Ibid.*
[50] Chown, "Giant Structure Spells Trouble," p. 24.

ing new universes all around us . . . new universes may be constantly coming into existence all around us, spontaneously and invisible . . . it is entirely possible that our own universe came into existence this way.[51]

Why not? If evolution can "evolve" one universe into existence, why not many? A Russian cosmophysicist has refined this idea somewhat, suggesting that our universe is perpetually reproducing itself with other universes.

> The evolution of inflationary theory has given rise to a completely new cosmological paradigm. . . . In it the universe appears to be both chaotic and homogeneous, expanding and stationary. Our cosmic home grows, fluctuates and eternally reproduces itself in all possible forms, as if adjusting itself for all possible types of life that it can support.[52]

In this wondrous scenario, the inflationary bubble expands from nothing in an infinitesimal fraction of a second to a size several orders of magnitude greater than the size of the observable universe, all the while reproducing other universes! There is not yet any experimental confirmation, of course, but mathematics and computers and lively imagination can go where mortals cannot.

There are also the "froth theory," the "string theory," the "superstring theory," and others, all presumably refinements of the big-bang theory. Robert Oldershaw of Dartmouth University is one of many who remain skeptical.

> During the past decade or so, two worrying trends have emerged in the two areas of physics that claim to explain the nature of everything — particle physics and cosmology. The first trend is that physicists are increasingly devising mathematically elegant hypotheses which they say are "compelling" but which nevertheless cannot be verified by experiments or observations. The second trend is that theorists are becoming reluctant to give up their elegant notions, preferring to modify the theory rather than discard it, even when observations do not support it.[53]

[51] M. Mitchell Waldrop, "Do-it-Yourself Universes," *Science*, vol. 235 (February 20, 1987), p. 845, 846.

[52] Andrei Linde, "The Self-Reproducing Inflationary Universe," *Scientific American*, vol. 271 (November 1994), p. 55.

[53] Robert Oldershaw, "What's Wrong with the New Physics?" *New Scientist*, vol. 128 (December 22/29, 1990), p. 56.

One reason for the plethora of cosmological theories continually appearing in the media is the very fact that cosmology must rely only on mathematics and computer simulations, actual experimentation being impossible. Oldershaw goes on to cite some examples:

> A lot of effort has been diverted into string theory, yet it has not led to a single prediction. In addition to these well-known theories, there are many other hypotheses of the "new physics" that suffer from a lack of testable predictions. Some that come to mind are the existence of "hidden dimensions," "shadow matter," "wormholes in space-time," and the "many worlds" interpretation of quantum mechanics.[54]

One might hesitantly add "black holes," "white holes," "anti-matter" and other esoteric concepts to such a list. Some would say, of course, that black holes have actually been observed, but there are not many, if any.

> That brings the number of serious black hole candidates to four, the candidates for extra-galactic black holes to one.[55]

No serious candidates for "white holes" have been proposed, and one hears very little about "anti-matter" these days.

As noted earlier, a significant number of cosmologists are seriously promoting alternative cosmologies to the big bang. These generally assume an eternal universe, without beginning and without end, yet continually evolving.

One is the "quasi-steady-state cosmology" recently put forth by Halton Arp, Fred Hoyle, and others. Another is the "plasma universe," proposed by Hannes Alfven and others. Like Arp and Hoyle, Hannes Alfven (who was a Nobel Prize winner in 1970) has found it almost impossible to get papers on cosmology published in the establishment journals ever since he repudiated the big bang!

Advocates of both these theories maintain that they can incorporate the evidences of the big bang (red shifts, background radiation, light-element genesis) into their theories, as well as avoiding its problems. Whether this is so remains doubtful; the big-bang cosmologists, who still constitute the great majority, certainly don't think so.

---

[54] *Ibid.*, p. 57.
[55] Barry Parker, "Where Have All the Black Holes Gone?" *Astronomy*, vol. 22 (October 1994), p. 39.

To the creationist, all such theories — especially these eternal-universe theories — deny the very existence of a Creator and are, therefore, evolutionary theories of the same genre basically as the big bang. Sometimes the steady-state-theory (or, now, the quasi-steady-state-theory) is called the "continuous creation" theory, but a more realistic term would be the "continuous-*ex nihilo*-evolution" theory.

A number of theists have even tried to correlate the big bang with creationism, arguing that the "big bang" itself (or the "quantum fluctuation from the primeval nothingness") was *the* act of special creation that brought the universe into being. While this concept may correlate with new-age pantheistic evolution (as well as with non-theistic evolution), it should not be called *special creation*. Paul Davies, who is himself a religionist of sorts, refutes any such notion.

> When the big-bang theory became popular in the 1950s, many people used it to support the belief that the universe was created by God at some specific moment in the past. And some still regard the big bang as "the creation" — a divine act to be left beyond the scope of science. . . . However, this sort of armchair theology is wide of the mark. The popular idea of a God who sets the universe going like a clockwork toy and then sits back to watch was ditched by the Church in the last century.[56]

Such theists need to remember that the big bang theory was not really a discovery of modern science, but essentially just an attempt to extend naturalism back to the very beginning by trying to explain even the origin of the universe without God. To impose God on a system that works *without Him* makes the special-creation idea altogether redundant.

Stephen Hawking has an interesting comment in this connection. He was invited to speak at a Papal conference on science, and then he had an audience with the pope.

> [The pope] told us that it was all right to study the evolution of the universe after the big bang, but we should not inquire into the big bang itself because that was the moment of creation and therefore the work of God. I was glad then that he did not know the subject of the talk I had just given at the conference — the possibility that space-time was finite but had no boundary, which means that it

---

[56] Paul Davies, "What Hath COBE Wrought?" *Sky and Telescope* (January 1993), p. 4.

had no beginning, no moment of creation.[57]

The creation model of origins, as applied to the universe itself, in no way harmonizes with the big bang or any other theory of evolutionary cosmology. The universe was created supernaturally in a period of special creation at the beginning, by an omnipotent and transcendent Creator, a universe fully functioning, perfect and complete, right from the start. As noted at the beginning of this chapter, such a creation fits perfectly and scientifically with the whole universe, just as it is.

Mysteries of the Heavenly Bodies

Evolutionary astronomers have developed elaborate theories of the evolution of all the stars and other bodies in the universe, making it all sound very pat, just as though they had observed it happening. All follows from the big bang, however, and since the big bang is a badly flawed theory, all of these sub-theories are brought in question, too. In addition, each has its own problems. The standard model goes something like this:

> Matter in the universe was born in violence. Hydrogen and helium emerged from the intense heat of the big bang some 15 billion years ago. More elaborate atoms of carbon, oxygen, calcium and iron, out of which we are made, had their origins in the burning depths of stars. Heavy elements such as uranium were synthesized in the shock waves of supernova explosions. The nuclear processes that created these ingredients of life took place in the most inhospitable of environments.[58]

> The composition of the earth is the natural by-product of energy generation in stars and successive waves of stellar birth and death in our galaxy.[59]

Just how the stars were formed from the big-bang explosion, however, remains a mystery. The big bang generated hydrogen and helium, they say, and the higher elements were generated later in the interiors of stars. But where did those stars come from? Presumably, they were composed of hydrogen and helium atoms that were somehow pulled together by gravity as they were rushing apart with the expanding universe.

---

[57] Hawking, *Brief History of Time*, p. 116.
[58] Robert P. Kirshner, "The Earth's Elements," *Scientific American*, vol. 271 (October 1994), p. 59.
[59] *Ibid.*, p. 65.

If so, where are they now? All of the stars whose spectra have been observed already have metallic elements in them.

> A recent paper by Cavrel adds an interesting twist to speculation on the whereabouts of those most elusive of astronomical objects, Population III stars. These are the stars of zero metallicity which must have formed before the Population I stars in galactic disks and Population II stars in galactic halos. The existence of such stars is inevitable because metals can be made only by stars themselves (unlike some of the lighter elements, such as helium and deuterium, which are produced through cosmological nucleosynthesis in the big bang). Thus the first stars must have contained no metals at all. . . . The problem is that despite extensive searches, nobody has ever found a zero-metallicity star.[60]

Stars are supposedly still coming into existence, accumulating by condensation out of interstellar gas. The Orion nebula has often been acclaimed as the classic example of protostars in the process of becoming stars, because of its unusual brightness and visible gas clouds. There seems to be a problem, however, even in this prized example.

> The discovery that at least some of the infrared sources once thought to be protostars are more probably very young, massive stars dramatically shedding mass has some important implications for the understanding of how new stars form. First of all, it means astronomers may have to start afresh for the precursors of typical main sequence stars. Second, the wind from a large luminous star may have a strong influence, either positive or negative, on the creation of smaller stars, such as those resembling the sun. On the one hand, the wind could so badly disrupt the cloud surrounding it that further star formation would be impossible. On the other hand the pressure of wind on the neighboring parts of the cloud could promote the collapse of further fragments. Third, if a strong wind is a feature of the early evolution of all stars, not just massive ones, it could adversely influence the formation of planetary systems.[61]

---

[60] Bernard Carr, "Where is Population III?" *Nature*, vol. 326 (April 30, 1987), p. 829.

[61] Gareth Wynn-Williams, "The Newest Stars in Orion," *Scientific American*, vol. 245 (August 1981), p. 55.

From the above description of the "protostars" in the glorious Orion nebula, supposedly the best example of new stars forming, these protostars are doing more *breaking up* than *building up*. The high outward and/or tangential pressures of the stellar winds would very likely overpower the inward pull of gravity. Stars can disintegrate more easily than they can form, it seems. Although there are various theories of stellar formation and evolution, there is little true knowledge.

> Nobody really understands how star formation proceeds; it's really remarkable.[62]

> It is also a bit disturbing that all these estimates of the ages and composition of the stars rest on elaborate calculations of what is going on inside them, but all that we observe is the light emitted from their surfaces.[63]

Consequently, there is very little real understanding of how stars could ever have evolved from gas clouds. There is even less understanding of how galaxies and galactic clusters form.

> Among the most important relics are the structures we see in the sky: many stars are grouped into clusters, and clusters themselves along with loose stars like our sun are grouped into galaxies, and the galaxies themselves are grouped into clusters of galaxies. . . . We do not even know whether the smaller structures formed first and then coalesced into the larger ones, or whether the large ones formed first and then broke up into the smaller ones.[64]

> Now, in the 1990s we can still say that we are only on the verge of understanding how galaxies are born, how they work, and what roles they play in the universe at large. . . . The process by which galaxies clump together poses a significant mystery for astronomers.[65]

The situation with respect to such esoteric objects as quasars and black holes is even more uncertain:

---

[62] Roger A. Windhorst, as quoted in Corey S. Power, "A Matter of Timing," *Scientific American*, vol. 269 (October 1992), p. 30. Windhorst is an astronomer at Arizona State University.

[63] Steven Weinberg, "Origins," *Science*, vol. 230 (October 4, 1985), p. 16.

[64] *Ibid.*

[65] Jay Gallagher and Jean Keppel, "Seven Mysteries of Galaxies," *Astronomy*, vol. 22 (March 1994), p. 39, 41.

> We see [quasars] today as the earliest sign-posts of galaxy-sized objects. But what happened in the time between the appearance of the cosmic background radiation and the first quasars? So far astronomers have no observations of this lengthy period.[66]

> Proving the existence of black holes continues to be one of the hot areas of astronomical research.[67]

It doesn't get any easier when it comes down to the origin of planets. The sample is not large, of course, since the only *known* planets are those in our own solar system. And the problem here is that they are all different from each other.

> The solar system used to be a simple place. . . . But 30 years of planetary exploration have replaced that simple picture with a far more complex image. "The most striking outcome of planetary exploration is the diversity of the planets," says planetary physicist David Stevenson of the California Institute of Technology. Ross Taylor of the Australian National University agrees: "If you look at all the planets and the 60 or so satellites, it's very hard to find two that are the same."[68]

As a result, all the old theories of the evolution of the earth and the solar system (the nebular hypothesis, the tidal theory, etc.) have just about been abandoned, and the whole subject is now open.

> The challenge will be to understand how, as Stevenson puts it, "you can start out with similar starting materials and end up with different planets." Stevenson and others are puzzling out how subtle differences in starting conditions such as distance from the sun, along with chance events like giant impacts early in solar system history, can send planets down vastly different evolutionary paths.[69]

Even the earth's moon is still of unknown origin, despite NASA's various *Apollo* missions. Since all the older theories have had to be

---

[66] Jay Gallagher and Jean Keppel, "Seven Mysteries of Galaxies," *Astronomy*, vol. 22 (March 1994), p. 40.

[67] *Ibid.*, p. 44.

[68] Richard A. Kerr, "The Solar System's New Diversity," *Science*, vol. 265 (September 2, 1994), p. 1360.

[69] *Ibid.*

abandoned, the planetary scientists are turning to catastrophism: that is, sudden ejection of the moon from the earth by a planet-sized object of some kind. Not only so, but the various planets and their respective satellites are believed now each to require a similar catastrophic type of origin. This type of approach to a geological explanation has been diligently eschewed in the past, but the times are changing!

> Unique events are difficult to accommodate in most scientific disciplines. The solar system, however, is not uniform. All nine planets (even such apparent twins as the earth and Venus) are different in detail from one another. . . . The planets all possess varying obliquities; the most extreme example is Uranus, lying on its side with its pole pointing toward the sun, probably the consequence of collision with an earth-sized body. In contrast to the earth, Venus rotates slightly backward, has a low magnetic field, no oceans, a thick atmosphere mainly of carbon dioxide, and no moon. All this diversity makes the occurrence of single events more probable in the early stages of the history of the solar system. Thus a giant collision with the earth becomes a reasonable possibility for the origin of the moon.[70]

The physical and chemical composition of the moon is very different from that of the earth, however, and it is difficult to see how the moon could have come from the earth, even as the result of such a hypothetical giant collision. Though the impact explanation is currently favored — for lack of anything better — it is surely not a very good one.

> In astronomical terms, therefore, the Moon must be classed as a well-known object, but astronomers still have to admit shamefacedly that they have little idea where it came from. . . . "Where did the moon come from?" is still an open and challenging question.[71]

If this is a problem with respect to the moon, from which our astronauts have brought back many measurements and samples, then it is a *far greater problem* with respect to the 9 planets and 60 satellites, which differ far more widely from each other than do the earth and the

---

[70] Stuart Ross Taylor, "The Origin of the Moon," *American Scientist*, vol. 75 (September/October 1987), p. 477.

[71] David W. Hughes, "The Open Question in Selenology," *Nature*, vol. 327 (May 22, 1987), p. 291.

moon. How could they all be so different in composition and motion, being all associated with the same sun and all presumably about the same age? It would seem that no naturalistic explanation makes sense, even in the absurdly unlikely happenstance of 70 different giant planetesimals striking them some time in the past.

Well, when all else fails, perhaps the evolutionists will try creation. The creation model may go against the psychological grain of establishment scientists, but it does fit all the facts. We may not know *why* each planet and satellite was created so uniquely, but "why" questions are theological. This book seeks to deal only with the scientific evidence, and *that* supports creation.

Chapter 9

The Circumstantial Evidences Say No to Evolution

Since long before Darwin published his famous book, and before anything of consequence was known about paleontology, genetics, or thermodynamics, evolutionists were speaking of what they thought were circumstantial evidences of evolution. They cited the features of comparative anatomy and physiology, the assumed recapitulation theory of embryology, the geographical distribution of plants and animals, the vestiges of once-useful organs, the classification hierarchy, and other such superficial evidences to defend their faith in evolution.

Vestigial Organs — Useful After All

Some of these "evidences" have long since been disproved, though introductory textbooks often still use them. The argument based on vestigial organs, for example, lost all its persuasive power when it was finally realized that practically all such organs have specific uses, and were not mere atrophied remnants of once-useful organs.

S. R. Scadding of Guelph University, in an important paper reviewed by Stephen Jay Gould, essentially settled this argument once and for all. He reviewed the famous list of vestigial organs in man, originally published by the German anatomist R. Wiedersheim in 1895, who in turn had updated and extended the list originally cited by Darwin, Haeckel, and other early evolutionists.

He first noted that this was never really a scientific argument, since it was essentially based on ignorance, and was supposedly a testimony against God, who (if He existed) would surely not have created useless organs.

> The vestigial organ argument is essentially a theological argument rather than a scientific argument.[1]

Then, after discussing the various categories of these supposed vestigial organs and concluding that practically all have at least minor functions at some time during life, as well as the impossibility of proving that any such organ or structure *never* had any function at all, he said:

> As our knowledge has increased, the list of vestigial structures has decreased. Wiedersheim could list about one hundred in humans; recent authors list four or five. Even the current short list of vestigial structures in humans is questionable. Anatomically, the appendix shows evidence of a lymphoid function. . . . The coccyx serves as a point of insertion for several muscles and ligaments. . . . The semilunar fold of the eye . . . aids in the cleaning and lubrication of the eye ball.[2]

> Since it is not possible to unambiguously identify useless structures, and since the structure of the argument used is not scientifically valid, I conclude that "vestigial organs" provide no special evidence for the theory of evolution.[3]

It is interesting that Gould has endorsed Scadding's analysis and conclusions, yet he has used a very similar type of argument when he cites "imperfections," such as the panda's thumb, as evidence for evolution. As discussed in chapter 2, this also is an argument from ignorance, at best, for the panda's thumb is beautifully adapted to the panda's uses in its own environment. The same would apply to the more recent argument based on what are called "pseudogenes" — mutant genes that presumably have no current purpose. These will be discussed later in this chapter.

Furthermore, even if this type of argument were scientifically valid, it would not be sound theologically, as Darwin and Haeckel thought. The fact that the Creator would make each structure "perfect" for its intended use in the beginning does not mean that it would stay that

---

[1] S. R. Scadding, "Do 'Vestigial Organs' Provide Evidence for Evolution?" *Evolutionary Theory*, vol. 5 (May 1981), p. 173.

[2] *Ibid.*, p. 175.

[3] *Ibid.*, p. 176.

way forever. Any organ or structure or gene that once was useful and has now lost its usefulness is simply an illustration of the creation model, which predicts that any "vertical change" will be downward, rather than upward. Evolutionists should (but probably won't) abandon this entire *type* of argument.

Evidence from Embryos

Another discredited evidence for evolution is the hoary "recapitulation theory" that "ontogeny recapitulates phylogeny": that is, that the development of the embryo from conception to birth recapitulates the evolutionary history of the species. Thus, the human conceptus or embryo was said to begin life as a one-celled animal in a liquid environment, developing then into a multi-celled invertebrate, into a fish with gill-slits, from there into an amphibian with a three-chambered heart, after that, into a monkey with a tail, and, finally — toward the beginning of the third trimester — into a human being.

This idea antedated Charles Darwin, originating in the ancient pantheistic philosophy of the "great chain of being," but was said by Darwin to be probably the main evidence for macro-evolution. It was especially popularized by the German biologist Ernst Haeckel, who later even was found guilty of "schematizing" his drawings of embryonic development, to make it appear as though the embryos of human beings looked just like those of rabbits, horses, and other animals, until well along in their development.

That idea has long been disproved, of course, although many evolutionists (including even some textbook writers and evolutionist debaters) continue to use it in an effort to convince people to accept evolution. Embryologic researchers have shown conclusively that the embryo never has gill-slits or a tail or any of the supposed evolutionary recapitulations at all. It is programmed — via the genetic code in the DNA molecules — to develop into a human being right from the start, and every stage in its development is essential to reaching that goal. A science writer reviewing the papers presented at an important 1981 Berlin conference on embryology noted the following:

> Drawing parallels between development and evolution was much in vogue a century ago — as captured in the tongue-twisting slogan still memorized by students, "Ontogeny recapitulates phylogeny." But interest shifted away from development in the period following the widespread acceptance of Darwin's theory of evolution.[4]

---

[4] Julie Ann Miller, "Return of the Embryo," *Science News*, vol. 120 (July 4, 1981), p. 12.

The reporter did not mention the real reason for this shift of opinion. The fact is that the theory had been proved false! Even Gould, who is trying to restore interest in embryology as important in understanding evolution, said that the recapitulation theory "should be defunct today."[5]

The reason that Gould (who has even written a book entitled *Ontogeny and Phylogeny*), and the 50 other biologists at the Berlin conference were trying to develop renewed interest in embryology was that the punctuated equilibrium theorists are desperately searching for some kind of mechanism that can explain sudden evolutionary spurts after thousands of generations of stasis, and they hope that the secret may be found somewhere in the embryo.

> The philosophical shift that has renewed interest in embryology is a concern for large and relatively sudden changes that take place in evolution. . . . And the major changes, which can create a new species, all crowd into a relatively short period. Then the discontinuous change creates a "hopeful monster," which can adapt to a new mode of life. . . . changes in an organism's development can be amplified into a major difference in the adult.[6]

Or so they hoped! However, neither the conference papers nor the 15 or so years of study after the conference have solved the problem.

> Raising questions rather than answering them was the stated intention of the meeting. In that it certainly succeeded.[7]

Embryological evidences or mechanisms for evolution should be considered a dead end. Manipulating genes or embryos normally will produce defective offspring, if anything, that would never survive in nature — let alone produce an evolutionary advance of any kind. This has been abundantly verified in countless experiments on fruit flies, over many decades. These poor little animals have been bombarded with radiations, chemicals, and other mutagenic agents, and many "monsters" have been generated: flies with misplaced legs, extra wings instead of the balancing organs, missing thorax segments, and other grotesque changes.

---

[5] Stephen Jay Gould, "Dr. Down's Syndrome," *Natural History*, vol. 89 (April 1980), p. 144.

[6] Miller, "Return of the Embryo," p. 12.

[7] *Ibid.*, p. 14.

Not one of these victims was a *"hopeful monster,"* however. All these "homeotic mutants," as such mutations are called, are either lethal, harmful, or neutral, at best. Such changes, however, are in accord with the universal law of entropy, and with the requirements of the creation model. They could never produce real evolution to a higher type.

The Witness of Biogeography

For some reason, the geographical distribution of animals and plants is often cited (and has been, since before Darwin's time) as an evidence of evolution. It has always been obvious, to both creationists and evolutionists, that different regions or habitats tend to support their own distinctive faunas and floras.

That does not mean that they must have *evolved* there, however. There has been in the past, and is at present, a great amount of migration when habitats or environments change. This could well have been the case even if all species had been specially created at the same spot on earth at one particular time in the past. If that were the case, it would not have taken many generations before population pressures and availability of many varieties of ecological niches around the world would have induced migration to just those habitats where each species is now found.

It is not at all obvious, therefore, how either past or present geographical distributions of animals can be used legitimately to differentiate between evolution of the species *in situ,* or migration from their point of origin. Marsupials, for example, even now are found not only in Australia, as some seem to think. Fossils of marsupials have also been discovered in several continents.

That seems true of fossils in general, as a matter of fact. The most famous fossil animal of all, the dinosaur, has been found in abundance *on every continent.*

Nevertheless, evolutionists have used geographical distribution as one of their arguments. Marjorie Grene, an eminent philosopher of science, confirms this, but also notes the importance of dispersal in understanding biogeography:

> Geographical distribution was one of the classic supports for descent with modification. . . . But birds do fly and so . . . do fishes swim. Why *no* dispersal, ever? Among, for example, North and South American fauna or Hawaiian *drosophila* it seems pretty well established.[8]

---

[8] Marjorie Grene, "Is Evolution at a Crossroads?" Chapter 2 in *Evolutionary Biology*, ed. Max K. Hecht, Bruce Wallace, and Ross J. MacIntire, vol. 24 (1991), p. 70.

In the context, Professor Grene was defending neo-Darwinism against punctuationism, but her defense could just as well apply to creation with subsequent dispersion. Dispersion may or may not have been aided, or inhibited, by continental splitting and drifting; but again there would be no difference between creationist and evolutionist explanations for any animal distribution caused thereby.

The main argument for evolution as related to geographical distribution seems limited to microevolution, the most widely mentioned example being "Darwin's finches."

As observed by Charles Darwin on his travels along the western coast of South America, there were different species of finches in the various Galapagos Islands off the coast. He argued that these different species (with different beak sizes and shapes as the main difference) had migrated from South America, and then each had evolved in an appropriate way to survive in the particular ecological habitat of each different island.

Creationists would probably explain the differences in the finches in essentially the same way, except that they would call the process "variation" or "recombination," instead of either "evolution" or even "micro-evolution." The finches are all still finches, with all probably inter-fertile with each other. The original finches were created with a genetic variation potential (like the famous peppered moth of England, already discussed) that would enable them to adapt to the different habitats as various groups from the mainland reached the various islands from time to time. However, this is not evolution, but variation, or possibly even speciation (depending on definition).

Detailed attempts to study how even this much change could take place have not been easy. A biology professor at the University of Michigan, after detailed study, concluded:

> There is a need for further research into the affinities of Darwin's finches with Central and South American species to solve the enigma of the phylogenetic origin of the finches.[9]

In any case, the changes took place very quickly, at least as geologists view time.

> Evidently the evolutionary radiation took place fairly rapidly in geological time, for the Galapagos are no more

---

[9] Peter R. Grant, "Speciation and the Adaptive Radiation of Darwin's Finches," *American Scientist*, vol. 69 (November/December 1981), p. 661.

than three to five million years old.[10]

As a matter of fact, it has been found in recent years that such variation in the finches can take place in just a very few years, as in the case of the peppered moth or in pesticide-resistant insects. The finches are all still inter-fertile, and so continue to constitute one species. Each variety is able to adjust its behavior and breeding habits whenever environmental changes necessitate.

In any event, the finches are all still of the finch type, with the ability to vary expeditiously and adjust to a change of habitat, thereby providing another confirmation of the "conservation" stipulation of the creation model.

The Insignificance of Similarities

A long-cherished "evidence" of evolution has been the study of comparative anatomy and physiology, or simply, comparative morphology. We could add the study of comparative embryology, calling the entire argument the evidence from similarities. Men look more like apes than elephants, which proves that they are more closely related to apes than to elephants, so goes the argument.

A common ploy is to note what are called "homologies." For example, the human arm is "homologous" to the forelimb of a horse, the wing of a bat, and the flipper of a dolphin. This fact is supposed to show that they all had a common ancestor.

No, it doesn't! It simply shows that man had need for his arm, the horse needed a strong fore leg, the bat needed strength to power his wings, and the dolphin needed to swim. The respective structures were all designed by the same Creator, who used a similar basic plan for each, with special variations to accommodate the specific needs.

This argument from homologous structures might possibly be explained by evolution from a common ancestor, but is much more naturally explained as design by a common Designer, with the ability to vary His design to meet particular environmental needs.

Sometimes these similarities, which are always easily explained by creation, become very difficult to explain by the evolutionist. He often then falls back on a semantic device called "convergent evolution." For example, consider the wing. Insects have wings, birds have wings, some reptiles had wings (e.g., the extinct pterosaur), and some mammals (i.e., bats) have wings. All these animals were designed to fly, but evolutionists have to assume that a structure intended for flight evolved along *four completely separate pathways*, finally "converging" on

---

[10] *Ibid.*, p. 655.

structures that look homologous, but are not!

Another example is the amazing organ called the eye. Fish and people both have eyes, not because they both came from a common ancestor, but because both have to see, so the Creator made eyes for them. But squids also have eyes, and the extinct trilobites had very remarkable eyes. So do butterflies! People did *not* inherit their eyes from marine invertebrates, however, and all evolutionists would agree that they didn't. Instead, they call such similarity of results "convergence."

In any case, the differences are far more significant than the similarities. No one has any problem distinguishing a man from a gorilla, yet evolutionists believe that the two came rather recently from a common ancestor. To the extent that similarities of form really relate to similarity of function, they can surely be explained just as well by creation by the same Creator, who would certainly be justified in creating similar structures for similar functions.

Sir Gavin de Beer noted another problem with the argument from homologies. He listed a number of cases in which structures that had very similar or identical functions in different animals, were nevertheless coded by altogether different genes and chromosomes.

> It is now clear that the pride with which it was assumed that the inheritance of homologous structures from a common ancestor explained homology was misplaced.[11]

A journal founded for the specific purpose of fighting creationism carried an article several years ago by a scientist with the National Institutes of Health in Maryland. The scientist, Edward E. Max, M.D., Ph.D., made an important admission concerning this old argument from similarities.

> Thus, the similarities between species in anatomy and protein structure can be interpreted in two entirely different ways. The evolutionists say that the similarity between features of, for example, humans and apes reflects the fact that these features were "copied" from a common ancestor; the creationists say that the two species were created independently but were designed with similar features so that they would function similarly. Both views

---

[11] Gavin De Beer, *Homology an Unsolved Problem* (London: Oxford University Press, 1971), p. 15.

seem consistent with the similarity data, but which view is correct?[12]

This author, of course, believes that evolution is correct, but he does acknowledge that the similarity data can be explained just as well by creation as by evolution. His own argument is based on "errors" in "pseudogenes."

Before discussing this particular argument, however, we first need to consider the supposed evidence from similarities in protein structure to which Dr. Max makes reference. These particular similarities have been widely used in recent years as a means not only of arguing against creation, but also as a means of constructing evolutionary family trees and even evolutionary chronologies.

In the meantime, the reader should keep in mind the fact that, while either creation or evolution can explain the *similarities*, only creation can explain the *differences*!

Chaotic Genetics

Since the old ideas of small, random point mutations have proven inadequate to explain evolution — and genetic mutations are now needed that will produce hopeful monsters or other large changes — the field of genetics has proliferated in all sorts of strange directions. Instead of the old Mendelian concept of a specific gene for each physical characteristic, modern molecular biology has introduced an amazing assortment of genes into the literature. There are structural genes, regulatory genes, selfish genes, coding genes, junk genes, split genes, pseudogenes, processed genes, jumping genes, repeating genes, satellite genes, converted genes, and various others.

Each functional gene affects many characteristics; every characteristic is affected by many genes, but most genes (superficially) seem to do nothing at all. Many gene sequences repeat themselves in various organisms, and in most cases the function of these repeating sequences is quite unknown. Then there are the DNA molecules, the RNA, and various other components of the cell, all playing various key roles in heredity, but all still very imperfectly understood.

This is hardly an appropriate place to try to discuss all these terms and concepts. Even specialists in molecular biology are still trying to sort them out. A little seems to be known about many things, but not much is known about anything specific in this unique field of study.

---

[12]Edward E. Max, "Plagiarized Errors and Molecular Genetics: Another Argument in the Evolution-Creation Controversy," *Creation/Evolution*, vol. 19 (1986), p. 36.

> The all-pervading message of the Cambridge meeting was that genomic DNA is a surprisingly dynamic state. . . . The most obvious comment to make about the genomes of higher organisms is that biologists understand the function of only a tiny proportion of the DNA in them.[13]

Obviously, it is hoped that this mysterious world of molecular biology will eventually provide desperately needed answers (needed by evolutionists, that is) as to what causes evolution. It must be embarrassing to be certain that evolution is true, and yet to have no idea how it works!

A great amount of money, possibly over three billion dollars per year, is being devoted to molecular biology, so evolutionists are hopeful that an explanation will one day be forthcoming.

But it hasn't yet! Creationists are amazed at the strong faith exercised by evolutionists. Over a century of intensive research into mechanisms of biologic change has still failed to turn up a plausible genetic model to explain evolution. Evolution is supposed to be an all-pervading process, still actively going on, yet no one has ever seen it happen, there are no evolutionary transitions recorded in the fossils, and no known genetic mechanism is capable of producing it. Yet evolutionists repeatedly insist that evolution is a proven fact of science! This is an amazing commentary on human nature in its perverse attempt to get rid of God.

However, genetic studies have provided a new set of data that evolutionists have started using again in recent years as an evidence for evolution. With the increasing recognition that the fossil record, as well as the mutation/selection mechanism of neo-Darwinism, really constitutes an argument *against* evolution instead of *for* evolution, a new line of evidence was urgently needed. Apparently, the best that they could come up with is the supposed hierarchical arrays of various proteins in different organisms, which are supposed to correspond to the chronological histories of their respective times of divergence from the common ancestral line. This is the so-called evidence from molecular homology.

For example, it is commonly asserted now that man and the chimpanzee must be very closely related because they are said to share 99 percent of their functional DNA. Similarly, the chimpanzee is allegedly man's closest relative based on hemoglobin similarities. By

---

[13] Roger Lewin, "Do Jumping Genes Make Evolutionary Leaps?" *Science*, vol. 213 (August 7, 1981), p. 634.

such comparison, it is asserted that a complete evolutionary family tree can be derived between man and all other organisms, with the time of divergence of each from the ancestral stock actually constituting a "molecular clock," which can even be used to give absolute dates by calibrating against radiometric ages. It is even alleged that the same evolutionary relationships are obtained from most other proteins in the various organisms, and that these all correspond to the paleontological record as well.

Now even if this were all true, it certainly would not prove evolution. This is nothing more nor less than the old argument from similarities, or comparative morphology. One of the traditional arguments for evolution has always been that of similarities: similarities in anatomy, similarities in embryology, etc. But that, of course, proves nothing. Similarities indicate a common designer *at least as much* as they indicate a common ancestor. Why is it surprising that chimpanzee DNA should be very similar to human DNA? The entire structure of chimpanzees is far more similar to that of humans than it is, for example, to that of fishes or scorpions.

The DNA, for that matter, even though it seems to carry the genetic information for all organisms, is mostly of uncertain function.

> In the human genome, for instance, these protein-coding genes constitute marginally more than one percent of all the DNA. The rest of the genome is the target of much speculation, but few secure answers.[14]

It would seem that, if the function of 99 percent of human DNA is unknown (more recent writers say 97 percent), the fact that 99 percent of the 1 to 3 percent of human DNA that *is* known corresponds to chimpanzee DNA really proves very little. It is only the, say three percent, difference, apparently, that does all the coding (if, indeed, the DNA is really responsible for all such genetic coding, a proposition that has never been satisfactorily demonstrated).

Furthermore, the supposed similarities have been much overrated. Blood proteins and cytochrome C are two types of proteins that have often been cited as supporting the imaginary evolutionary hierarchy. Yet, note the following evaluations of these two systems by two eminent biologists:

> If blood proteins are a representative sample of proteins coded by structural genes, the most similar species

---

should have the most similar blood proteins. Wilson (Univ. Calif. of Berkeley) and his colleagues found, however, that structural genes for blood proteins accumulate mutations at rates that appear independent of anatomical evolution. . . . It thus seems evident that the old method of comparing proteins of different species may no longer be the primary tool for investigating the mechanisms underlying the evolution of organisms.[15]

The cytochrome c of man differs by 14 amino acids from that of the horse, and by only 8 from that of the kangaroo. Similar facts are found in the case of hemoglobin; the chain of this protein in man differs from that of the lemurs by 20 amino acids, by only 14 from that of the pig, and by only 1 from that of the gorilla. The situation is practically the same for other proteins.[16]

By all other physical measures, of course, man should have been much more closely related to the horse, than to the kangaroo and the lemur than the pig. In a very provocative paper presented at the American Museum of Natural History, Dr. Colin Patterson, senior paleontologist at the British Museum of Natural History, cited several such anomalies and contradictions in the molecular data. Even though he is a leading evolutionist, he then concluded:

In other words, evolution may very well be true, but basing one's systematics on it will give bad systematics.[17]

Systematics, of course, is the discipline that tries to classify organisms in appropriate taxonomic groups supposed to reflect relationships.

As these protein-sequencing data continue to be accumulated in various labs, more and more unexpected — even bizarre — relationships have been found. For example:

The most controversial feature of Gardiner's cladogram is the close relationship that is suggested between birds and mammals . . . one French paleontologist has even

---

[15] Gina Bara Kojata, "Evolution of DNA: Changes in Gene Regulation," *Science*, vol. 189 (August 8, 1975), p. 446-447.

[16] Pierre P. Grassé, *Evolution of Living Organisms* (New York: Academic Press, 1977), p. 194.

[17] Colin Patterson, "Evolutionism and Creationism," Speech at the American Museum of Natural History (New York, N.Y.: November 5, 1981), p. 14 of transcript.

published a restoration of the hypothetical common ancestor of birds and mammals — a sort of warm-blooded hairy/feathery, climbing insect eater![18]

Yet, we are currently being told that birds evolved from dinosaurs — some scientists even say that birds *are* dinosaurs! Now, however, the relationship between mammals and birds that was suggested by cladistic analysis seems to be supported by the molecular data.

> Adrian Friday and Martin Bishop of Cambridge have analyzed the available protein sequence data for tetrapods. ... To their surprise, in nearly all cases, man (the mammal) and chicken (the bird) were paired off as closest relatives, with the crocodile as next nearest relative.[19]

Thus, both cladistics and molecular biology seem to imply that birds evolved from mammals. Hemoglobin was one of the proteins indicating this mammal-to-bird order.

Little has been heard from this theory in the past decade, however. The reptile-to-bird lobby has evidently prevailed.

Protein similarities continue to yield many surprises — in the evolutionary context, that is.

> Proteins with nearly the same structure and function (homologous proteins) are found in increasing numbers in phylogenetically different, even very distinct taxa (e.g., hemoglobin in vertebrates, in some invertebrates, and even in certain plants).[20]

Would this suggest that man is closely related to "certain plants?"

Dr. Christian Schwabe, a research biochemist in the Medical University of South Carolina, has been studying this field of evolutionary evidences for many years, especially the insulin and relaxin families of proteins, searching for reasonable phylogenetic relationships. He finds no indication of evolution anywhere, however, though he is clearly anti-creationist in his own beliefs.

Molecular evolution is about to be accepted as a

---

[18] Mike Benton, "Is a Dog More Like a Lizard or a Chicken?" *New Scientist*, vol. 103 (August 16, 1984), p. 19.

[19] *Ibid*. Benton was a research scientist at the time in the Museum of the University of Oxford, in England.

[20] Paul Erbich, "On the Probability of the Emergence of a Protein with a Particular Function," *Acta Biotheoretica*, vol. 34 (1985), p. 53.

method superior to paleontology for the discovery of evolutionary relationships. As a molecular evolutionist I should be elated. Instead it seems disconcerting that many exceptions exist to the orderly progression of species as determined by molecular homologies; so many, in fact, that I think the exception, the quirks, may carry the more important message.[21]

In Schwabe's studies of relaxins, for example, he found many odd "relationships."

Against this background of high variability between relaxins from purportedly closely related species, the relaxins of pig and whale are all but identical. The molecules derived from rats, guinea pigs, man, and pigs are as distant from each other (approximately 55 percent) as all are from the elasmobranch's relaxin. . . . Insulin, however, brings man and pig closer together than chimpanzee and man.[22]

Although his major research dealt with the relaxin and insulin families, Schwabe also noted similar phenomena in other protein molecules.

The relaxin and insulin families do not stand alone as exceptions to the orderly interpretation of molecular evolution in conventional monophyletic terms. . . . Additional examples of anomalous protein evolution . . . cover a range of *ad hoc* explanations apparently limited only by imagination.[23]

He cites for examples similar anomalies in lysozymes, cytochromes, and various hormones. In fact, Schwabe goes so far as to suggest that traditional monophyletic evolution should be replaced by polyphyletic evolution — that there are multiple evolutionary trees stemming from many separate origin-of-life events. He notes that the proteins all seem to have been present from the beginning, and that there are no "transitional" evolutionary forms among the molecules, just as

---

[21] Christian Schwabe, "On the Validity of Molecular Evolution," *Trends in Biochemical Sciences*, vol. 11 (July 1986).

[22] Christian Schwabe, "Theoretical Limitations of Molecular Phylogenetics and the Evolution of Relaxins," *Comparative Biochemical Physiology*, vol. 107B (1974), p. 171, 172.

[23] Christian Schwabe and Gregory W. Warr, "A Polyphyletic View of Evolution," *Perspectives in Biology and Medicine*, vol. 27 (Spring 1984), p. 473.

there are none among the fossils.

Many more such inconsistencies have been observed by others in this *assumed* evidence from molecular homologies. Probably the most thorough discussion of them is found in a book by the molecular geneticist Michael Denton. In summarizing, he says the following:

> Thousands of different sequences, protein and nucleic acid, have now been compared in hundreds of different species but never has any sequence been found to be in any sense the lineal descendant or ancestor of any other sequence . . . there are hundreds of different families of proteins and each family exhibits its own unique degree of interspecies variation, some greater than haemoglobin, some far less than the cytochromes . . . each ticking at its own unique and highly specific rate.[24]

The Unstandard Time of Molecular Clocks

Even more difficulties become apparent when these supposed molecular homologies are used as a molecular "clock." A recent authoritative study of this subject first defines this so-called clock as follows:

> The fundamental tenet of the molecular clock hypothesis is that evolutionary rates of homologous proteins are regular, so that the interval separating living species from common ancestors is reflected in the degree of protein dissimilarity between them.[25]

This assumption of uniform protein-divergence rates, that is, of constant nucleotide mutation rates, is an assumption implicitly based on neo-Darwinian population genetics. Korey shows that the critical factors of generation length, and numbers of individuals in the population have been ignored. This, of course, invalidates the whole procedure.

> Coupled with complementary findings regarding the significance of species bottlenecks to protein divergence rates, these effects undermine the main premise of the clock thesis, especially as it applies to the dating of lineages not remotely separated.[26]

---

[24] Michael Denton, *Evolution: A Theory in Crisis* (London: Burnett Books, Inc., 1985), p. 289, 296.

[25] Kenneth A. Korey, "Species Number, Generation Length, and the Molecular Clock," *Evolution*, vol. 35, no. 1 (1981), p. 139.

[26] *Ibid.*, p. 146.

Steven Stanley, who has rejected such gradualistic and uniformitarian premises for other reasons, is much less enamored with this molecular-homology idea than are the more traditional evolutionists.

> Simple estimates of overall genetic distance between species reveal little about degrees and rates of morphologic divergence.[27]

Korey has pointed out that the method as currently used will regularly give ages that are too "short" (that is, will underestimate the difference between the two organisms being compared, and, therefore, will underestimate the time since their assumed evolutionary divergence from a common ancestor). In particular, he criticizes the supposed close similarity between man and chimpanzee that has been inferred from the uniformitarian premise of the molecular clock.

> Certainly the widely contested date for the separation of *pan* and *Homo* that Sarich and Wilson suggest is subject to this bias.[28]

Dr. Vincent Sarich and A. C. Wilson, of the University of California at Berkeley, are the two scientists primarily responsible for the widespread notion that man, chimpanzee, and gorilla diverged from their "common ancestor" about five million years ago, as based on these interpretations of molecular chronologic homology.

In a review of an early symposium on the applications of these molecular homologies to evolutionary anthropology, the reviewer made the following cynical, but appropriate, concluding comment:

> On the current state of theoretical evolutionary work as described in this volume, I quote higher authority: the Red King acting as judge in *Alice in Wonderland*. . . . "If there's no meaning in it, that saves a lot of trouble, you know, as we needn't try to find any."[29]

The situation since that time (1977) with respect to the molecular-clock idea has continued to deteriorate.

Specifically, how accurate is the "molecular evolu-

---

[27] Steven M. Stanley, *Macroevolution: Pattern and Process* (San Francisco, CA: W. H. Freeman and Co., 1979), p. 61.

[28] Korey, "Species Number," p. 145.

[29] Roy J. Britten, review of *Molecular Anthropology*, eds. Morris Goodman, R. E. Tashian, and J. H. Tashian (New York: Plenum, 1976), 466 pp., in *Science*, vol. 198 (October 21, 1977), p. 287.

tionary clock"? . . . The very reasonable conclusion is that "using the primary structure of a single gene or protein to time evolutionary events or to reconstruct phylogenetic relationships is potentially fraught with error." . . . There is no such thing as *the* molecular clock: there are several, each with different attributes.[30]

Research from a number of labs is showing that clocks based on different molecules tick at different, and often varying, rates. . . . Moreover, the rates of DNA clocks based on different cellular sources of DNA can differ within the same organisms.[31]

Even Allan Wilson, one of the main promoters of the molecular-clock idea, later came to agree that the clock's timekeeping is unreliable.

The molecular clock, however, does not tick at the same rate at every position along the DNA molecule.[32]

In order to be very useful, the molecular clock somehow needs to be correlated with the chronology of the fossil record (which, of course, is highly variable itself). When the clock ticks differently for every molecule, this becomes a serious problem.

One of the major problems with molecular clocks is that they need to be located in an absolute time frame determined by the fossil record. Undoubtedly the best such clock available at the moment is the DNA–DNA hybridization clock of Sibley and Ahlquist, but Peter Houde argues that the DNA–DNA clocks needs to be reset. . . . If the picture envisaged by Houde is correct . . . then the datum on which DNA–DNA hybridization data is tied in to the fossil record is out by tens of millions of years.[33]

If the "best clock" is wrong in its timekeeping by tens of millions of years, then what value could *any* of the others have?

The most publicized application of molecular clocks has to do with

---

[30] Roger Lewin, "Molecular Clock Scrutinized," *Science* (May 3, 1985), p. 571.

[31] Ivan Amato, "Ticks in the Tocks of Molecular Clocks," *Science News*, vol. 131 (January 31, 1987), p. 74.

[32] Allan C. Wilson, "The Molecular Basis of Evolution," *Scientific American*, vol. 253 (October 1985), p. 165.

[33] Michael E. Howgate, "The German 'Ostrich' and the Molecular Clock," *Nature*, vol. 324 (December 11, 1986), p. 516.

the evolution of apes and men. Even here, however, the results are equivocal:

> Hence, for the gorilla-chimp-human portion of the phylogeny, there is a strong rejection of the molecular clock hypothesis.[34]

> Morphology and molecular data are congruent in indicating that Homo and African apes are more closely related to each other than the orang. The position of chimps is equivocal, however; amino acid sequencing links them with humans, morphology links them with gorillas, and DNA sequencing has produced ambiguous results.[35]

A more recent analysis of the whole subject of protein molecular clocks has led to a completely negative conclusion concerning their value and validity.

> In fact, with growing numbers of sequences available, it becomes increasingly difficult to demonstrate a protein class at all which may be considered as a reliable molecular clock.[36]

The scientist drawing this conclusion, Dr. Siegfried Scherer, is professor of biology at the University of Konstanz in Germany. After comprehensive analysis of all the data, he concludes:

> Considering the strong demands usually applied in experimental biology, it is hard to understand why the concept survived such a long period at all.
> The protein molecular clock hypothesis . . . has been tested empirically using ten different proteins representing more than 500 individual sequences from plants, animals, and prokaryotes. In no case a linearity within reasonable limits of confidence could be found. . . . This holds also for proteins such as cytochrome c or fibrinopeptides which

---

[34] Alan R. Templeton, "Phylogenetic Inference from Restriction Endonuclease Cleavage Site Maps with Particular Reference to the Evolution of Humans and the Apes," *Evolution*, vol. 37 (March 1983), p. 238.

[35] Timothy Rowe, "New Issues for Phylogenetics," review of *Molecules and Morphology in Evolution*, ed. Colin Patterson (Cambridge University Press, 1987), in *Science*, vol. 239 (March 4, 1988), p. 1183.

[36] Siegfried Scherer, "The Protein Molecular Clock: Time for a Re-evaluation," *Evolutionary Biology*, ed. Max K. Hecht, Bruce Wallace, and Ross J. MacIntyre, vol. 24 (1991), p. 94.

usually have been considered as being reliable molecular clocks. . . . It is concluded that the protein molecular clock hypothesis should be rejected.[37]

Junk DNA and Vestigial Genes

Two other supposed molecular evidences of evolution need to be discussed briefly. One is the so-called "junk DNA," or surplus DNA, the 97 percent of the DNA molecule that does not code for proteins in the reproduction process. The other is what are called "pseudogenes": genes which presumably once had useful functions, but have mutated and lost those functions, becoming mere vestiges of what they once were.

The DNA molecule itself contains all the genes, whether active or vestigial, whether useful or surplus. It is remarkable that this infinitely varying molecule is still DNA (deoxyribose nuclei acid), and that it is the basic substance in all living organisms, specifying and coding their own reproduction, so that every individual is unique and yet the same type as its progenitors. It is even more remarkable, however, that evolutionists somehow think that this fact is an evidence for evolution.

> The outstanding example of a universal homology is the genetic code. . . . The code, although it is arbitrary, is known to be universal. . . . Now, if different species had been created separately, we should be very surprised if they had all been built with exactly the same genetic code. It would indeed be surprising if they had all used DNA as their genetic material; but even more surprising if they had all hit on the same code.[38]

This particular deduction is a blatant *non sequitur* if there ever was one! Just *why* should it be surprising that all living organisms would be structured on the same basic blueprint of life? They did *not* "all hit on the same code," but were all designed by the same infinitely wise designer. It would indeed be surprising, on the other hand, if their common ancestor hit on the genetic code by chance, as evolution would imply.

The code always involves the same basic molecular structure, but is so organized as to be able to program millions of distinct species, and, indeed, trillions of distinct individuals. Information scientists have calculated that there are more units of information in the genetic code than in all the books ever written. That would surely

---

[37] *Ibid.*, p. 102, 103.
[38] Mark Ridley, *The Problems of Evolution* (London: Oxford University Press, 1985), p. 10.

be quite a "hit" for blind chance to hit on!

Furthermore, all that information is contained in just 3 percent or less of the human genome. Thus, 97 percent of the DNA is "junk DNA," as they call it. This supposedly is just some of the excess baggage produced and accumulated by "neutral mutations" in the long course of evolution.

Now, however, evidence is becoming available to indicate that even the "junk DNA" is also organized for some distinct purpose.

> The protein-coding portion of the genes account for only about 3 percent of the DNA in the human genome; the other 97 percent encodes no proteins. Most of this enormous, silent genetic majority has long been thought to have no real function — hence its name: "junk DNA." But one researcher's trash is another researcher's treasure, and a growing number of scientists believe that hidden in the junk DNA are intellectual riches that will lead to a better understanding of diseases (possibly including cancer), normal genome repair and regulation, and perhaps even the evolution of multicellular organisms.[39]

The main clue that some sort of information has been programmed in the "junk DNA" is that it seems to be structured in a non-random fashion, even though it does not code any protein.

> By applying statistical methods developed by linguists, investigators have found that "junk" parts of the genomes of many organisms may be expressing a language. These regions have traditionally been regarded as useless accumulations of material from millions of years of evolution. . . . Over the past ten years, biologists began to suspect that this feature is not entirely trivial.[40]

This is bound to be a fruitful area of research for years to come. The fact that the supposedly surplus 97 percent of the DNA in humans is not really surplus after all, but is designed for some yet-to-be-discovered purpose makes the amazing structure of this molecule more interesting than ever, and strengthens the already strong evidence for its special creation by an omniscient, omnipotent Creator.

---

[39] Rachel Nowak, "Mining Treasures from 'Junk DNA,'" *Science*, vol. 263 (February 4, 1994), p. 608.

[40] Philip Yam, "Talking Trash," *Scientific American*, vol. 23 (March 1995), p. 45.

Enough genes have already been uncovered in the genetic midden to show that what was once thought to be waste is definitely being transmitted into scientific code.[41]

But there is still another argument that evolutionists have advanced concerning the genetic system. This is based on the so-called "pseudogenes." These entities involve a similar argument to that of the junk DNA. The difference is that junk DNA was thought to have been useless from the start, whereas pseudogenes are genes that were once believed to be useful but now to have lost their utility through one or more mutations.

A pseudogene is (probably) a molecular equivalent of the appendix in humans. It is a functionless vestige of a formerly functional gene; for instance, some pseudogenes lack one of the parts that are needed for a gene to be translated into a protein. If the gene is not translated, it must lie dormant inside its bearer.[42]

These pseudogenes have been most extensively studied in simple organisms, but that is now changing:

Pseudogenes are now thought to be common in vertebrates and perhaps in other organisms as well.[43]

In fact, homologous pseudogenes have been found recently in both humans and gorillas. It is *this* bit of evidence that has been touted as a conclusive proof of evolution from ape to man. Edward Max, who acknowledged that the argument from similarities was as effective an argument for creation as for evolution,[44] then argued that a pseudogene shared by man and gorilla proved conclusively that the two shared a common ancestor, a mutation in whose genome produced the pseudogene in question. Here is a summary of the reasoning employed:

This pseudogene [i.e., the processed immunoglobulin epsilon pseudogene] is apparently shared by man and gorilla, but is not found in other apes and monkeys. . . . The appearance of the same "error" — that is, the same useless pseudogene in the same position in human and ape DNA — cannot logically be explained by independent origins of

---

[41] Nowak, "Mining Treasures from 'Junk DNA,'" p. 610.

[42] Ridley, *The Problems of Evolution*, p. 71.

[43] G. Ledyard Stebbins and Francisco J. Ayala, "The Evolution of Darwinism," *Scientific American*, vol. 253 (July 1985), p. 75.

these two sequences. . . . The possibility of identical rare genetic accidents creating the same two pseudogenes in ape and human DNA by *chance* is so unlikely that it can be dismissed . . . the existence of the two shared pseudogenes leads to the logical conclusion that both the human and ape sequences were copied from ancestral pseudogenes that must have arisen in a *common ancestor of humans and apes*.[45]

At first, Max may seem to have a point, though one wonders why this pseudogene was not found in other apes, since they also were thought to have the same common ancestor as gorillas and humans. But then he undermines his own case by the following victory statement:

Evolutionists as early as Darwin pointed to vestigial structures . . . as supporting the evolutionary viewpoint. . . . Vestigial genetic sequences — that is, pseudogenes — provide exquisite examples of vestigial structures and, thus, especially compelling evidence for evolution.[46]

The fact is, however, that vestigial structures do *not* support the evolutionary viewpoint. If they are really vestiges of once-useful structures, they represent deteriorations or losses, not gains or advances, in perfect accord with one of the stipulations of the basic creation model.

However, as already emphasized by S. R. Scadding, "vestigial organs provide no special evidence for the theory of evolution,"[47] but rather are simply expressions of contemporary ignorance concerning their function. Ridley mentioned the human appendix as analogous to pseudogenes, which he said were "functionless vestiges of formerly functional genes."[48] The appendix, however, is no vestige of anything, but is now known to have an important lymphoid function in early life.[49]

Just as the long list of more than 100 vestigial organs in man has long since vanished as discoveries of the functions of these organs gradually accumulated, so will this likely prove true for the "vestigial" genes. If certain human and gorilla homologous genes actually have a useful function not yet discovered, then there is no need whatever to

---

[44] See footnote 12, this chapter.
[45] Edward E. Max, "Plagiarized Errors and Molecular Genetics: Another Argument in the Evolution-Creation Controversy," *Creation/Evolution*, vol. 19 (1986), p. 42.
[46] *Ibid.*, p. 43.
[47] See footnote 3, this chapter.
[48] See footnote 42, this chapter.
[49] See footnote 2, this chapter.

imagine a common ancestor for the two. The fact that we do not yet know what that function may be is simply a statement of current ignorance, just as was the appellation of "junk" to 97 percent of the human genome.

It is probable that future research will reveal that many of these so-called pseudogenes — just like the vestigial organs once thought to prove evolution — have *real functional purpose*. That has already been shown to be true in some cases. It seems possible — pending future research — that at least some pseudogenes can be activated on certain occasions to prevent harmful chromosome rearrangements resulting from radiations or other mutagenic influences. There may be other uses; at least it is always dangerous to "argue from silence." The fact that biologists do not yet know the function of pseudogenes does not prove that they do not have any!

Therefore, the evidence continues to mount that creation is a far better model than evolution by which to explain and correlate the known facts of science.

Chapter 10

The Rocks and Fossils Tell of Sudden Death

In chapters 3–5, the testimony of the fossils — fossils that now are resting by the multi-billions in the sedimentary rocks of the earth's crust — was shown clearly to favor special creation of each basic kind of organism and to deny evolution. No true evolutionary transitions between any two basic kinds of organisms are found anywhere among the fossils. Furthermore, the extreme complexity of each type and its marvelous symbiotic adaptation to its environment could never have organized themselves by random processes.

Our survey in chapter 2 — biologic processes as they exist at present (e.g., mutation and natural selection) — could never in a trillion years generate higher, more complex organisms, as evolutionary theory demands. Mutation is a *random process*, working to *disorder* any ordered system, and natural selection is a conservation process, sieving out the harmful mutations and thereby keeping the population essentially unchanged.

Consequently, the fossil record does not and cannot speak of evolution over the geologic ages. The question remains, however, as to what its real significance may be. It obviously speaks of death, because fossils are the dead remains of once-living plants and animals. But how and when their deaths occurred is a key question in the conflict between the creation and evolution models.

The geologic ages of the earth have, somewhat arbitrarily, been organized in terms of five great "eras," as follows, proceeding from ancient to recent: (1) Archaeozoic (no life); (2) Proterozoic (preliminary life); (3) Paleozoic (early life); (4) Mesozoic (intermediate life); and (5)

Cenozoic (recent life). Each of the eras is subdivided into periods, and the periods into epochs.

The resulting construct is called the geologic timetable, or the geologic column (the term "column" referring to an imaginary cross-section through the earth's crust, with the oldest rocks at the bottom, the youngest at the top). If this column is real, there is at least a superficial appearance of evolution preserved there, with "simple" forms of life preserved as fossils in the oldest rocks, and more and more complex forms in progressively younger rocks.

Nevertheless, there are still no transitional forms, and the laws of thermodynamics and probability seem to stipulate that real evolution is impossible, so just what do all these rocks and fossils, with their respective "ages" actually represent? The situation is further complicated by the contention that radiometric dating has proved that the geologic ages are spread out through 4.6 billion years of earth history.

If such ages are real, then many would argue that there has at least been *time* for evolution, whether we see evidence of it or not. They would also impugn the wisdom of any presumed "creator" who would create by such a wasteful, inefficient, cruel process as evolution over billions of years, when He supposedly would be wise enough and powerful enough to choose and use a better way.

So, once again, if the rocks and fossils are not telling us about slow evolution over vast ages, just what *are* they saying? This is the question that we want to discuss in the present chapter and the following.

In this chapter it will be shown that the real testimony of geology and paleontology is not the evolution of life over many ages, but the cataclysmic destruction of life in one age. Then, in the next chapter, it will be demonstrated that the weight of all the combined scientific evidence is of one creation of all things, in a brief creation period not very long ago.

Return to Catastrophism

For almost two centuries, the dogma of uniformitarianism reigned unchallenged in the study of historical geology. The belief that "the present is the key to the past" governed almost all geological interpretation, and the age-long slow processes of erosion and sedimentation seemed a natural accompaniment to the age-long gradual processes of organic evolution. This dogma was like an albatross whose foreboding presence was stultifying any true understanding of earth history.

> Our science is too encumbered with uniformitarian concepts that project the modern earth/life system as the

primary model for interpretation of evolution and extinction patterns in ancient ecosystems. Detailed paleoenvironmental data tell us the past is key to the present, not vice versa. . . . Abrupt, even catastrophic, regional to global mass mortalities and extinctions (bioevents) are predictable and commonly observed in phanerozoic strata.[1]

The term "phanerozoic" is used by geologists to refer to almost all the fossil-bearing stratigraphic layers in the rocks, corresponding to all "ages" from the Cambrian onward. Therefore, numerous regional — and sometimes global — catastrophic events are now believed to have occurred in earth history after the coming of multi-cellular life to the earth. These "bioevents" are believed to have caused massive extinctions of life on earth.

The most publicized such "event" has been the supposed asteroid bombardment of earth that many believe caused the extinction of the dinosaurs, but geologists now are talking also about many others. A recent article says that there are no less than "15 phanerozoic mass extinctions known," so that "a synthesis of mass extinction theory now seems possible."[2]

This is all sharply in contrast with the long-held dogmas of uniformitarianism and slow-and-gradual evolutionism. These two dogmas have gone hand-in-glove ever since the days of Lyell and Darwin.

Sir Charles Lyell, a slightly older contemporary (and mentor) of Charles Darwin, is considered to be the "father of uniformitarianism." He was a bitter opponent of the earlier "catastrophism" in geology, as advocated by Georges Cuvier and others, and even more so of what he called the "mosaic" geology and chronology. He was untiring in his efforts to discredit the Book of Genesis, even though he still professed belief in some form of "creation."

His efforts largely succeeded, and soon the intellectuals of Darwin's era had accepted the Lyellian doctrine of long ages of earth history, with present geologic processes deemed adequate to explain all the earth's geologic systems and formations. Charles Darwin often acknowledged his debt to Lyell, stating that Lyell had provided him with the vast ages of time he needed to make his theory of evolution by natural selection feasible.

---

[1] Eric Kauffman, "The Uniformitarian Albatross," *Palaios*, vol. 2, no. 6 (1987), p. 531.
[2] E. S. Kauffman and D. H. Erwin, "Surviving Mass Extinctions," *Geotimes*, vol. 40 (March 1995), p. 14.

But they were both wrong! Lyell's uniformitarianism is rapidly being displaced by neo-catastrophism, and Darwin's gradual evolutionism is being rejected in favor of long ages of "stasis," followed by extinctions and evolutionary bursts. Although these younger geologists and paleontologists are every bit as committed to evolutionism as those of the older school, their arguments sound much like the same ones that creationists have been using since long before punctuationism and neo-catastrophism came along. In fact, these latter-day evolutionists tend to complain about this very similarity, and we creationists cannot help but suspect that our arguments are having an effect (though the evolutionists, of course, would never admit such a thing!). Note, for example, just two observations by leading modern geologists:

> If the creationists could mount a successful attack on the validity of uniformitarianism, they would succeed in their effort to discredit modern geology.[3]

Creationists, of course, have never sought to "discredit modern geology." Geology is a wonderful and worthwhile science, and has made many vital contributions to civilization and human happiness. It is only so-called "historical geology" — which has gotten far off the track in advocating great ages and evolution — that creationists have debated and factually discredited. These latter constructs are concepts of naturalistic philosophy, not observational science, and have contributed nothing at all to civilization and human happiness.

Anyway, Shea goes on to complain that his fellow geologists have misunderstood uniformitarianism, and thereby given creationists ammunition to use against it.

> This clearly creates a problem for anyone who tries to show that the creationist concept of uniformitarianism is not the concept actually followed by geologists.[4]

What he means is that modern geologists are now allowing for great geological catastrophes within the overall framework of uniformitarianism, which basically consists of their geologic-age system.

Another leading younger geologist also complains about Lyellian uniformitarianism and the dangers of creationism because of such misunderstandings.

---

[3] James H. Shea, "Creationism, Uniformitarianism, Geology and Science," *Journal of Geological Education*, vol. 31 (1985), p. 105.
[4] *Ibid.*, p. 107.

> But the working hypothesis of the last century [that is, Lyell's dogma] has been turned into a dogma of today. Substantive uniformitarianism has been adopted as an article of faith, and catastrophists have been labeled fellow travelers of creationists.[5]

> In my presidential address to the International Association of Sedimentologists, I pointed out the fallacy of the Lyellian dogma and coined the term "actualistic catastrophism."[6]

Whether geologists will adopt Hsu's actualistic catastrophism as somehow different from other types of geologic catastrophism remains to be seen.

Creationists have always been aware, of course, that uniformitarian geologists (even Lyell) have allowed for local catastrophes (floods, volcanic flows, earthquakes, etc.), but it is only recently (Shea and Hsu notwithstanding) that most geologists have been willing to consider such things as regional and even global catastrophes, as well as sudden global extinctions of many forms of plant and animal life. Creationists have been citing evidences of global catastrophism for years, and at last secular, evolutionist geologists are beginning to recognize them too.

Another somewhat snide (and fallacious) reference to the influence of creationists on the resurgence of catastrophism is found in a recent review of the last book written by Derek Ager, the man whom many would consider the prime mover of neo-catastrophism.

> Indeed geology appears at last to have outgrown Lyell. In an intellectual shift that may well rival that which accompanied the widespread acceptance of plate tectonics, the last 30 years have witnessed an increasing acceptance of rapid, rare, episodic, and "catastrophic" events. Two aspects of this shift are noteworthy. First, it represents a powerful response to creationists, who often argue for wholesale rejection of all of historical geology whenever they find any indication of rapid geological phenomena. . . . Yet by the eminence of its author and the

---

[5] Kenneth J. Hsu, "Actualistic Catastrophism and Global Change," *Paleogeography, Paleoclimatology, Paleoecology*, Global and Planetary Change Section, vol. 89 (1990), p. 309.
[6] *Ibid.*, p. 310.

straightforwardness of its tone, this volume may mark the arrival of catastrophism as the status quo.[7]

So, catastrophism is back — whether *because* of the creationists or as a *defense against* the creationists may be a matter of point of view. Dr. Ager had been president of the British Geological Association. His earlier book, *The Nature of the Stratigraphic Record*, which is referred to later in this chapter, had a profound and widespread influence on modern geologists. No doubt this last book, written shortly before his death, will have an even greater impact. He has shown that all types of geological structures, formations, and systems were formed catastrophically. As Allmon says, catastrophism in geology is about to become the status quo.

This new catastrophism in geology goes along with the new saltationism in biology. Gould, Eldredge, and others — as discussed in chapter 5 — have postulated lengthy periods of stasis followed by mass extinctions, as the "motor" of evolution.

Creationists, of course, have been postulating long periods of stasis (that is, "no evolution") and mass extinction (that is, global catastrophism) as the true explanation of earth history since long before either Gould or Ager, but the latter-day paleontologists and geologists are now trying to put these phenomena into an over-all framework of evolutionary uniformitarianism.

The attempt is strained, to say the least. How can anyone realistically get the evolution of living organisms out of stasis and extinction? And how does one get over-all uniformitarianism out of nothing but catastrophically formed geologic systems? Science used to require observation, but all one ever really observes in the records of both past and present is stasis, catastrophe, and extinction — never evolution!

The records of past life are preserved in the fossils, and fossils — in order to become fossils — must be buried catastrophically.

> Because mass mortality or instantaneous death and burial create the optimal initial conditions for fossilization, it is possible that a significant portion of our fossil record is due to such exceptional events. . . . Once an organism dies . . . there is usually intense competition among other organisms for the nutrients stored in its body. This com-

---

[7] Warren D. Allmon, "Post-Gradualism," review of *The New Catastrophism*, by Derek Ager, *Science*, vol. 262 (October 1, 1993), p. 122. Allmon himself is with the Paleontological Research Institute associated with Cornell University in Ithaca, New York.

bined with physical weathering and the dissolution of hard parts soon leads to destruction unless the remains are quickly buried.[8]

That means that older ideas of fossil production, such as the slow accumulation of organic debris at the bottom of a lake or ocean, will not produce fossils. It takes rapid, permanent burial.

These mechanisms contrast with the popular image of burial as a slow accumulation of sediment through long periods of time, a gentle fallout from air or water that gradually covers organic remains.[9]

For remains with simple or complex taphonomic histories, burial is still the most critical step in the process of preservation, and only permanent burial will produce lasting fossils.[10]

Not even stagnant, anaerobic conditions on sea floors are sufficient to preserve skeletons without rapid burial.

Studies of Allison (1988) on the decay and early diagenesis of arthropods and other types of weakly skeletonized organisms demonstrate that burial in anaerobic muds leads to rapid destruction of organic matter (within a few months) by anaerobic bacteria; such tissues can only be preserved if early mineralization inhibits further decay.[11]

Therefore, many if not most, extraordinary fossil biotas record unusual, stressed environments.[12]

Thus, the regular existence of great fossil "graveyards," in every geological "age," clearly speaks of *massive catastrophism* in all these supposed "ages."

Surprising Testimonies of Catastrophism

More and more evidence of rapid burial of fossils and rapid

---

[8] Anna K. Behrensmeyer, "Taphonomy and the Fossil Record," *American Scientist*, vol. 72 (November/December 1984), p. 560.

[9] *Ibid.*, p. 360.

[10] *Ibid.*, p. 361.

[11] Carlton E. Brett, "Comparative Taphonomy and Ecology of Fossil 'Mother Lodes,'" review of *Extraordinary Fossil Biotas*, eds. H. B. Whittington and Conway Morris (London: *Philosophical Transactions of the Royal Society*, Series B, 311, 1985, 191 pp.), reviewed in *Paleobiology*, vol. 14 (Spring 1988), p. 216.

[12] *Ibid.*, p. 217.

formation of geologic structures seems to be coming in all the time. Great fossil graveyards of mammoths in Siberia, of amphibians in Texas, of hippopotami in Sicily, of fishes in California, Wyoming, Scotland, and many other places, and of dinosaurs on every continent, are well-known.

One of the more recent fossil lodes has been found in the Gobi Desert.

> The Gobi Desert of Central Asia is one of the earth's most desolate places. . . . Yet the Gobi is a paradise for paleontologists. . . . dinosaurs, lizards and small mammals in an unprecedented state of preservation. . . . Among them are 25 skeletons of therapod dinosaurs . . . more than 200 skulls of mammals . . . an even greater number of lizard skulls and skeletons.[13]

It was disappointing to paleontologists, in a way, to find so many fossils of dinosaurs along with so many mammals. These two groups of animals were supposed to have been separated from each other by "a gap of at least several million years." There was no indication of the "iridium boundary" that was presumed to mark the asteroid impact which many believe wiped out the dinosaurs at the Cretaceous/Tertiary boundary, opening the way for mammals.

> Whatever cataclysm wiped out the dinosaurs (and many other species . . .), its mark on Central Asia seems to have been erased.[14]

Evolutionists are embarrassed by this unexpected abundance of both Cretaceous reptiles and Tertiary mammals in the same formation. In fact, the dinosaur deposits are believed to be one of the best in the world!

> The Cretaceous Gobi is unquestionably one of the world's great dinosaur hunting grounds.[15]

In any case, dinosaur fossils in abundance are found all over the world, as already mentioned. Dinosaur graveyards are known in Europe, Africa, Australia, North America, South America — even as far north as Spitzbergen. In recent years they have also been found near the South Pole.

---

[13] Michael J. Novacek et al., "Fossils of the Flaming Cliffs," *Scientific American*, vol. 271 (December 1994), p. 60, 62.

[14] *Ibid.*, p. 69.

[15] *Ibid.*, p. 66.

> Scientists have reported discovering the first set of dinosaur fossils ever to be found in the interior of Antarctica. The fossils are said to be the remains of a plant eating dinosaur, 25 to 30 feet long . . . about 400 miles from the South Pole.[16]

Not only is there an abundance of dinosaur bones, but even of their footprints, though the latter are not usually found with their bones.

> Tracks, trailways, nests, eggs, and coprolites of the reptilian masters of the Mesozoic are chronicled from all over the world. . . . Lockley and Conrad report North American occurrences of dinosaur tracks in alluvial fans, fluvial flood-plains, desert dunes, interdune environments, lacustrine settings, deltas, and marine shoreline systems.[17]

It is not necessary to multiply examples of great fossil deposits, though it would easily be possible, because it is now commonly accepted knowledge that fossil beds require catastrophic burial of some kind. It is also universally recognized that fossils are used to identify and date the ages of the rocks where they are found (this will be discussed later). Therefore, all fossil deposits, which means practically all sedimentary rocks, speak of catastrophism rather than of uniformitarianism.

An often-cited example of uniformitarianism and long ages has been the great salt beds of the world. The traditional explanation of these has been that they were formed by long-continuing evaporation of salt-laden waters trapped in inland seas with no outlet, such as the present Dead Sea. They have even been called "evaporites," in deference to their presumed method of formation.

As the extent of the deposits has become better known, however, this interpretation has become essentially impossible:

> Many salt domes of the Gulf Coast would tower above Mount Everest if they were above ground. Some reach as much as eight miles above the bed of salt that formed them. At their caps the domes average two miles in diameter, and they are still broader at greater depth. From east Texas through Louisiana and Mississippi to Alabama,

---

[16] Chris Raymond, "Scientists Report Finding Fossils of Dinosaurs in Antarctica's Interior," *Chronicle of Higher Education* (March 20, 1991), p. A11.

[17] A. A. Ekdale, "Dinosaur Tracks and Traces," review of *Dinosaur Tracks and Traces*, eds. D. D. Gillette and M. S. Lockley (New York: Cambridge University Press, 1989, 454 pp.), in *Palaios*, vol. 5 (April 1990), p. 199.

and offshore under the Gulf itself, more than 500 salt domes have been identified.[18]

These are only the salt deposits along the Gulf Coast, of course, and there are many others all over the world.

For example, the "evaporites" under the Mediterranean are more than a kilometer thick, and have been made the basis of an elaborate theory about one or more times in the past when the Mediterranean was presumably a desert. This fantastic theory becomes unnecessary when it is realized that these vast salt beds are not "evaporites" at all.

> In referring to "evaporite" of the evaporitic facies, the term begs the question as it implies desication. For clarity, geology needs a new term; namely, "precipitite," rock created by precipitation. Hence, rocks of the evaporitic facies could be evaporites resulting from evaporation of precipitites, deposited by precipitation from a super-saturated solution. Our view is that the sub-Mediterranean salts are precipitites.[19]

Precipitation from a supersaturated solution, say a thick brine, or slurry, would not require long ages of time, but only appropriate levels of pressure and temperature, as well as massive amounts of dissolved or suspended salts. We may not know of a similar situation occurring today, but at least the precipitite concept seems much more plausible than the evaporite concept.

Other former arguments for uniformitarianism have included the formation of coal and oil, the growth of coral reefs and massive limestones, the formation of stalagmites in caves, the growth of successive petrified forests, and others. All are now known to lend themselves better to some form of catastrophic interpretation.

Consider the formation of oil, for example. Although the ultimate source of oil (whether great masses of fossil invertebrates (possibly algae) or inorganic exudations from the earth's mantle) has been a matter of dispute among geologists for many years, it has generally been assumed that the process takes a very long time.

More and more, however, it is being shown that oil can be produced very quickly under the right conditions. One of the most recent

---

[18] Joseph D. Martinez, "Salt Domes," *American Scientist*, vol. 79 (September/October 1991), p. 480.

[19] Robert S. Dietz and Mitchell Woodhouse, "Mediterranean Theory May Be All Wet," *Geotimes*, vol. 33 (May 1988), p. 4.

laboratory demonstrations of this fact has been conducted by Exxon Oil Company scientists, in tests on organic-rich shales from all over the world. These samples were heated and pressurized in a reaction vessel, vastly speeding up the time required to generate oil from the such organic-rich shales.

> These hotter than natural conditions sped up the transformation from a geologic time frame of millions of years to one measured in days and hours.[20]

However, it was found that just high pressure and temperature were not quite enough to produce the oil.

> They discovered that high temperatures cause an organic molecule to break into fragments — and so does water and brine, sometimes more effectively. . . . The results indicate that hot water becomes a catalyst for a series of ionic reactions — creating a second pathway for the cascade of molecular transformations that leads to oil. The acidic and basic nature of hot water — rather than heat — drives this cascade.[21]

Therefore, oil can be produced rapidly from oily rock (whatever causes *that*) in a hot-water, pressurized, briny, cataclysmic environment.

Thus coal and oil, which are the most important geological resources economically, and provide employment for more geologists than all other occupations combined, are increasingly being recognized as catastrophic in origin, *not requiring long ages at all*, as once believed. In fact, they can each be formed quite rapidly in the laboratory.

> A group at Argonne National Laboratory near Chicago, Illinois, recently uncovered some clues as to the origin of coal. The studies indicate that currently accepted theories of the development of coal probably are wrong. . . . The group heated undecomposed lignin, the substance that holds plant cells together, in the presence of montmorillite, or illite clay. The process led to simple coals, whose rank depended on the length of exposure to the 300° F temperature.[22]

---

[20] Elizabeth Pennisi, "Water, Water Everywhere," *Science News*, vol. 143 (February 20, 1993), p. 124.

[21] *Ibid.*, p. 125.

[22] "Basic Coal Studies Refute Current Theories of Formation," *Research and Development* (February 1984), p. 82.

With large quantities of plant material uprooted and transported by flooding waters, and with eroded and/or erupted clay materials abundantly available, plus heat from volcanism, conditions would be ideal for the formation of tremendous quantities of coal. The same is true for oil and for gas.

> For six years, two Australian researchers patiently watched over a set of 1-gm samples of organic material sealed inside stainless steel "bombs." The samples were derived from brown coal and a type of oil shale called torbanite. Each week, the temperature of the samples was increased by 1° C, gradually heating the material from 100° to 400° C. . . . The researchers found that after four years a product "indistinguishable from a paraffinic crude oil" was generated from the torbanite-derived samples, while brown coal produced a "wet natural gas."[23]

There are also more and more indications that oil can be formed rapidly in nature:

> Oceanic hot springs, the site of strange colonies of marine life, may also be a breeding ground for new sources of oil and gas, according to new findings from a research mission in the Gulf of California.
>
> Scientists say that the discovery, in the Guaymas basin off Baja California, indicates that petroleum may be rapidly produced in nature under the pressure-cooker environment of these deep-sea springs — in thousands of years, rather than millions.[24]

Another interesting development is the recognition that the formation of stalactites and stalagmites in caverns does not require the millions of years commonly cited by tour guides and older textbooks. They have been found in mine tunnels and underneath various structures, and have even been produced in the laboratory. Even more surprising was the discovery that they have been produced *organically*, not just by evaporation of calcium-carbonate from water dripping from a cavern roof.

> One has always held that the calcareous concretions in caves are the work of water and the chemical constituents of the rock. Surprise! The true workers in the kingdom

---

[23] *Science News*, vol. 125 (March 24, 1984), p. 187).
[24] *Copley News Service* (January 30, 1982).

of darkness are living organisms. . . . Indeed, an electron microscope photograph . . . shows that a web of mineralized bacteria is also an integral part of the stalactite's structure. Laboratory simulations have shown that microorganisms take an active role in the process of mineralization. . . . Besides being a surprising adjustment of our ideas of stalactite growth, the recognition that micro-organisms may play an active role in the subterranean world stimulates two new questions: (1) Can we believe any longer that a stalactite size is a measure of age? (2) Is the immense network of known caves (some as long as 500 kilometers) the consequence *only* of chemical action?[25]

Stop Continental Drift

Not because it is particularly germane to the creation/evolution question, or even to the age of the earth, but because it has so captivated the popular imagination, it is worth while to inject here a few words of caution about the current concept of continental drift, with all the accompanying scenario of sea floor spreading, magnetic reversals, plate tectonics, and other phenomena. This is a very far-reaching model, or even a paradigm, but it is much like evolution. That is, it is so flexible that anything can be made to fit it, and it is therefore non-testable. R. A. Lyttelton, one of the world's outstanding astro/geophysicists, has called attention to this weakness:

> As for the vast verbal and pictorial literature of plate tectonics, with its assumptions, it may surprise some to learn that it simply fails to qualify as a scientific theory. I am sure Jeffries fully agrees with this. Long ago, the great Poincare explained that such descriptive accounts are not the role of physical theories, which should not introduce as many or more arbitrary constants (or verbal assumptions) as there are phenomena to be accounted for; they should establish connections between different experimental facts, and above all they should enable predictions to be made.[26]

The continental drift/plate tectonics paradigm does *not* yield "predictions" that can be tested experimentally, but only "retrodictions"

---

[25] W. A. Corliss, "Living Stalactites," *Science Frontiers*, no. 57 (May/June 1988), p. 3. Corliss is referring to an article by Georges Dupont, "Et Si les Stalactites Etalent Vivantes" in the French science journal, *Science et Vie* (August 1987), p. 86.

[26] R. A. Lyttelton, *Nature*, vol. 305 (October 20, 1983), p. 672.

at best, which may possibly fit the model, of course, since it is so completely plastic and allows as many modifying assumptions as may be needed to make it fit. Lyttelton gives in both this article and elsewhere many examples of the weakness of this concept, especially in explaining past periods of mountain building. Sir Harold Jeffries, who was also one of the world's top astro-geophysicists, whom Lyttelton mentioned, also rejected the whole idea, for many good reasons, as do various other competent geologists and geophysicists, today.

The nearest thing to an experimental test of the idea would be an actual measurement of the distance between two continents, to see whether that distance is changing. This has actually become possible by the development of astronomical interferometers. So far, the results have been controversial, the weight of evidence still indicating no movement.

> Interferometry is a technique for combining signals received simultaneously from a given astronomical source at two or more different telescopes. . . . They have done geodetic and astronometric measurements since 1979 and in that time have noticed no significant changes in the distances between the telescopes. Theories of continental drift and gravity theories in which the earth expands over time would expect change.[27]

> Meanwhile, since the continents drift as slowly as one's fingernails grow — from one to ten centimeters per year — even the most precise surveying methods available today have not yet detected drift.[28]

This negative result, of course, does not prove that the continents have not drifted or moved in the past. Nor, for that matter, would any future positive result prove that they *did* drift in the past. Even *if* they did, it would not prove that they did not drift *much faster* in the past. The problem is that the whole concept is simply too flexible to be testable.

In the meantime, it is unnecessary for creationists to take any specific position on this subject, since it does not affect the creation/evolution issue one way or another. When it is incorporated as an integral part of the long-age evolutionary model, of course, as some have done, then it can and should be rejected as unscientific and false.

---

[27] *Science News*, vol. 123 (January 8, 1983), p. 20.

[28] Robert Dietz, "In Defense of Drift," *The Sciences*, vol. 23 (November/December 1983), p. 26.

Closely associated with continental drift, of course, is the concept of sea floor spreading, which, in turn, was based on parallel patterns of reversals of the so-called magnetic stripes of the Mid-Atlantic Ridge. The reversals of the magnetized particles in these stripes are taken to mean that the earth's magnetic poles reverse their polarity about every 700,000 years, so that the magnetic field changes directions by 180° at these intervals. The sea floor is assumed to be emerging from the earth's mantle at the Ridge, then moving away from the Ridge in opposite directions, carrying the continents (e.g., Africa and South America) with it. The great ages of these stripes have been determined mainly by potassium-argon dating of the lava rocks being formed by this process. This has been going on, evolutionists say, since at least the end of the Cretaceous "period" about 75 (or more) million years ago (at that time, all the continents are assumed to have been together in one super-continent, Pangea).

Apart from the exorbitant time periods involved in this supposed process, most creationists would not be greatly concerned whether or not the continental drift/sea floor spreading/plate tectonics paradigm is valid. The long ages, however, will be shown in the next chapter to be very doubtful. Like evolution itself, the theory is excessively flexible and adaptable, capable of being made to fit many geological and paleontological phenomena. Like evolution, it cannot be observed in operation, so it cannot be either proved or disproved, scientifically.

Its main evidence, however — the laterally symmetrical reversals of the magnetic stripes on the sea floor — has in recent years been brought into serious question. That is, there are now known to be "vertical-stripe reversals," as well as lateral, and this tremendously complicates any notion of a globally changing magnetic field.

> Internal polarity changes with depth in a drilled sequence of oceanic crustal rocks do not match the observed magnetic "stripe" polarity measured on the surface.[29]

Thus, there is a three-dimensional complex pattern of reversals in the sea floor that seems to negate the simple dipole-field reversal hypothesis, which is the main "proof" offered for sea floor spreading.

> These several vertically alternating layers of opposing magnetic polarization directions found in cored oceanic crust

---

[29] J. C. Pratsch, "Petroleum Geologist's View of Oceanic Crust Age," *Oil and Gas Journal*, vol. 84 (July 14, 1986), p. 114.

disproves one of the basic parameters of sea floor spreading theory, namely that the oceanic crust was magnetized entirely as it spread laterally from the magmatic center.[30]

Among other things, these mixed-up stripes completely negate their use in age determinations.

It appears today that oceanic magnetic stripes have no value for age determinations of oceanic crusts; they are originating beneath oceanic basalt levels, and they originate in linear fault or fracture systems.[31]

Since sea floor spreading is the chief evidence for continental drift, the latter is also questionable.

But we would be well advised to reconsider the mechanics and scales of continental drift . . . none of the geological and geophysical data from subduction zones indicate absolute motions of oceans or adjacent continents.[32]

For some reason, these facts seem not to have had much effect on the confidence of geologists in the drift paradigm. However, the author cited above is not the only one who has reported these disturbing phenomena.[33]

Furthermore, the whole concept of plate tectonics now is under a cloud, despite the mountain of evolutionary applications and interpretations that have been erected on it. There are other difficulties with it as well.

But plate tectonics, too, has its faults. While the theory is very successful at explaining how oceans and oceanic crust form, in many ways it leaves the continents high and dry. In the case of the India-Asia collision, for instance, it doesn't explain why the oldest part of the Indian plate has survived the collision intact while sections of Asia have been evidently deformed.[34]

---

[30] *Ibid.*, p. 115.

[31] *Ibid.*

[32] J. M. Hall and P. T. Robinson, "Deep Crustal Drilling in North Atlantic Ocean," *Science*, vol. 204 (May 11, 1979), p. 573-586.

[33] Richard A. Kerr, "How Is New Ocean Crust Formed?" *Science*, vol. 205 (September 14, 1979), p. 1115-1118.

[34] Stefi Weisburd, "Rooting for Continental Roots," *Science*, vol. 130 (December 13, 1986), p. 380.

After discussing the evidences that the assumed "plates" are not of the same thickness under continents and oceans (as assumed in plate-tectonics theory), but that the thickness under the stable continental cores is much thicker, this author concludes:

> Continental roots may not represent another geosciences revolution in the making, but they certainly demonstrate that the conventional plate tectonics theory is not gospel.[35]

It has long been recognized that the chief difficulty with the whole idea of dipole magnetic reversals, with all the theoretical baggage heaped on that assumption, is the lack of a mechanism in the earth's core — or anywhere else — to cause such a remarkable turnover, and to move whole continents apart. The usual suggestion (still utterly unobserved and unexplained) is that there are huge "convective cells" or heating cells of some sort deep in the earth's mantle, driven somehow by a tremendous "dynamo" in the core. Soon after this idea was introduced, Dr. A. E. J. Engel, professor of geology at the California Institute of Technology, made an interesting — and still relevant — comment:

> Large convective cells in the earth's mantle caused by terrestrial reheating have been invoked to move the continents, make the mountains, spread the ocean's floor, and create the tremendous secular changes that we see manifest in the surficial complexity of the earth's crust. The mechanism of large convective cells as agents of these several major dynamic events is a most functional, if untestable, hypothesis. Belief in cells is akin to belief in an orthodox God. Few earth scientists, I suspect, really believe in either completely; yet none is clever enough to invent working hypotheses less testable, more tantalizing, self-sufficing, and all encompassing as God or the convective cell.[36]

The whole paradigm associated with plate tectonics (including continental drift, sea floor spreading, magnetic-field reversals, mountain-building, biogeographical evolution, etc.) is thus still largely — like evolution — a matter of faith.

One Worldwide Cataclysm

Examples of catastrophic, rapid formation of rock systems in the

---

[35] *Ibid.*, p. 382.
[36] A. E. J. Engel, "Time and the Earth," *American Scientist*, vol. 57 (Winter 1969), p. 475.

geologic systems of the earth, like those cited above in this chapter, could be multiplied, eventually covering every component of the geologic column. There is literally *no* geologic system or structure or formation that *requires* for its explanation long, slow processes extending over thousands or millions of year. Dr. Derek Ager said in the closing sentence of his famous book *Nature of the Stratigraphic Record*:

> The history of any one part of the earth, like the life of a soldier, consists of long periods of boredom and short periods of terror.[37]

That is, every thing we can actually see in the geologic records indicates formation by very rapid processes.

Ager was not a creationist, of course. In fact, he complained about being quoted by creationists. Nevertheless, he did argue strongly against any form of uniformitarianism. If there is any doubt about his conclusion, one should look also at the following statement:

> To me the whole record is catastrophic . . . in the sense that only the episodic events — the occasional ones — are preserved for us.[38]

Dr. Ager continued to believe in long geological ages, but he pointed out that the actual geological record in the rocks does not include "the long ages of boredom" (these would correspond to the paleontologist's long ages of *stasis*), but only "the short periods of terror" (corresponding to the mass extinctions and evolutionary punctuations).

As noted earlier, Ager was not merely an eccentric catastrophist in a profession still dominated by uniformitarians. He was a highly respected professional, serving as president of the British Geological Association, and he is now widely recognized as leader of the neo-catastrophist school, which probably is the dominant position among current geologists.

We are justified, therefore, in concluding that all components of the actual geological structures, formations, and systems in the earth's crust have been formed catastrophically and rapidly. The remaining question is whether they have all been formed recently, essentially in one

---

[37] Derek Ager, *Nature of the Stratigraphic Record*, 3rd Ed. (New York: John Wiley and Sons, Inc., 1993), p. 141. This sentence has now become a common cliché among the younger school of geologists.

[38] Derek Ager, in *Catastrophes and Earth History*, eds. W. A. Berggren and J. A. Van Couvering (Princeton University Press, 1984), p. 93.

period of great upheaval on the earth, or intermittently, in the traditional 4.6-billion-year framework of assumed earth history.

Uniformitarianism did dominate standard geological thought and teaching for 150 years. Now, suddenly, almost the entire geological community seems to have swung over to neo-catastrophism. Still unwilling to accept again the catastrophism of the founding fathers of geology, centered in a worldwide deluge, the emphasis currently is on the necessity of postulating all sorts of other catastrophes (asteroids, meteorites, comets, volcanoes, regional floods, slipping crusts, splitting continents, sudden pole reversals, and other similar phenomena) to explain practically all such geological data. Two fairly recent summaries may be taken as typical. Reviewing an important meeting, Dr. Roger Lewin says this:

> "It is a great philosophical breakthrough for geologists to accept catastrophism as a normal part of earth history." This comment, made by Erle Kauffman at a meeting on the dynamics of extinction held recently at Northern Arizona University, Flagstaff, identifies a currently important, perhaps revolutionary, shift in collective professional perspectives among paleontologists as well as geologists. . . . The new catastrophism, if such an emotive phrase can be permitted, for many would disavow the designation, merely allows for asteroid impact as one of many agents that from time to time profoundly perturb global conditions important to life, including atmospheric and oceanic circulation, temperature gradient, and sea level.[39]

One of the men largely responsible for this notable new science of the "dynamics of extinction" is Dr. David Raup, head of geology of the University of Chicago and curator of geology at the Field Museum. He says:

> A great deal has changed, however, and contemporary geologists and paleontologists now generally accept catastrophism as a "way of life," although they may avoid the word catastrophe. In fact, many geologists now see rare, short-lived events as being the principal contributors to geological sequences. . . . The periods of relative quiet contribute only a small part of the record.[40]

---

[39] Roger Lewin, *Science*, vol. 221 (September 2, 1983), p. 935.
[40] David Raup, *Field Museum of Natural History Bulletin*, vol. 54 (March 1983), p. 21.

Geological uniformitarianism, which creationists have been vigorously opposing for over 50 years, has thus suddenly been all but abandoned by the geologists themselves, so there is hardly any point any more in citing the many weaknesses of the uniformitarian concept, or the numerous evidences of catastrophe in the rock strata. For those wanting more documentation, the ICR Technical Monograph *Catastrophes in Earth History* by Dr. Steven Austin (1983) contains extensive annotated bibliographies on this neo-catastrophist movement among evolutionary geologists. This has been kept updated in his ICR computer disc CATASTROREF.

Perhaps it is because evolutionists have been, for 150 years, so singularly unsuccessful at learning the mechanics of evolution, that they have been turning to the "dynamics of extinction." The current abandonment of gradualism in biological evolution has coincided with the recent abandonment of gradualism in geological evolution. Punctuationism (rapid evolution in a small population) has come into vogue in biology, concurrently with neo-catastrophism in geology, and it is naturally very tempting to relate — or even to equate — the two. Many contemporary evolutionists are doing just that, though with reservations.

For example, T. H. Van Andel commented as follows several years ago, after first pointing out that the geological record is essentially one of rare catastrophic events separated by long gaps when nothing much was happening:

> Among the many ideas fermenting today in the study of evolution there is one, frequently heard, that ascribes the major evolutionary steps to a jump advance, a concentration of major change in a very brief interval of time. There seems to be no good reason why such pulses of evolutionary change should coincide with the major rare events that built the sedimentary sequence in which the record of evolution is contained. Thus, the new "catastrophist" view of the sedimentary record implies that key elements of the evolutionary record may be forever out of reach.[41]

This pessimistic view concerning the impossibility of ever learning how evolution worked was written before the "discovery" by Raup and Sepkowski that massive extinctions have occurred at what they interpreted to be 26 million-year intervals throughout geologic history (it has since been shown that the statistical controls on this study were so weak as to disqualify its conclusions).

[41] T. H. Van Andel, *Nature*, vol. 294 (December 3, 1981), p. 398.

At any rate, the fossils do seem to record many extinctions (e.g., the dinosaurs), so evolutionists are hopeful that this may somehow provide the key to the evolution of life. Michael Benton, in the zoology department at Oxford University, has said:

> There is increasing evidence that major physical changes have caused more large-scale evolutionary changes than has competition. . . . Competition may increase the probability of extinction of a particular lineage, but it will rarely be the sole cause, whereas it could be postulated that a catastrophic change in the physical environment is sufficient on its own.[42]

Likewise, Roger Lewin of the American Association for Advancement of Science comments on the necessity — but the overwhelming difficulty — of trying to relate evolutionary advances to geologic catastrophes:

> Each mass extinction in a sense resets the evolutionary clock and so makes the history of life strikingly spasmodic and governed by a greater element of chance than is palatable in strict uniformitarianism. . . . The notorious paucity of the fossil record combines with a greatly varying sedimentation rate to make time resolution of faunal changes little short of a nightmare.[43]

At the 1983 annual meeting of the Geological Society of America, held in Indianapolis, there seemed to be, especially among the paleontologists, an overwhelming consensus developing that catastrophes and their accompanying mass extinctions somehow hold the key to understanding evolution. Dr. Stephen Gould, describing this development with his enthusiastic endorsement, reported:

> There . . . a group of my colleagues in paleontology began to dismantle an old order of thinking about old objects, and to construct a new and striking approach to a major feature of life's history on earth: mass extinction . . . mass extinctions have been more frequent, more unusual, more intense (in numbers eliminated), and more different (in effect versus the patterns of normal times)

---

[42] Michael Benton, *Nature*, vol. 302 (March 3, 1983), p. 16, 17.

[43] Roger Lewin, "Extinctions and the History of Life," *Science*, vol. 221 (September 2, 1983), p. 935.

than we had ever suspected.[44]

Now, mass extinctions — unusual, intense, different — correlate nicely with the concept of cataclysm, but it is difficult to see how extinctions can tell us anything about evolution! The *extinction* of life would seem to be the polar opposite of the *evolution* of life. Even if we could determine for sure, say, that an asteroid impact resulted in the extinction of the dinosaurs, this would tell us nothing whatever about how they evolved in the first place. Nevertheless, Gould wistfully clings to this hope:

> Heretofore, we have thrown up our hands in frustration at the lack of expected pattern in life's history — or we have sought to impose a pattern that we hope to find on a world that does not really display it. . . . If we can develop a general theory of mass extinction, we may finally understand why life has thwarted our expectations — and we may even extract an unexpected kind of pattern from apparent chaos.[45]

Well, "hope springs eternal," and to the evolutionists anything is apparently preferable to creationism. Nevertheless, Gould is here retreating again to his Marxist faith that chaos and destruction, in some utterly mystical way, somehow generate higher order and a better society. In any case, this absurd current notion of evolution generated suddenly by catastrophism, extinction, chance preservation, and quantum speciation of hopeful monsters speaks more loudly than any creationist critique could do, of the utter hopelessness of the scientific case for evolution.

In seeking to determine whether the multitudinous evidences of catastrophism in the earth's crust represent many local catastrophes spread over billions of years, or one complex of catastrophes occurring essentially contemporaneously in a global cataclysm, it is well to note that the various "ages" are determined mainly by their so-called "index fossils." This will be discussed in the next chapter.

Although there are many, many different types of rocks and minerals and structural features, they are each and all scattered indiscriminately through the various ages. That is, any so-called geologic age can include shales, basalts, limestones, and any other petrologic complex; any geologic age may yield quartz, feldspar, iron, or any other

---

[44] Stephen J. Gould, *Natural History* (February 1984), p. 14.
[45] *Ibid.*, p. 23.

mineral or metal; any geologic age may have rocks containing coal or oil or natural gas; and any age may exhibit any type of fold, fault, intrusion, or other structural features. The rocks all seem to be *one* age as far as their physical and chemical characteristics are concerned!

It is even more important to note that the *only* global unconformity in the geologic column occurs right at the bottom of the column, where it rests on the crystalline basement. What this means is that the sedimentation process that deposited the sediments which eventually became the sedimentary rocks that make up the geologic column was continuous, from bottom to top, without a significant time break, with the exception of the surficial sediments deposited intermittently during the few thousand years of recorded history.

Now, an "unconformity" is the contact surface between two rock formations (say, for example, where a shale formation overlies a sandstone formation) when the sediments above and below the surface do not "conform" to each other in terms of the direction of the strata (or "layers" of sediment) that comprise the two formations. Flat lying strata may overlie a set of planed-off inclined strata, for instance, with the interface surface between the two sets called an unconformity.

The significance of all this is that an unconformity surface represents an erosional surface and, therefore, an unknown lapse of time between the time when the strata of the lower formation stopped being deposited and the strata of the upper formation began to be deposited. An unconformity, in short, represents a time gap in the process of sedimentary deposition when the sediments that would eventually be hardened into sedimentary rocks were first being laid down.

A conformity, on the other hand, is an interface between two formations in which the sedimentary strata above and below conform to each other in orientation and angle, with no evidence of time lapse between them — no soil profile, bioturbation, etc. The implication in such a case would be that the deposition process was continuous, with the formation above laid down immediately after the one below, with no opportunity for any intervening earth movements or sea-level drop or other physical change to initiate erosion instead of deposition on the surface.

There are some conformity surfaces, however, where it is thought that a time lapse may have occurred, because of a sudden change in the evolutionary stage of the contained fossils above and below. Such situations have been called "deceptive conformitives" or "paraconformities," but, since their main mark of recognition is the absence of an assumed intervening evolutionary stage, they are questionable, to say the least.

In general, therefore, a conformity surface indicates continuous deposition, whereas an unconformity indicates a significant gap in time in that part of the geologic column. The missing time may be long or short; there is no way to tell from the unconformity itself.

With this background discussion, it should be easy to see that, if there were such a thing as a worldwide unconformity, say between the Cambrian period and the Ordovician period (or any two other geological "ages"), it would be an ideal way of demarking the various geological ages and dating the rocks. As a matter of fact, in the very early days of the development of historical geology, this was actually believed to be the case.

This idea, however, was abandoned long ago, not only on a worldwide basis, but even on a local basis. Note the following recommendation by two top authorities, written soon after World War II:

> The employment of unconformities as time-stratigraphic boundaries should be abandoned. Because of the failure of unconformities as time indices, time-stratigraphic boundaries of Paleozoic and later age must be defined by time — hence by faunas.[46]

Once again, it is emphasized that rocks are "dated" not by any physical criteria — even such obvious time boundaries as unconformities — but only by fossils, which means by assumed evolution.

A more recent, and authoritative, confirmation of the very important fact that "unconformities" in the geologic column, which represent time gaps of unknown duration in the formations where they occur, are *not* worldwide, and, therefore, cannot represent worldwide time gaps, is noted in the following statement:

> Bounding unconformities were the basis for establishing many of the earliest stratigraphic units in western Europe. Many of the systems of the present accepted Standard Global Chronostratigraphic Scale were originally unconformity-bounded units. This procedure has not been restricted, however, to the earliest days of stratigraphic work or to western Europe; it has been used, and continues to be used, in all parts of the world. Unconformity-bounded units became very popular at the time tectonic

---

[46] H. E. Wheeler and E. M. Beesley, "Critique of the Time-Stratigraphic Concept," *Bulletin of the Geological Society of America*, vol. 59 (1948), p. 84.

episodes were considered essentially synchronous world-wide, but did lose favor among geologists when synchroneity was found not to hold true.[47]

Very important for our immediate discussion, therefore, is the now-recognized fact that there are no worldwide unconformities (either physical unconformities or fossil unconformities, for that matter) and, therefore, no worldwide time break within the main sedimentary deposits in the geologic column.

This means — and this is very important — that essentially *the entire sedimentary geologic column, all over the world, is a unit, deposited continuously from bottom to top without a significant time break*. It is a unitary phenomenon, and, therefore, must have a unitary cause.

We have already shown that catastrophism is now generally accepted even by most evolutionary geologists. That is, every unit in the geologic column was formed by some kind of "rare event" or "catastrophe": a local flood, volcanic eruption, landslide, tsunami, or some other violent phenomenon.

Now, if every unit in the geologic column was produced by at least a local catastrophe, and all the units are connected through an essentially continuous deposition process, then the entire series must represent merely different local components of the same worldwide cataclysm. The whole is the sum of its parts.

Even though this chain of reasoning may appear simplistic, it is straightforward and seems compelling, if the assumptions on which it is based are valid. There are really only two assumptions: (1) every formation in the geologic column was formed rapidly, in some kind of catastrophic depositional environment; (2) there is no worldwide unconformity, or time gap in the sedimentary fossil-bearing geologic column.

Some die-hard uniformitarians would still question the first assumption, but, as documented above, more and more in the modern school of geologists are saying that everything in the geologic column is a record of catastrophe. Robert Dott, in his June 1982 presidential address to the Society of Economic Paleontologists and Mineralogists, said:

---

[47] Amos Salvador, "Unconformity-Bounded Stratigraphic Units," *Bulletin of the Geological Society of America*, vol. 98 (February 1987), p. 232. Salvador was writing as Chairman of the Geological Society's International Subcommission on Stratigraphic Classification.

> The sedimentary record is largely a record of episodic events . . . episodicity is the rule, not the exception.[48]

As far as the second assumption is concerned, practically all geologists would now agree that there are no worldwide unconformities in the so-called Phanerozoic part of the geologic column, but a few still would say that a global unconformity exists at the base of the Cambrian system, supposedly the oldest of the geological ages with multi-cellular life forms. In the Precambrian (Proterozoic Era) there are great thicknesses of sedimentary rocks, but for a long time it was believed that there were no fossils in these rocks. Later, many reports began to come in of different deposits of protozoan fossils (one-celled organisms) in the Precambrian, but many still maintained that there was a worldwide unconformity between the Precambrian and Cambrian.

In recent years, however, there have been several sites around the world where an odd assortment of soft-bodied multi-celled animals have been found in Precambrian rocks. These are known as the Ediacaran fauna, named after the Australian site where they were first discovered. A particularly significant site has also been found in eastern Siberia. In this region are located what so far are considered "the best sequences of rocks spanning the boundary, about 570 million years old, between the Cambrian and Precambrian geological periods."[49]

A photograph of the site has the following caption:

> These rocks along the Aldan River in Siberia span the boundary with little or no disruption, and clearly log the evolution of shelled animals and their soft-bodied anteced-ents.[50]

The caption is unrealistic in one respect, however: there are no intermediate fossils between the Ediacaran soft-bodied animals and the shelled animals of the Cambrian. In fact, Adolph Seilacher of Germany, supported by Stephen Gould and others, have shown that the Ediacaran fossils were so different as to be completely unrelated to the later animals, dying off without descendants.[51]

But, in any case, the so-called unconformity *did not exist*, at least at this site in Siberia.

There is really no basis any longer for assuming an unconformity

---

[48] Robert Dott, *Geotimes* (November 1982), p. 16.
[49] Cheryl Simon, "In With the Older," *Science News*, vol. 123 (May 7, 1983), p. 300.
[50] *Ibid.*
[51] Stephen J. Gould, *Natural History*, vol. 93 (February 1984), p. 15.

of worldwide extent anywhere, even at the Cambrian–Precambrian boundary. The example cited above could be augmented by many others:

> In the 19th century the boundary between the Precambrian and the Cambrian was relatively easy to find, because the areas then under study showed major gaps or unconformities (representing an interval of time in which there was no preservation or deposition of rocks) between Precambrian and Cambrian sedimentary layers. The expanded data base available to 20th century paleontologists has actually complicated the task of locating the boundary precisely, because many regions are now known where Precambrian and Cambrian formations grade continuously into each other.[52]

Now if the sediments of the Precambrian are continuous with those of the Cambrian, there is, indeed, no worldwide time break in the sediments of the geologic column. And, again, if there is no universal time gap in the geologic column, and if all individual formations represent intense depositional episodes (many geologists still don't like the word "catastrophe"), then the entire column must represent *one continuous intense depositional episode*, a one-of-a-kind "rare event." Instead of depicting the evolution of life over many ages, the sedimentary geologic column in the earth's crust really represents the *vast destruction and burial of life in one age*.

At the very least, this model ought to be given serious scientific consideration, as a possible alternative to the failed model of evolutionary uniformitarianism. The idea of long geologic ages is not at all needed, by all the factual evidences, to explain the phenomena of earth history.

This idea of long ages is so ingrained in modern opinion, however, that we need to study at some length the methods of geologic dating. And that is the subject of the next chapter.

---

[52] Mark A. S. McMeramin, "The Emergence of Animals," *Scientific American*, vol. 256 (April 1987), p. 98.

Chapter 11

The Geologic Ages Are Vanishing

In earlier chapters, we have seen that vertically upward evolution has never been observed to occur in the present, and that the ubiquitous absence of transitional forms in the fossils indicates that it never occurred in the past. Furthermore, the laws of probability, of thermodynamics, and of causality show that evolution is impossible and that it will never occur in the future either. Finally, in these last two chapters, it will be shown that, even if it were possible, there has not been time enough for evolution to occur.

The only remaining argument for evolution is the long geological ages, which supposedly provide time for evolution. However, such tremendous spans of time depend completely upon the assumption of uniformitarianism. This assumption is invalid, however, as shown in the preceding chapter, and that fact is now recognized by most geologists. All the great rock strata, fossil beds, and other geological systems have been formed rapidly and catastrophically, not slowly and gradually over long ages.

Furthermore, it was shown in the last chapter that these catastrophes were all interconnected and continuous, with no worldwide time break, so that the entire fossiliferous geologic column was formed essentially during and following *one global cataclysm*. This cataclysm was primarily hydraulic in nature (that is, a worldwide flood), but was also accompanied by great volcanic, tectonic, and other geophysical phenomena.

All of this, in turn, brings the whole concept of geologic ages and billions of years of terrestrial and celestial antiquity into serious doubt.

Just why do scientists think that they know these ages ever existed? How do they arrive at billions of years for the antiquity of the earth, and how do cosmophysicists arrive at an even greater age for the universe?

To the creationist the answer to these questions is that evolutionists are repeatedly making *ad hoc* assumptions to try to justify an atheistic evolutionary world view, and that the pseudo-rationale for all these assumptions is the discredited premise of uniformitarianism. Even a few evolutionary geologists let an acknowledgment slip every now and then that this is all founded on speculation.

> The fact that the calculated age of the earth has increased by a factor of roughly 100 between the year 1900 and today — as the accepted "age" of the earth has increased from about 50 million years in 1900 to at least 4.6 eons today — certainly suggests we clothe our current conclusions regarding time and the earth with humility.[1]

The author of this cautionary statement was a distinguished geologist, professor of geology at the California Institute of Technology and the Scripps Institute of Oceanography. He went on to say:

> We will speculate a lot about the first eon or more of earth's history . . . but in the foreseeable future it will be mostly speculations — essentially geopoetry.[2]

Although Dr. Engel's critique was published more than a quarter century ago, nothing really has changed. When one of the writers (H. Morris) was just a young instructor some 50 years ago, the scientific books and articles on this subject agreed that there were some six independent lines of evidence (radioactive decay, expanding universe, etc.) that converged on a date of about two billion years for the age of both the earth and the cosmos. Now, of course, the "age" of the earth is 4.6 billion years, and that of the universe about 18 billion years. (Perhaps this is a clue to the great age of the writer!) But note the honest conclusion of Professor Engel:

> The most honest concede freely we know almost nothing of the earth or its processes.[3]

In any case, the continual insistence of evolutionists that "we

---

[1] A. E. J. Engel, "Time and the Earth," *American Scientist*, vol. 57 (Winter 1969), p. 461.
[2] *Ibid.*, p. 462.
[3] *Ibid.*, p. 480.

know" the earth is billions of years old is unwarranted. There is a great deal of good scientific evidence that the earth is *far too young* for evolution to be a feasible option in explaining origins.

Before discussing the question of "absolute age," however, we need to look first at the "relative ages," as implied in the evolution-based geologic column. That is, just how do evolutionists know (or *think* that they know) that a given rock or fossil is of Cambrian age or Jurassic or Tertiary or something else?

Circular Reasoning in Geology

So we ask the question. Suppose we find a certain rock formation that interests us, and we would like to know how to go about determining the geologic age in which it was formed. We go to the encyclopedia to get the answer:

> Paleontology (the study of fossils) is important in the study of geology. The age of rocks may be determined by the fossils found in them.[4]

That sounds simple enough. All we have to do now is find some fossils in the rock, and that will tell us how old it is.

But how do fossils tell us the age? Somehow we must first know the age when those fossils lived. How do we do that? We go again to the same encyclopedia, to an article written by the very same paleontologist. Here is how he says to do that.

> Scientists determine when fossils were formed by finding out the age of the rocks in which they lie.[5]

This is becoming confusing! Still another article, in the same encyclopedia, tells us again how to know the age of the rocks, so that they can tell us the age of their fossils.

> Fossils help geologists figure out the ages of rock strata and the times at which plants and animals lived.[6]

Isn't there some way out of this circle of reasoning? Rocks give us

---

[4] Samuel Paul Welles, Article on "Paleontology," *World Book Encyclopedia*, vol. 15 (1978), p. 85. Welles was a research scientist in the Museum of Paleontology at the University of California at Berkeley.

[5] Samuel Paul Welles, Article on "Fossils," *World Book Encyclopedia*, vol. 7 (1978), p. 364.

[6] Samuel P. Ellison, Jr., Article on "History of the Earth," *World Book Encyclopedia*, vol. 6 (1978), p. 16d. Ellison was Professor of Geological Science at the University of Texas.

the age of the fossils, and the fossils tell us the age of the rocks. But surely there must be a starting place somewhere!

And indeed there is. The key is the *assumption* of evolution.

The age does not depend on radiometric dating, as is obvious from the fact that the geologic-age system had been completely worked out and most major formations dated before radioactivity was even discovered. Neither does the age depend upon the mineralogic or petrologic character of a rock, as is obvious from the fact that rocks of all types of composition, structure, and degree of hardness can be found in *any* "age." It does not depend upon vertical position in the local geologic strata, since rocks of any "age" may, and do, rest horizontally and conformably on rocks of any other age. No, a rock is dated *solely* by its fossils.

> The only chronometric scale applicable in geologic history for the stratigraphic events exactly is furnished by the fossils. Owing to the irreversibility of evolution, they offer an unambiguous time scale for relative age determinations and for worldwide correlations of rocks.[7]

Obviously, fossils could be distinctive time-markers only if the various kinds each had lived in different ages. But how can we know which fossils lived in which ages? No scientists were there to observe them, and true *science* requires *observation*. Furthermore, by analogy with the present (and uniformitarianism is supposed to be able to decipher the past in terms of the present), many different kinds of plants and animals are living in the present world, including even the "primitive" one-celled organisms with which evolution is supposed to have begun. Why, therefore, is it not better to assume that all major kinds also lived together in past ages as well? Some kinds, such as the dinosaurs, have become extinct, but practically all present-day kinds of organisms are also found in the fossil world.

The only reason for thinking that different fossils should represent different ages is the assumption of evolution. If evolution is really true, then, of course, fossils should provide an excellent means for identifying the various ages, an "unambiguous time scale," as Schindewolf put it. Hollis Hedberg, former president of the Geological Society of America, adds his own confirmation that evolution is the key, as follows:

---

[7] O. H. Schindewolf, "Comments on Some Stratigraphic Terms," *American Journal of Science*, vol. 255 (June 1957), p. 394. Derek Ager also says that "fossils have been and still are the most accurate method of dating and correlating the rocks in which they occur" (*New Scientist*, vol. 100, November 10, 1983), p. 425.

> Fossils have furnished, through their record of the evolution of life on this planet, an amazingly effective key to the relative positioning of strata in widely-separated regions, and from continent to continent.[8]

The use of fossils as time-markers thus depends completely on "their record of evolution." But, then, how do we know that *evolution* is true? Why, because of the fossil record!

> Fossils provide the only historical, documentary evidence that life has evolved from simpler to more and more complex forms.[9]

So, the only *proof* of evolution is based on the *assumption* of evolution! The system of evolution arranges the fossils, the fossils date the rocks, and the resulting system of fossil-dated rocks proves evolution! Around and around we go.

How much more simple and direct it would be to explain the fossil-bearing rocks as the record in stone of the destruction of the ancient world by one great flood. The various fossil assemblages represent, not evolutionary stages developing over many ages, but, rather, ecological habitats in various parts of the world in one age.

Fossils of marine invertebrate animals are normally found at the lower elevations in each local geologic column, for the simple reason that they live at the lowest elevations and would be first affected and buried in a global cataclysm. Fossils of birds and mammals are found only at the higher elevations because they live at higher elevations, are lower in weight density, more mobile, and could escape burial longer. Human fossils are extremely rare because men would only very infrequently be trapped and buried in flood sediments at all because of their high mobility. The sediments of the "ice-age" at the highest levels are evidence of the drastically changed climate that would be caused by such a global cataclysm.

The flood theory of geology, which was so obvious and persuasive to the founders of geology, is thus once again beginning to be recognized as the only theory that is fully consistent with the actual *facts* of geology.

As suggested above, creationists have long insisted that the main evidence for evolution — the fossil record — involves a serious case of circular reasoning. That is, the fossil evidence that life has evolved from

---

[8] H. D. Hedberg, "The Stratigraphic Panorama," *Bulletin of the Geological Society of America*, vol. 72 (April 1961), p. 499.

[9] C. O. Dunbar, *Historical Geology* (New York: Wiley, 1960), p. 47.

simple to complex forms over the geological ages depends on the geological ages of the specific rocks in which these fossils are found. The rocks, however, are assigned geologic ages *based on* the fossil assemblages which they contain. The fossils, in turn, are arranged on the *basis of* their assumed evolutionary relationships. Thus, the main evidence for evolution is based on the *assumption* of evolution!

A significant development in recent years has been the fact that many evolutionary geologists are now also recognizing this problem. They no longer ignore it or pass it off with a sarcastic denial, but they admit that it is a real problem that deserves a serious answer.

The use of "index fossils" to determine the geologic age of a formation, for example, was discussed in an interesting way in an important paper by J. E. O'Rourke.

> These principles have been applied in *Feinstratigraphie*, which starts from a chronology of index fossils, and imposes them on the rocks. Each taxon represents a definite time unit and so provides an accurate, even "infallible" date. If you doubt it, bring in a suite of good index fossils, and the specialist without asking where or in what order they were collected, will lay them out on the table in chronological order.[10]

That is, since evolution always proceeds in the same way all over the world at the same time, index fossils representing a given stage of evolution are assumed to constitute infallible indicators of the geologic age in which they are found. This makes good sense and would obviously be the best way to determine relative geologic age — if, that is, we knew infallibly that evolution were true!

But how do we know that? There is such a vast time scale involved that no one can actually observe evolution taking place.

> That a known fossil or recent species, or higher taxonomic group, however primitive it might appear, is an actual ancestor of some other species or group, is an assumption scientifically unjustifiable, for science never can simply assume that which it has the responsibility to demonstrate. . . . It is the burden of each of us to demonstrate the reasonableness of any hypothesis we might care to erect about ancestral conditions, keeping in mind that we

---

[10] J. E. O'Rourke, "Pragmatism versus Materialism in Stratigraphy," *American Journal of Science*, vol. 276 (January 1976), p. 51.

have no ancestors alive today, that in all probability such ancestors have been dead for many tens of millions of years, and that even in the fossil record they are not accessible to us.[11]

There is, therefore, really no way of proving scientifically any assumed evolutionary phylogeny, as far as the fossil record is concerned.

Likewise, paleontologists do their best to make sense out of the fossil record and sketch in evolutionary sequences or unfossilized morphologies without realistic hope of obtaining specific verification within the foreseeable future.[12]

It would help if the fossil record would yield somewhere at least a few transitional sequences demonstrating the evolution of some kind of organism into some other more complex kind. So far, however, it has been uncooperative, as discussed earlier.

The abrupt appearance of higher taxa in the fossil record has been a perennial puzzle.... If we read the record rather literally, it implies that organisms of new grades of complexity arose and radiated relatively rapidly.[13]

Transitions are well-documented, of course, at the *same* levels of complexity — within the "kinds," that is — but never into "new grades of complexity." *Horizontal* changes, however, are not really relevant to the measure of geologic time, since such changes occur too *rapidly* (e.g., the development of numerous varieties of dogs within human history) to be meaningful on the geologic time scale, and are reversible (e.g., the shift in the population numbers of the peppered moth of England from light-colored to dark-colored and back again).

Thus, *vertical* evolutionary changes in fossils are essential to real geologic dating, but they are impossible to prove. They must simply be assumed.

The dating of the rocks depends on the evolutionary sequence of the fossils, but the evolutionary interpretation of the fossils depends on the dating of the rocks. No wonder the evolutionary system, to thoughtful

[11] Gareth V. Nelson, "Origin and Diversification of Teleostean Fishes," *Annals* (New York Academy of Sciences, 1971), p. 27.

[12] Donald R. Griffin, "A Possible Window on the Minds of Animals," *American Scientist*, vol. 64 (September/October 1976), p. 534.

[13] James W. Valentine and Cathryn A. Campbell, "Genetic Regulation and the Fossil Record," *American Scientist*, vol. 63 (November/December 1975), p. 673.

outsiders, implies circular reasoning.

> Are the authorities maintaining, on the one hand, that evolution is documented by geology and, on the other hand, that geology is documented by evolution? Isn't this a circular argument?[14]

> The intelligent layman has long suspected circular reasoning in the use of rocks to date fossils and fossils to date rocks. The geologist has never bothered to think of a good reply, feeling the explanations are not worth the trouble as long as the work brings results. This is supposed to be hard-headed pragmatism.[15]

The main "result" of this system, however, is merely the widespread acceptance of evolution. But uniformitarian assumptions and evolutionary geology are altogether useless in locating oil or other economically useful deposits. Perhaps, however, geologists feel that, since biologists have already proved evolution, they are justified in assuming it in their own work. But biologists in turn have *simply assumed evolution to be true.*

> But the danger of circularity is still present. For most biologists the strongest reason for accepting the evolutionary hypothesis is their acceptance of some theory that entails it. There is another difficulty. The temporal ordering of biological events beyond the local section may critically involve paleontological correlation, which necessarily presupposed the non-repeatability of organic events in geologic history. There are various justifications for this assumption but for almost all contemporary paleontologists it rests upon the acceptance of the evolutionary hypothesis.[16]

And, as far as the "ordering of biological events beyond the local section is concerned," O'Rourke reminds us again:

> Index fossils . . . are regarded as the features most reliable for accurate, long-distance correlations.[17]

---

[14] Larry Azar, "Biologists, Help!" *Bioscience*, vol. 28 (November 1978), p. 714.

[15] J. E. O'Rourke, "Pragmatism versus Materialism in Stratigraphy," p. 48.

[16] David B. Kitts, "Paleontology and Evolutionary Theory," *Evolution*, vol. 28 (September 1974), p. 466.

[17] J. E. O'Rourke, "Pragmatism versus Materialism in Stratigraphy," p. 48.

As mentioned earlier, more and more modern geologists are now recognizing the existence of circular reasoning in their geological methodologies. Among these, in addition to those already mentioned, is Dr. Derek Ager, former president of the British Geological Association.

It is a problem not easily solved by the classic methods of stratigraphical paleontology, as obviously we will land ourselves immediately in an impossible circular argument if we say, firstly that a particular lithology is synchronous on the evidence of its fossils, and secondly that the fossils are synchronous on the evidence of the lithology.[18]

In another article, Dr. Ager, who was also head of the geology department at Swansea University, notes the problem involved in trying to use minor differences in organisms (that is, what creationists would call *horizontal changes* or *variations*) as time markers.

We all know that many apparent evolutionary bursts are nothing more than brainstorms on the part of particular paleontologists. One splitter in a library can do far more than millions of years of genetic mutation.[19]

It would seem that this innovative tendency would lead to great uncertainty in the use of extinct marine organisms (about whose intraspecific variability while they were living we know nothing whatever) as index fossils.

Another geologist who recognized the circulatory problem was Dr. Ronald West at Kansas State University, who noted:

Contrary to what most scientists write, the fossil record does not support the Darwinian theory of evolution because it is this theory (there are several) which we use to interpret the fossil record. By doing so, we are guilty of circular reasoning if we then say the fossil record supports this theory.[20]

Still another comment on the circular reasoning process involved

---

[18] Derek V. Ager, *The Nature of the Stratigraphic Record*, 3rd ed. (New York: John Wiley and Sons, 1993), p. 98.

[19] Derek V. Ager, "The Nature of the Fossil Record," *Proceedings of the Geological Association*, vol. 87, no. 2 (1976), p. 132.

[20] Ronald R. West, "Paleontology and Uniformitarianism," *Compass*, vol. 45 (May 1968), p. 216.

in developing paleontological sequences appears in an important symposium paper.

> The prime difficulty with the use of presumed ancestral-descendant sequences to express phylogeny is that biostratigraphic data are often used in conjunction with morphology in the initial evaluation of relationships, which leads to obvious circularity.[21]

In view of such admissions from many leading evolutionists, it is clear that there neither is, nor can be, any *proof* of evolution. The evidence for evolution is merely the assumption of evolution!

The most extensive discussion of the circular-reasoning problem in evolutionary geology is probably the paper by O'Rourke.[22] Although he attempts to explain and justify the process as being based on induction from observed field data, he does admit many important problems in this connection. With reference to the geologic column and its development, he says:

> Material bodies are finite, and no rock unit is global in extent, yet stratigraphy aims at a global classification. The particulars have to be stretched into universals somehow. Here ordinary materialism leaves off building up a system of units recognized by physical properties, to follow dialectical materialism, which starts with time units and regards the material bodies as their incomplete representatives. This is where the suspicion of circular reasoning crept in, because it seemed to the layman that the time units were abstracted from the geological column, which has been put together from rock units.[23]

The fiction that the geological column is actually represented by real rock units in the field has long been abandoned, of course.

> By mid-nineteenth century, the notion of "universal" rock units had been dropped, but some stratigraphers still imagine a kind of global biozone as "time units" that are supposed to be ubiquitous.[24]

---

[21] B. Schaeffer, M. K. Hecht, and N. Eldredge, "Phylogeny and Paleontology," Ch. 2 in *Evolutionary Biology*, vol. 6, eds. Th. Dobzhansky, M. K. Hecht, and W. C. Steere (New York: Appleton-Century-Crofts, 1972), p. 39.

[22] J. E. O'Rourke, "Pragmatism versus Materialism in Stratigraphy," p. 47-55.

[23] *Ibid.*, p. 49.

[24] *Ibid.*, p. 50.

Behind all such assumed time units is the doctrinaire assumption of evolution, which is the basic component of materialism.

> The theory of dialectic materialism postulates matter as the ultimate reality, not to be questioned. . . . Evolution is more than a useful biologic concept: it is a natural law controlling the history of all phenomena.[25]

And if physical data in the field seem in any instance to contradict this assumed evolutionary development, then the field data can easily be reinterpreted to correspond to evolution! This is always possible in circular reasoning.

> Structure, metamorphism, sedimentary reworking, and other complications have to be considered. Radiometric dating would not have been feasible if the geologic column had not been erected first. . . . The axiom that no process can measure itself means that there is no absolute time, but this relic of the traditional mechanics persists in the common distinction between "relative" and "absolute" age.[26]

In this exposition, O'Rourke decries the common reliance on an implicit circular argument that he attributes to the assumption of dialectical materialism, and he urges his colleagues to deal pragmatically with the actual stratigraphic rock units as they occur in the field, in confidence that this will eventually correlate with the global column that was built up gradually by similar procedures used by their predecessors.

He does recognize, however, that if the actual physical geological column is going to be used as a time scale, it is impossible to avoid circular reasoning:

> The rocks do date the fossils, but the fossils date the rocks more accurately. Stratigraphy cannot avoid this kind of reasoning if it insists on using only temporal concepts, because circularity is inherent in the derivation of time scales.[27]

Although the above references are 20 years old, they are not outdated, for this method of geological "dating" has been in use for more than 100 years and is still standard. Rocks are assigned a geologic age

---

[25] *Ibid.*, p. 51.
[26] *Ibid.*, p. 54.
[27] *Ibid.*, p. 53.

based essentially on the assumed stage-of-evolution of their fossils. Such a method, of course, has to presume that evolution is a known fact, and that its various stages, with their respective forms of life, are already settled.

But how could all this be known, if it all took place millions of years ago? As we have seen, there is no evidence of any vertical evolution occurring today, nor are there any evolutionary intermediates in the billions of known fossils from the past.

As hard as it may be to believe at this late date, the fact is that most of these imaginary evolutionary stages were originally developed deductively in the early 19th century by studies of comparative morphology and physiology of existing animals, especially utilizing inferences drawn from Ernst Haeckel's infamous "recapitulation theory." Stephen Gould referred to this fact as follows in his study of the racist implications of this theory:

> In Down's day, the theory of recapitulation embodied a biologist's best guide for the organization of life into sequences of higher and lower forms.[28]

But the recapitulation theory has long since been proved false, so how could it have been a reliable guide for determining evolutionary sequences? Many people, of course, have maintained that the fossil record gives an actual documented history of evolution. But we have just seen that the so-called fossil record is based on the assumption of evolution, and it is then used to date the rocks to provide the framework of "history" in which to interpret and correlate those rocks as an evolutionary series. And thereby, of course, the fossils have been neatly ordered in the same "evolutionary series" in which they have already arranged the rocks!

As previously noted, creationists have long argued that this is circular reasoning, and we are glad that evolutionists are finally admitting it. Raup says, for example:

> The charge that the construction of the geologic scale involves circularity has a certain amount of validity. . . . Thus, the procedure is far from ideal and the geologic ranges of fossils are constantly being revised (usually extended) as new occurrences are found.[29]

---

[28] Stephen Jay Gould, *Natural History* (April 1980), p. 144.
[29] David M. Raup, "Geology and Creation," *Field Museum of Natural History Bulletin*, vol. 54 (March 1983), p. 21.

One portion of the geological time scale was, however, supposedly developed by a sort of inductive process from actual fossil deposits in the rocks. The most recent of the geologic eras, the Cenozoic (involving the Tertiary and Quaternary Periods) was subdivided by Sir Charles Lyell in the early part of the 19th century, by a method that was supposed to be quantitative. A leading modern paleontologist and his colleagues have described this process as follows:

> In about 1830, Charles Lyell . . . developed a biostratigraphic technique for dating Cenozoic deposits based on relative proportions of living and extinct species of fossil mollusks. . . . Strangely, little effort has been made to test this assumption. This failure leaves the method vulnerable to circularity. When Lyellian percentages alone are used for dating, it remains possible that enormous errors will result from spatial variation in the temporal pattern of extinction.[30]

Lyell made his original studies almost exclusively on the rocks of the Paris Basin in France, so it was presumptuous and invalid to apply this all over the world. As Stanley and his associates point out:

> One source of error for Lyellian data that may, in general, bias estimates of extinction rates is a failure to recognize living representatives of some fossil species.[31]

These and other problems were real fallacies. The authors conclude:

> Thus our analysis casts doubt on the universal utility of the Lyellian dating method, even for faunas at a single province.[32]

These Tertiary and Quaternary subdivisions actually represent the most systematic attempt to develop a truly "inductive" (that is, "erected step-by-step from actual data in the field") technique for organizing a portion of the geological-age system. This is the most "recent" part of the time scale and, thus, presumably, the clearest and best preserved. Yet it did not work even here. The larger divisions, based on the recapitulation

---

[30] Steven M. Stanley, Warren O. Addicott, and Kujotaka Chinzei, "Lyellian Curves in Paleontology: Possibilities and Limitations," *Geology*, vol. 8 (September 1980), p. 422.

[31] *Ibid.*, p. 424.

[32] *Ibid.*, p. 425.

theory and other subjective criteria, are, therefore, even *less* reliable. Yet geologists still use it. Raup explains:

> In spite of this problem, the system does work! The best evidence for this is that the mineral and petroleum industries around the world depend upon the use of fossils in dating. . . . I think it quite unlikely that the major mineral and petroleum companies of the world could be fooled.[33]

Evidently, even such a careful and competent geologist as Dr. Raup can apparently be fooled, however. Oil companies use fossils (actually micro-fossils) only to trace out a given formation in a given region. They could hardly be used to locate oil-bearing rocks associated with a particular geological age, since oil is found in rocks of *all* ages! Actually, oil geologists and other economic geologists do their prospecting for new deposits on the basis of geometric and geophysical criteria, not paleontological assumptions.

And *whatever* they use, it is surely wishful thinking to boast that "the system does work," only about 1 out of 40 (very costly) wildcat oil wells discovers a new pool!

The bottom line is that the geological ages of rocks depend on the assumption of evolution, and that assumption is wrong! That being the case, there is no objective way to determine the geological age of a rock or fossil deposit. Consequently, for all that can be proved to the contrary, they could all well be of essentially the *same* age!

The Supposed Order of the Fossils

The foregoing discussion has shown that there is no way to tell the geologic age of rocks and their fossils, except on the assumption of evolution. Since there is no real evidence for evolution except the supposed geologic ages of the rocks and fossils, there is no reason *not* to conclude that all the rocks and fossils might have the *same* geologic age. This implication correlates with the compelling evidence that all such rocks have a catastrophic origin, and that all the individual catastrophes were connected and continuous components of a global hydraulic cataclysm. Instead of representing the evolution of life over many ages, the rocks and fossils represent the global destruction of life in one age.

An obvious question, however, involves the general order of the strata in the geologic column. Even though the entire geologic column may have been deposited in one great hydraulic-based cataclysm, why are the fossils arranged in a vertical order that at least *looks* like

---

[33] David M. Raup, "Geology and Creation," p. 21.

evolution? Why are there different forms of life found as fossils in the different rock systems that evolutionists have attributed to different ages?

The answer is twofold. In the first place, the supposed order is to a considerable extent artificial, since each local geological column varies from every other, and since each local column never constitutes more than a very small fraction of the total column. In the second place, such order as does exist is mainly an order of ecological zonation, and is exactly what a great flood would cause.

It is significant that every one of the great phyla and most of the classes of the animal kingdom appear in the Cambrian rocks, supposed by evolutionists to be the oldest of the fossil-producing geological ages. All the animals preserved in these rocks are marine animals, reflecting the marine fauna that lived in the pre-Flood oceans — and, therefore, normally were buried most deeply in the flood sediments. They comprise the same phyla and classes that live in the present oceans, except for some that have apparently become extinct, and they often are animals practically identical with living types (sponges, starfish, jellyfish, etc.).

Evolutionists used to claim that the vertebrates did not evolve until 60 million years or so after the Cambrian period. Now, however, even vertebrates (specifically fishes) have been found in Cambrian rocks.

> Until recently, vertebrates have been known from rocks no older than the Middle Ordovician (about 450 million years ago). In 1976 and 1977 the known range of the vertebrates was extended about 20 million years by discoveries of fish fossils in rocks of latest Early Ordovician and earliest Middle Ordovician age in Spitzbergen and Australia. This report of fish material from Upper Cambrian rocks further extends the record of the vertebrates by approximately another 40 million years.[34]

If practically *all* the animal classes and phyla are found in *all* the geologic "ages," or more accurately, the rock systems of the geologic column, there is very little left of even a superficial appearance of evolution.

Furthermore, ecological zonation accounts for what may still appear to be a semblance of evolutionary development in any local geological column. That is, the vertical order in the rocks (to the extent that any order exists at all) is usually from marine invertebrates at the

---

[34] John E. Rapetski, "A Fish from the Upper Cambrian of North America," *Science*, vol. 200 (May 5, 1978), p. 529.

lowest elevations to marine vertebrates, then amphibians (at the interface between land and sea in the pre-Flood world), then reptiles, mammals, birds, and men. This is essentially the order of increasing elevation in the ecological habitat. It does *not* represent evolution at all, though it has long been so interpreted. Some evolutionists are now recognizing the validity of this concept:

> It is worth mentioning that continuous "evolutionary" series derived from the fossil record can in most cases be simulated by chronoclines — successions of a geographic cline population imposed by the changes of some environmental gradients.[35]

Whether we are able yet to sort out all the details of every local geological column in the context of a global flood model, however, the important point is that the entire geological column really bears witness to *continuous catastrophism*.

Anomalies in the Evolutionary Order

There are, indeed, many evidences that the basic forms of life have been essentially the same throughout all the geologic ages, with the exception of the many types that have become extinct. The same is true of the physical constituents of the rocks: the petrologic types, the minerals, the faults, and other features. There is really nothing in either the physical or paleontological components of the rocks that would necessarily require identification of rocks as belonging to different ages.

In addition to that very basic fact, there also exist many anomalous deposits in the sedimentary column that make it still more difficult to believe in the standard geologic ages. One of these is the frequent occurrence of fossils that are found in deposits that contradict the "official" evolutionary order. This phenomenon is more or less brushed off with the term "stratigraphic disorder."

> Any sequence in which an older fossil occurs above a younger one is stratigraphically disordered. Scales of stratigraphic disorder may be from millimeters to many meters. . . . Stratigraphic disorder at some scale is probably a common feature of the fossil record.[36]

Evolutionists can, of course, explain away such anomalies by

---

[35] V. Krassilov, "Causal Biostratigraphy," *Lethaia*, vol. 7, no. 3 (1974), p. 174.

[36] Alan H. Cutler and Karl W. Plessa, "Fossils Out of Sequence: Computer Simulations and Strategies for Dealing with Stratigraphic Disorder," *Palaios*, vol. 5 (June 1990), p. 227.

various hypothetical "mixing" processes that rework the sediments after initial deposition, whether or not these are evident in the sedimentary environments themselves. At any rate, such "out-of-order" deposits are common, and do pose a problem for those whose presuppositions would require them to assume different depositional ages.

> The extent of disorder in modern and ancient sediments is not well documented; however, the widespread occurrence of anomalies in dated sections suggest that disorder should be taken seriously by paleobiologists and stratigraphers working at fine stratigraphic scales.[37]

Not only are there many places where fossils from different ages are found out of order, or even mixed together, but there are also numerous locations around the world where entire formations are apparently missing or even inverted.

Practically every local column has examples of "missing ages" in the sequences, many of which are replaced by what are wishfully called "paraconformities," with the missing ages evident only because of the missing fossils, but with no unconformity present to signal a period of erosion. Even more significant are the many examples of "reversed ages," and "old" formations resting conformably on "young" formations.

The most basic rule of stratigraphy (the study of the sequences of "strata," or layers, in the rocks) is that sedimentary rock formations on the bottom are older than those on the top. Sedimentary rocks are formed by the erosion, transportation, and deposition of sediments, and nothing could be more obvious than the fact that deposits on top were laid down after the sediments below them. However, this common sense rule often seems not to work in the presupposed evolutionary scenario.

> In many places, the oceanic sediments of which mountains are composed are inverted, with the older sediments lying on top of the younger.[38]

If this is the case, then how did the geological authorities ever decide that the bottom rocks were younger? The answer is that, as already discussed, they are dated by the fossils!

For true believers in evolution, it may be logical to date rocks this way, even when this requires devising a method for explaining how the

---

[37] *Ibid.*, p. 234.
[38] *Science News*, vol. 98 (October 17, 1970), p. 316.

sediments got out of order. Since, however, we do not observe evolution taking place today, one must ask how they can be so confident that evolution was true in the past. The "answer" is that the evolutionary history of life is revealed by the fossil record in the sedimentary rocks. Dr. Pierre P. Grassé who for more than 20 years held the Chair of Evolution at the Sorbonne in Paris, one of the world's leading universities, has noted this fact:

> Naturalists must remember that the process of evolution is revealed only through fossil forms.[39]

That is, ancient rocks just *have to* contain fossils of organisms in an early stage of evolution; younger rocks are bound to contain fossils representing a more advanced stage of evolution. We "know," of course, which rocks are ancient, because they are the ones on the bottom, with the younger ones on top. But, then, we have just noted that there are many places where this order is reversed. We "know" that they are reversed because of the evolutionary stages of their respective fossils.

Now, if one again senses a feeling of dizziness at this point, it is because we are once again going in circles. Maybe it will help settle our queasiness if we find some *actual physical evidence* that these gigantic old rock blocks have really ridden up and over (over-thrust) the younger ones. We would expect to find, if this is true, a tremendous amount of rock breakage (brecciation) and ground-up rock powder at the interface, along with deep grooves and scratches (striations) along the undersurface, and a general mixture of the upper and lower rocks along the thrust plane. Is this what is found?

Not usually. Usually, the contact surface is sharp and well-defined, with the older rocks on top of the younger, often with many expected "ages" missing in between.

> The following observations about "overthrusts" seem to have universal validity: 1. The contact is usually sharp and impressive in view of the great amount of displacement. . . . 5. Minor folding and faulting can usually be observed in both the thrust plate and the underlying rocks. The intensity of such deformations is normally comparatively weak, at least in view of the large displacements these thrust plates have undergone.[40]

---

[39] Pierre P. Grassé, *Evolution of Living Organisms* (New York City, NY: Academic Press, 1977), p. 4.

[40] P. E. Gretener, *Bulletin of Canadian Petroleum Geology*, vol. 25 (1977), p. 110.

It is true, of course, that some "overthrusts" do exhibit evidence of brecciation and other such indicators of relative movement. Does this not prove that they are really overthrusts?

Not at all — at least not necessarily. Many types of movement may occur besides overthrusting.

> Late deformations, particularly by normal faulting, are present in many thrust plates. They should be recognized for what they are: post-thrusting features completely unrelated to the emplacement of the thrust plates.[41]

Then what deformations can be identified with confidence as caused by the thrust itself? The author of the above quotation says that "basal tongues" from the lower plate are often injected into the base of the overthrust plate, and that these sometimes merge together. Also secondary "splay" thrusts may be found.

But now suppose that all these physical phenomena — brecciation, rock powder, striations, basal tongues, splay thrusts, etc., that a real overthrust would produce — are actually present, does this finally prove that the rocks have really been moved out of their original depositional order?

Of course not. Such phenomena merely prove that the upper block has moved *somewhat* with respect to the lower block. This is quite common, even with formations in the "correct" sedimentary order, resulting from the different physical properties and times of deposition of the two formations, and proves nothing whatever about overthrusting!

Admittedly, such phenomena do not *rule out* the possibility of overthrusting, as their absence might do. They are necessary, but not sufficient, conditions for overthrusting. More evidence is needed: notably, evidence of the "roots" from which the alleged thrust block was derived, along with evidence that its *incredible journey* was physically possible.

Are the sources of the overthrust plates usually discernible? Only rarely, and with much speculation. Furthermore, in most cases, there are not any genuine evidences of overthrusting at all.

> Different lithological units, usually with stratigraphic separation measured in kilometers, are in juxtaposition along a sharp contact, often no more impressive than a bedding plane.[42]

---

[41] *Ibid.*
[42] *Ibid.*, p. 111.

Why, then, could it not be a simple bedding plane? And how do geologists explain the incredible forces and motions in the earth that can accomplish the remarkable feat of moving a gigantic mass of rock great distances up and over another great rock formation? Titanic compressive forces and rock strengths must be generated, and tremendous frictional forces overcome, before such an operation could ever be accomplished! The mechanism of the presumed phenomenon has always been mysterious, however, and some of the most competent geophysicists have said it was impossible.

In 1959, however, William Rubey and M. King Hubbert felt that they had solved the problem, proposing that water trapped in the pores of the sediments as they were deposited, gradually became so compressed with the accumulating overburden that they developed "geostatic" pressures, capable actually of *floating* the formation above into location.[43]

This suggestion was enthusiastically accepted by most geologists, and, for nearly three decades, was by far the most widely adopted solution to the overthrusting problem.

It is obvious, however, that these very high pore pressures can be maintained only if (1) the pores in the rock section near the interface are inter-connected, so that the pressure will be applied over the entire base of the floating slab, (2) the permeability of the cap rock is so low that it provides an effective seal against the water's escaping under the high pressure gradient to which it is subjected, and (3) this seal is maintained throughout the movement.

This is a highly unlikely combination of circumstances, however, and some geologists recognize it to be a serious fallacy in such a proposed solution.

> At high enough pressure and temperatures, plastic flow will certainly reduce pore space inter-connectivity. To be effective mechanically, pore space must be inter-connected pore space; it is not clear that this is always the case during metamorphism. . . . Our preliminary results suggest that the effective permeability of the upper plate must be on the order of 10^{-3} mD or less for gravity gliding to be feasible. Otherwise, the fluid will leak away from the zone of decollement before pore pressure can reach the levels needed for gravity gliding. Although *in situ* rock

---

[43] William Rubey and M. King Hubbert, *Bulletin of Geological Society of America*, vol. 70 (February 1959), p. 155-166.

permeabilities are poorly known, the few existing measurements suggest that effective permeabilities as low as 10^{-3} mD are rare in the geologic column.[44]

But suppose that, in some cases, rocks such as shales and evaporites do have sufficiently low permeabilities to seal off the high pressure zone. Now the problem becomes one of rock strength — the pressures become so high as to fracture the rocks!

> When the pore fluid pressure exceeds the least compressive stress, fractures will form normally to that stress direction . . . we suggest that pore pressure may never get high enough to allow gravity gliding as envisaged by Hubbert and Rubey.[45]

If fractures develop, of course, this increases the permeability, and the water flows out, lowering the pressure and stalling any incipient flotation. Furthermore, it is simply inconceivable that these huge (often many miles long, wide and thick) slabs of rock could traverse the long distances necessary without fractures developing from other causes as well. There seems no way to avoid escape of pore water through at least *some* fractures. By Pascal's law, if the pressure is lowered *at any point* in a continuous water body, it must drop by the same amount throughout the entire body. The whole scenario seems impossible, hydraulically, over any significant distances.

> We suspect that over the areas of large thrust sheets such as those in the Appalachians or the Western Cordillera, effective permeabilities would have been too large to allow gravity gliding, even with shale or evaporite cap rocks.[46]

Therefore, it begins to appear that overthrusting by floating is impossible on any noteworthy scale. But this is not quite the last resort of those who must salvage the evolutionary order in the rocks at all costs.

> Simple gravity gliding under the influence of elevated pore pressure cannot explain the Heart Mountain fault. . . . Pierce has suggested a catastrophic genesis for the Heart Mountain allochthon.[47]

---

[44] J. H. Willemin, P. L. Guth, and K. V. Hodges, *Geology* (September 1980), p. 405.

[45] *Ibid*., p. 406.

[46] P. L. Guth, K. V. Hodges, and J. H. Willemin, *Geological Society of America Bulletin* (July 1982), p. 611.

[47] *Ibid*.

William Pierce[48] studied the Heart Mountain "over-thrust" (Paleozoic over Eocene) for many years. Originally, he thought it was caused by simple gravity sliding, but this proved impossible mechanically. Then it was suggested that the mechanism might have involved the Hubbert and Rubey fluid-pressure concept. When he found that that did not work either, he invoked catastrophism, and catastrophism with a vengeance, postulating an *explosive* transplantation of the thrust blocks! Catastrophic events, however, obviously can neither be observed in process nor modeled in the laboratory:

> Catastrophic processes are beyond the scope of this analysis.[49]

One can *believe* in catastrophic overthrusting if his motivation to do so is sufficiently strong, of course. If evolutionists want to retain their cherished evolutionary sequences, therefore, they must do so only by faith in catastrophism. Floating rock formations won't float!

Thus, the supposed "order of the fossils" in the geologic column is really not much of an order at all. There are numerous examples of out-of-order fossils, as well as entire regional formations out of order. Even when everything is in the "correct" order according to evolutionary theory, there are — more often than not — whole missing "ages" in local geologic columns. All these anomalies require various *ad hoc* explanations as to how they got that way. If, however, all the "ages" were really the *same age*, and if all the now-fossilized plants and animals were actually *living contemporaneously* in that age, then the anomalies are not anomalous any more.

And even when they are all in the proper order in a given locality, Gould and others have pointed out that still there is no evolutionary "vector of progress" evident in the column. To the extent that there is any vertical order in the fossils at all, such statistical order is only that which a worldwide hydraulic cataclysm, such as has already been inferred from the physical phenomena in the strata, would be expected to produce.

As a general rule, it is obvious that — other things being equal — such a global cataclysm would tend to deposit organisms in ecological burial zones corresponding to the ecological life zones where they were living when caught up by the global flooding. Thus, organisms living at lower elevations (deep-sea marine invertebrates) would usually be

---

[48] William Pierce, *Clastic Dykes of Heart Mountain Fault Breccia*, USGS Prof. Paper 1133 (1979), 25 p.

[49] Guth, Hodges, and Willemin, *Geological Society of America Bulletin*, p. 611.

buried at lower elevations, while organisms living at higher elevations (bears, birds, etc.) would tend to be deposited at higher elevations.

Another factor necessary to consider is that of mobility. Animals that are capable of running, swimming, climbing, or flying can escape burial longer than others. One would, for example, expect to find few fossils of birds or human beings for this reason. Even though finally overtaken and drowned in the rising floodwaters, they would be much less likely to be trapped in the sediments and preserved as fossils than other less mobile animals.

In general, therefore, it is clear that such a worldwide flood would often tend to produce fossil sequences roughly corresponding to those in the standard geological column. There would be many exceptions, of course, and there *are* many exceptions to the standard order, as already discussed.

It should be noted again in this connection that each local geologic column normally incorporates only a few of the geological "periods." If both marine and terrestrial formations are found in the same column, the marine formations usually (as expected) would be on the bottom, and the land sediments on top. Only rarely is a formation containing fossils of land animals found interspersed between two marine formations from different periods. The main exception to this rule is in the cyclic deposits (e.g., coal seams) along the interface between the lands and the rising waters, as sediments are brought in and deposited first from one direction and then from the other. Normally, all these, however, would be from the same geological "period."

Even assuming that each geological deposit was laid down rapidly, as discussed previously, many have argued that it would take great lengths of time to convert these sediments into the solid rocks of the geological column. The great thickness of non-lithified sediments in offshore delta deposits, or in deep-sea sediments, are offered as cases in point.

However, the rate of lithification (that is, conversion of loose sediment into stone) depends on many variables, chief of which is the presence or absence of a cementing agent, such as calcite, silica, or others. In the context of a worldwide flood, such materials would be abundant everywhere. Also there would, of course, be plenty of water, as well as conditions of changing pressure and temperature, all of which are conducive to rapid lithification under the right conditions.

As a very relevant example, one need only think of the conversion of a "sediment" of sand, gravel, and water (plus cement!) into solid rock (concrete) in a matter of a few hours. This kind of phenomenon would have been common during and after any such hydraulic/tectonic/volcanic complex of catastrophes.

The Anomalous Climates of the Ancient World

The present climatic regime of the world is one of varied temperatures zones — arctic, temperate, subtropical, and tropical zones — and these have varied little during recorded history. If this historical regime is considered "normal," however, then the geologic column contains two important special fossil anomalies. The first is the global temperate-to-subtropical zone throughout most of the geologic column, providing still further testimony to the contemporaneity of all the "ages." The second is a worldwide glacio-pluvial period (the so-called "Ice Age") following the global warm period.

Following the cataclysmic death and burial of that ancient world, however, the post-cataclysm sediments of the column indicate a global regime of rain and cold continuing up to the early periods of recorded history.

The great coal measures of the world dating from the late Paleozoic era onward, of course, speak of semi-tropical vegetation essentially everywhere in the world, as does the worldwide prominence of dinosaurs and other reptiles during the Mesozoic era. Furthermore, the atmosphere was richer and heavier, contributing to lush vegetation and abundant animal life everywhere.

> The earth's atmosphere 80 million years ago contained 50 percent more oxygen than it does now, according to an analysis of microscopic air bubbles trapped in fossilized tree resin. . . . One implication is that the atmospheric pressure of the earth would have been much greater during the Cretaceous era, when the bubbles formed in the resin.[50]

The cause of such increased atmospheric pressure (hyperbaric pressure) is conjectural, but it would have had a number of advantages for plants, animals, and people living in it. In fact, hyperbaric pressure chambers are increasingly being used today for medical and therapeutic purposes.

One interesting insight is its provision of an explanation for the once-dominant flying reptiles and their later demise when the atmospheric pressure was reduced to present levels.

A dense atmosphere could also explain how the

---

[50] Ian Anderson, "Dinosaurs Breathed Air Rich in Oxygen," *New Scientist*, vol. 116 (November 5, 1987), p. 25.

ungainly pterosaur, with its stubby body and wing span of up to 11 meters, could well have stayed airborne.[51]

The higher atmospheric pressure could have been caused by an extensive blanket of water vapor in the upper atmosphere, although there is only a very small amount of water vapor (averaging about an inch of liquid water equivalent) there today. It is difficult to imagine any other cause for the higher pressure.

Such a canopy would have served also as a thermal blanket, maintaining a greenhouse-like environment on the earth in the age before it condensed and fell to earth. This correlates, of course, with the evidence of a global warm climate in that age, even in the higher latitudes. Scott Wing and David Greenwood, two paleobotanists with the Smithsonian Museum of Natural History, have compiled much evidence that the winters of the Tertiary era were mild even in such presently frigid states as Wyoming and Montana.

> The fossil fauna records compiled by Wing and Greenwood include abundant signs of mild Eocene winters in continental interiors; cold-sensitive land turtles too large to burrow for protection during the winter, diverse communities of tree-living mammals dependent on year-round supplies of fruit and insects, and crocodile relatives, all found as far into the continental interior as Wyoming. . . . The fossil plant data, Wing and Greenwood's specialty, also call for equable continental climate 50 million years ago. Palms, cycads (resembling a cross between ferns and palms), and tree ferns extended into Wyoming and Montana in the Eocene.[52]

The mild, warm climates extended even deep into the Antarctic Continent during the late Tertiary.

> The discovery of thousands of well-preserved leaves in Antarctica has sparked a debate among geologists over whether the polar region, rather than being blanketed by a massive sheet of ice for millions of years enjoyed a near-temperate climate as recently as three million years ago.[53]

---

[51] *Ibid.*

[52] Richard A. Kerr, "Fossils Tell of Mild Winters in An Ancient Hothouse," *Science*, vol. 261 (August 6, 1993), p. 682.

[53] Chris Raymond, "Discovery of Leaves in Antarctica Sparks Debate over Whether Region Had Near-Temperate Climate," *Chronicle of Higher Education* (March 20, 1991), p. A9.

These leaves were found on a cliff in the Trans-Antarctic Mountains, only 250 miles from the South Pole.

> The leaves, compressed by subsequent layers of ice, look like fossils. But unlike fossils, which leave only mineral traces of the original organism, the leaves retain their original cellular structure and organic content.[54]

Just as a possible thermal vapor canopy (assumed to be present in the upper atmosphere since the primeval creation) could account for the warm climates and hyperbaric pressures that evidently characterized earth's ancient age, so its condensation and precipitation might account for the global hydraulic cataclysm implicit in the geologic column and also the subsequent regime of cold and rain. At least it seems to provide a model worthy of serious study by geologists and climatologists.

We have indicated that the late Paleozoic era (the *early* Paleozoic is recognized almost entirely by marine fossils), the Mesozoic era, and the Tertiary period of the Cenozoic era were characterized by a global warm climate. On the other hand, the immediate post-Tertiary period — the Pleistocene epoch — is widely known as the Ice Age. It is characterized by many geological phenomena (glacial tills, moraines, striated rocks, etc.) that strongly suggest continental ice sheets in the polar and sub-Arctic latitudes, as well as phenomena indicating a pluvial, or rainy, period in the lower latitudes.

There have been well over 30 theories published purporting to explain the cause of the Ice Age, all of them controversial, and none of them universally accepted. The sudden change in climate resulting from the precipitation of a previous thermal vapor blanket would seem to be the most promising explanation of all. That would also provide much of the water required for the global inundation implicit in the unified sediments of the earth's crust, as discussed in the preceding chapter.

As to the trigger that initiated the condensation and precipitation of the canopy, several suggestions could be offered, but all are necessarily speculative. Some event (e.g., volcanic eruptions, cometary dust swarms, meteor showers) that would provide condensation nuclei for the vapor particles could be one possible cause.

Another obvious evidence of a worldwide flood is the worldwide drying up of inland lakes and seas, along with the evidence that all river valleys once carried much larger quantities of water and alluvium than

---

[54] Chris Raymond, "Discovery of Leaves in Antarctica Sparks Debate over Whether Region Had Near-Temperate Climate," *Chronicle of Higher Education* (March 20, 1991), p. A9.

they do now. The Pleistocene Epoch, also known as the Ice Age, is the most recent of the supposed geological ages. The Ice Age in higher latitudes was accompanied by a Pluvial Age in lower latitudes, a rainy period in which the great deserts of the world were all well watered, many having towns and extensive agricultural works; and there were great lakes and deep-flowing rivers everywhere, including regions now arid and barren.

Sir Fred Hoyle and Elizabeth Butler have written a fascinating description of this period, which they attributed to a similar worldwide catastrophe, a sudden impact of cometary dust over the world as a comet swept by:

> Acquisition by the upper atmosphere of some 10^{14} gm. of cometary dust would have major implications on the earth's climate. Pluvial activity would increase dramatically as temperature differences between sea and land widened. Global distribution of precipitation would be controlled by the density of the dust in the atmosphere; for a partially reflective blanket, a fraction of solar energy would still reach ground level creating new climatic zones. The totally undecomposed state of the interiors of Siberian Mammoths and the curious distribution, often uphill, of erratic boulders point to unbelievably sudden and severe conditions at the onset and possibly end of a glacial period. We suggest that a reflective blanket of particles could promote such conditions.[55]

With only slight change, this paragraph by two eminent astrophysicists could describe what would happen when the postulated primeval vapor canopy suddenly condensed and precipitated. In fact, one possible cause of its precipitation could well be the earth's passage through a cloud of cometary or meteoritic dust. Hoyle and Butler go on to describe other probable aftereffects:

> Streams and rivers would flow for a while in enormous abundance, and inland lakes would fill to exceptionally high levels, as in fact they did. The concurrence of pluvial conditions with ice ages is another challenge to "small cause" theories, since a slow cooling together of oceans and lands over a time scale of approximately 10^4 years would decrease

---

[55] Fred Hoyle and Elizabeth Butler, "On the Effect of a Sudden Change in the Albedo of the Earth," *Astrophysics and Space Science*, vol. 60 (1979), p. 505.

evaporation and precipitation, which the known pluvial conditions clearly show to be wrong. . . . The mammoths became
extinct during the last ice age. . . . But if the ice came slowly,
over a time-span of approximately 10^4 years, a slow migration
to the south would not only be possible, but we think inevitable.[56]

Hoyle and Butler are surely correct in repudiating the various
slow-and-gradual theories that have been proposed for the onset of the
Ice Age. A worldwide cataclysm, however, provides the only fully
satisfactory explanation. The worldwide warm climate indicated in the
rocks and fossils of almost all the world's other "geological ages" finds
an eminently satisfactory explanation in the greenhouse effect caused by
an ancient water-vapor canopy over the earth, the sudden precipitation
of which brought on a worldwide flood and, probably, the immediately
subsequent Ice Age and Pluvial Age.

In this chapter we have seen abundant evidence that the so-called
"geological ages" — the 4.6 billion years of the supposed evolutionary
history of the earth and its inhabitants — really constituted only *one*
primeval age, characterized by a year-round pleasantly warm climate
everywhere, lush vegetation, and a great variety of animal life. That age
came to a dramatic and traumatic end in a global hydraulic/tectonic/
volcanic cataclysm that produced the earth's great fossil-bearing sedimentary crust. The cataclysm was followed by a relatively brief glacio-
pluvial period that eventually settled down into the present more or less
quiescent regime with sharp latitudinal and annual climatic variations.

All of this evidence brings into serious doubt the supposed multi-
billion-year history of the earth, as commonly taught today. The earth
could well be quite young, more or less coextensive with the duration of
human occupation and civilization.

The actual physical evidences related to the age of the earth — a
few suggesting an old age, but many implying a young age — will be
surveyed in the following chapter.

---

[56] Fred Hoyle and Elizabeth Butler, "On the Effect of a Sudden Change in the Albedo of
the Earth," *Astrophysics and Space Science*, vol. 60 (1979), p. 508.

Chapter 12

Really, How Old Is the Earth?

In the last analysis, the only evidence for evolution is the assumed multi-billion-year age of the earth. No one has ever observed macro-evolution taking place in the present, there are no transitional forms in the fossils to show it taking place in the past, and the basic laws of observed change in nature clearly indicate that it could never happen at all.

Yet the scientific and intellectual establishments are so reluctant to believe in a Creator who could create all things by His own omnipotence, that they still insist that we *must* believe in evolution. To do that, of course, they must first insist that we believe in a very old earth, arguing that since there has been enough time for evolution, therefore, evolution must be true. The evidence for the earth's great antiquity is so strong, they assert, that believing in a young earth is as unreasonable today as believing in a flat earth.

This intellectual peer pressure has intimidated even many creationists, who, therefore, have opted for some compromise that mixes creation with evolution in one way or another. As shown in Volumes 1 and 3 of this Trilogy, however, such attempts at compromise involve overwhelming theological and sociological problems which, in effect, impugn the character of God.

That area of study, however, is not the purpose of *this* volume. Here we wish, rather, to critique the supposed scientific evidence itself — that is, the scientific data that have been used to determine the so-called "absolute" age of the earth. It turns out, as we shall see, that the weight of the *scientific* evidence alone gives strong evidence that the earth is *far too young* for evolution to be even a feasible model of earth history.

The Beginning of History

Modern intellectuals speak of "millions" or "billions" of years just as though they knew what they were talking about! The fact is, of course, that no human being could *possibly* relate experientially to such numbers.

The rise and fall of kingdoms that thrived two or three thousand years ago is considered *ancient* history. The very *beginning* of *real* history — that is, of events which have been recorded and preserved in actually written accounts, goes back only a few thousand years at the most. Anything earlier than that must necessarily be a matter of some degree of speculation, since there *are no records*.

That this is as far back as we can go *historically* was confirmed many years ago (as if we needed confirmation!) by no less an authority than Colin Renfrew, the premier living archaeological and linguistic scholar in England. He argues that 3100 B.C. is approximately the date of the founding of Egypt's first dynasty. Then he adds the following:

> The Mesopotamian chronology is less reliable than the Egyptian, and it does not go back so far.
>
> This date of 3100 B.C. thus sets the limit of recorded history. No earlier dates can be obtained by calendrical means, and indeed the dates cannot be regarded as reliable before 2000 B.C. . . . Any dates before 3000 B.C. could be little more than guesswork, however persuasive the arguments and the evidence after that period.[1]

There are even some Egyptologists who argue that Egypt's first dynasty did not start until around 2000 B.C., pointing out that Manetho, the Egyptian historian on whom many depend for their chronological calculations, may not have distinguished whether certain dynasties in the two kingdoms of upper and lower Egypt were contemporaneous or sequential.

Renfrew did overlook one chronology more ancient than that of Egypt: one that would extend history back an additional two thousand or so years. That, of course, is the Mosaic chronology as preserved in the ancient Book of Genesis, which — if accepted — would make the early chapters of Genesis the most ancient historical record in the world. Liberal scholars reject Genesis, however, and since the purpose of this

---

[1] Colin Renfrew, *Before Civilization* (New York, NY: Alfred A. Knopf, 1973), p. 28. Renfrew is Professor of Archaeology at Cambridge University.

volume does not include defending the Bible, we shall simply assume that real history begins no more than 5,000 or so years ago.

Therefore, any dates that are older than that — especially the dates assigned to the supposed geological ages and to the evolutionary history of life — must necessarily be speculative. Any calculated age exceeding 5,000 years before the present must be based on some natural process whose rate of operation in some defined system can be measured as it exists at present, plus one or more assumptions as to how it may have functioned in the past. The components of the system must be known as they exist in the present, and then one or more assumptions made as to their state in the past.

Therefore, to make an age calculation on a very simple system of only one changing component, the following quantities must be either known or assumed:

1. Quantity of the component existing at present in the system.

2. Average rate of change of the component in the past.

3. Quantity of the component at the beginning.

It must also be assumed that the system has been closed throughout its history, with no ingress or egress of the component being measured.

That sounds simple enough in principle. In practice, however, it often becomes very complicated, especially when one realizes that there is no way of *knowing* that the assumptions are valid. For example, there is no way to know how the rate of change of the process may have varied in the past. It is usually *assumed*, therefore, that it has not changed.

Secondly, there is no way of *knowing* that the system has been closed throughout its history. It is very likely that it has *not* been closed. If not, then further guessing is necessary as to how any possible external influences may have affected the changes in the system.

Even more importantly, there is certainly no way of *knowing* what the state of the system may have been at its beginning. No one was there to observe and measure it. One can assume that there was nothing there at all, and that the whole system has grown from scratch, as it were. But that is strictly an assumption, and a very unreasonable assumption at that.

It is especially unlikely in the context of special creation, and that is the very issue we are discussing. How does one know, for example, that the system and its components were not created "full-grown," so to speak? If an omnipotent Creator exists at all (and, again, that is the very point at issue), why would He have to "create" something by a slow, wasteful, cruel process requiring millions of years? It would be far more reasonable for Him to create every system in His universe *fully mature and functioning* in its intended purpose right from the start.

Presumably — allowing the existence of God as at least a possibility — His ultimate purpose in creation would involve man, the highest and most complex of His creatures. So why would He waste millions of years in developing trilobites and dinosaurs and other creatures that would die out *before* man ever appeared?

Thus, the calculation of an "age" for anything without taking into full account the possibility of its initial creation as a fully functioning, already completely developed, entity is tantamount to denying God's existence right from the start. One cannot *prove* evolution simply by denying the possibility of creation!

The usual rejoinder of evolutionists to the concept of the creation of maturity (or "apparent age") is that it would make God out to be a deceiver, making something "look" old when it was really young.

No it wouldn't! If anything at all has been truly *created*, it must have been created with *an appearance of at least some prior history*. There could be no creation otherwise. It would only "look" old to one who rejects the very possibility of special creation.

It is, therefore, impossible to make a certain determination of the age of the earth, or of anything else before the beginning of written records. The assumptions that have to be made in order to calculate an "apparent age" are simply the assumptions of uniformitarianism: that is, (1) closed system, (2) constant process rate, and 3) zero starting point. Since none of these assumptions can be known to be valid — especially the third — one can never be sure that a calculated apparent age even approximates the true age of the system.

The only terrestrial processes which, even with these uniformitarian assumptions, will give ages ranging into the desired billion-year realm for the age of the earth are those based on radioactive decay (e.g., uranium/lead, potassium/argon, rubidium/strontium). These will be discussed later in this chapter. On the other hand, there are many worldwide processes which, *even with the traditional uniformitarian assumptions*, will yield earth ages far too young to allow evolution as a viable model of origins.

In this book, we are not trying to determine the true age of the earth. As we have seen, that is impossible scientifically, because of the built-in fallacies in the assumptions that one has to make to calculate an apparent age. We can show scientifically, however, that there is strong *evidence* (not "proof") that the earth is too young for evolution to have taken place, even if evolution were possible at all!

That being true, it is quite legitimate to conclude that the earth need not be much older than the beginning of human recorded history. If creation is a better scientific model of origins than evolution (as we have been showing in many ways all through this book), it seems much more *realistic* to start with a completed, functioning creation, fresh from the powerful creative voice of God. There is no need for millions of years, and there is no *sure* scientific evidence of millions of years.

This fact can be illustrated if we take several specific examples of *worldwide processes* that — even with the standard uniformitarian examples — yield apparent ages far too small for evolution to be feasible. There are scores of such processes, with only a very few that can be forced to yield billion-year ages. These few, however, are all that most people hear about, for it is only these that appear large enough to allow for the possibility of evolution.

The Human Population

The worldwide growth process that is of most direct concern to society today is the growth of human population. This began to be of great concern only about 30 or 40 years ago, when people suddenly began to realize that over-population could become a serious world problem if its growth continued at present rates (about 2 percent per year) indefinitely. As a matter of fact, Thomas Malthus had raised this problem early in the 19th century, and his writings had been of great influence in leading Charles Darwin and Alfred Russel Wallace to their "discovery" of the struggle for existence, survival of the fittest, and natural selection as the supposed scientific basis for evolution.

Darwin and Wallace, as well as Malthus, all assumed an exponential growth of population, as do most writers on the subject. It is easy to show mathematically that, starting with just one man and one woman, it would take only about 1,100 years of exponential growth to produce the present world population of around six billion people, if the population were increasing by 2 percent each year. This cannot have been going on for very long in the past, or the world would long ago have been overrun with people.

In the 1970s the rate of increase has slightly exceeded 2 percent per year. That means a doubling time of less than 35 years; the number currently being doubled is a very large one. Projection of such growth for very long into the future produces a world population larger than the most optimistic estimates of the planet's carrying capacity. In the long run near-zero growth will have to be restored — either by lower birth rates or by higher death rates.[2]

This kind of alarmist writing has led to rationalizing such Draconian measures as abortion, homosexuality, infanticide, and euthanasia as measures of population control. For our purposes here, of course, population-growth statistics seem to place severe constraints on the age of man's existence on earth.

Not much is known about ancient population sizes, but the exponential-growth model assumed by Malthus, Darwin, and others still seems as reasonable as any, at least during recorded history. However, the present 2 percent growth rate must have been smaller in the past, or the planet would long since have been completely filled with people.

Any numerical description of the human population cannot avoid conjecture, simply because there has never been a census of all the people in the world. . . . The earliest date for which the global population can be calculated with an uncertainty of only, say, 20 percent, is the middle of the 18th century. The next-earliest time for which useful data are available is the beginning of the Christian era, when Rome collected information bearing on the number of people in various parts of the empire.[3]

Dr. Ansley Coale, who was director of the Office of Population Research at Princeton University, estimated from such data that the world population at the time of Christ was about 300 million.

From A.D. 1 to 1750 the population increased by about 500 million to some 800 million (the median of a range estimated by John D. Durand of the University of Pennsylvania).[4]

Such estimates are, of course, little better than guesses. Who *knows* what the populations of China or India or other distant nations may have been during those years? It becomes even more speculative when

---

[2] Ronald Freedman and Bernard Berelson, "The Human Population," *Scientific American*, vol. 231 (September 1974), p. 31. Freedman, professor of sociology at Michigan University, was President of the Population Council.

[3] Ansley J. Coale, "The History of the Human Population," *Scientific American*, vol. 231 (September 1974), p. 41.

[4] *Ibid.*, p. 43.

researchers attempt to guess at the size of still-earlier world populations. To do this, they simply assume the standard chronology of supposed human evolution from the Paleolithic era, and make it fit.

> For still earlier periods the population must be esti-
> mated indirectly from calculations of the number of people
> who could subsist under the social and technological insti-
> tutions presumed to prevail at the time.[5]

This presumption leads, however, to absurdly small growth rates, for which no valid evidence exists.

> Thus whatever the size of the initial human popula-
> tion, the rate of growth during man's first 990,000 years
> (about 99 percent of his history) was exceedingly small.
> Even if one assumed that in the beginning the population
> was two — Adam and Eve — the annual rate of increase
> during this first long interval was only about 15 additional
> persons per million of population. . . . Even if we again
> assume that humanity began with a hypothetical Adam and
> Eve, the population has doubled only 31 times, or an
> average of about once every 30,000 years.[6]

This corresponds to an annual percentage growth rate of only 0.000015 percent. Is it really plausible to believe that for *almost a million years*, populations increased annually by only 15 people per million, and now they have suddenly exploded to 20,000 *each year* per million? Or that the doubling time has suddenly decreased from 30,000 years to 35 years? This is evolutionary philosophy at its most preposterous, and is contrary to all known history and human nature.

As we have seen, the period of real history, as recorded by those who were there, occupies only about 5,000 to 6,000 years or so. Assuming only 4,000 years, to be conservative, and an initial population of only two people, to be even *more* conservative, an annual rate of growth of only 0.5 percent (one-fourth the present rate) would produce the present world population.

This is eminently reasonable, allowing adequately for periods of slow growth because of wars and pestilences and famines (actually, the world's greatest wars, famines, and pestilences have occurred in this present century). But to try to place the start of the human population

---

[5] *Ibid.*, p. 41.
[6] *Ibid.*, p. 43.

much earlier than this is not reasonable. To place it at a million years ago, as Coale assumed, would seem to be beyond all justification, at least as far as population statistics are concerned.

While this line of reasoning does not prove that the earth is young or that the first humans lived only a few thousand years ago, it is far more consistent with the facts of human history and known demographics than is the evolutionary scenario.

Radiocarbon and the Young Earth

It is interesting to recognize that radiocarbon (that is, Carbon 14, the unstable isotope of natural Carbon 12), which has been the basis of the main argument for human antiquity, actually yields a strong argument in support of a *young earth*. Radiocarbon (or C-14) is formed in the atmosphere by the action of cosmic rays on the atoms of Nitrogen 14 in the air. However, the radioactive instability of this C-14 causes it immediately to begin to decay to N-14, the stable isotopic form of carbon. The "half-life" of C-14 (that is, the time it takes for half of the C-14 in a given system to decay back to N-14) is approximately 5,730 years. Therefore, by about six such half-lives, or about 35,000 years, there would be practically no C-14 left to measure (some claim to be able to measure extremely small amounts out to as much as 80,000 years, or 14 half-lives, but that is very doubtful).

Thus, if the cosmic rays were somehow shut off, so that no more C-14 could be generated, it would take about, say, 50,000 years before all the radiocarbon in the earth's atmosphere, biosphere, and hydrosphere would have decayed back to nitrogen. Similarly, if the cosmic radiation were then turned on again, at the same rate as before, it would take about 50,000 years to build the C-14 back up to a level at which it would be in a "steady-state," with as much being produced worldwide as the amount decaying.

The problem is that all measurements show that the worldwide "assay" of radiocarbon is not yet at this level, indicating that its production has only been going on for much less than 50,000 years! It is not yet in a steady state, but is still building up in the world. Yet radiocarbon datings on human artifacts are invariably based on the assumption that, regardless of what the data show, the radiocarbon assay of the world *must* be in a steady state. The atmosphere and the earth are far older than 50,000 years, so the reasoning goes, and so that fact requires that radiocarbon *must* be in a steady state.

But the data clearly show otherwise!

We have now learned that one of the basic implicit

assumptions of the method — namely, the constancy of the atmospheric inventory of $C^{14}O_2$ — is not strictly correct.[7]

The authors refer to $C^{14}O_2$ (that is, carbon dioxide) because carbon combines with oxygen to form carbon dioxide, a compound that is very important in all plant and animal life processes. Normally, this compound is present as $C^{12}O_2$ — that is, natural carbon dioxide. However C-14 and C-12 are identical, as far as ordinary chemistry goes, so the proportion of radioactive carbon dioxide to natural carbon dioxide in any living organism is presumably the same as that in any other organism at that time, assuming that the C-14 has been distributed uniformly around the world.

When the plant or animal dies, however, it ceases to take in CO_2, while its C-14 content continues to decay to N-14. Consequently, the ratio of C-14 to C-12 in the organism at any time after death becomes an index to how long it has been dead, or the last date at which it was still living. This is the concept behind the radiocarbon dating method. It has been reasonably confirmed by historical dates back to about 3,000 years ago, though with many obviously incorrect results. For older dates, however, the invalidity of the steady-state assumption is bound to result in radiocarbon dates that are *too high*, with the error increasing as the age increases! The steady-state assumption actually has been known to be wrong ever since the method was first suggested back in the 1940s by Willard Libby.[8]

> We now know that the assumption that the biospheric inventory of C^{14} has remained constant over the past 50,000 years or so is not true.[9]

For those who wish to have a quantitative indication of just how wrong this assumption is, the following authoritative assessment is given:

> We note in passing that the total natural C-14 inventory of 2.16×10^{30} atoms . . . corresponds to a C-14 decay rate of 1.63×10^4 disintegrations/ m^2s of the earth, considerably below the estimated production rate of C-14 atoms

---

[7] Elizabeth K. Ralph and Henry N. Michael, "Twenty-five Years of Radiocarbon Dating," *American Scientist*, vol. 62 (September/October 1974), p. 553. Dr. Ralph is professor of archaeology and radiocarbon at the University of Pennsylvania.

[8] W. F. Libby, *Radiocarbon Dating* (Chicago, IL: University of Chicago Press, 1955), p. 7.

[9] Ralph and Michael, "Twenty-five Years of Radiocarbon Dating," p. 555.

averaged over the last 10 solar cycles (111 years) of 2.5 x $10^4 \pm 0.5$ x 10^4 atoms/m2s. From a geophysical point of view, it would be very surprising if the decay rate and the production rate were out of balance as seriously as the two numbers would suggest. It is difficult to reconcile this discrepancy by errors in computing the C-14 inventory since the bulk of the C-14 is in the sea, where the C-14 concentration relative to the terrestrial biosphere is known fairly well.[10]

Thus, there are 25,000 C-14 atoms per square meter per second being generated, and only 16,300 disintegrations. That is, about 50 percent more is being produced than is decaying, and this can mean only that the earth's atmosphere (where the production takes place) is far younger than 50,000 years!

The source of the discrepancy is therefore unknown unless the present-day production rate is indeed significantly higher than the average production rate over the last 8,000 years, the mean life of C-14.[11]

The authors of this assessment, of course, cannot allow themselves to consider that the earth's atmosphere (and, therefore, the earth itself) must be significantly younger than 50,000 years old. So, instead, they propose the seemingly outlandish conclusion that the cosmic-ray incidence on the earth must be much higher now than it used to be. This could be true only if the atmosphere had been shielded by some sort of protective canopy (say of water vapor!), or a much stronger magnetic field in the past. But either of these assumptions will also yield a much younger earth! It does seem clear — at least to those not blinded by evolutionary presuppositions — that the continuing worldwide build-up of radiocarbon is strong evidence for an earth *far too young* for evolutionism to be feasible.

The Decaying Magnetic Field

As a matter of fact, there is definitely strong evidence that the intensity of the earth's magnetic field was much stronger in the past than it is today! This fact was first emphasized by a creationist physicist, Dr. Thomas G. Barnes, then professor of physics at the University of Texas (El Paso) and director of its Shellenger Research

---

[10] A. W. Fairhall and J. A. Young, "Radiocarbon in the Environment," in *Advances in Chemistry*, vol. 93 (1970), p. 401-418.

[11] *Ibid.*

Laboratory.[12] However, it is now a widely recognized — though not yet explained — fact:

> Measurements of the main field . . . show that the over-all intensity of the field is declining at a rate of 26 nanoteslas per year. . . . If the rate of decline were to continue steadily . . . the field strength would reach zero in 1,200 years. . . . Moreover, little is known about what may cause the field — which is created by currents churning in the earth's molten core — to decline in strength.[13]

Dr. Barnes had previously pointed out that the main magnetic field of the earth, also called the dipolar field of the earth, with magnetic north and south poles slowly varying in location around the earth's axial poles, had been decaying in the intensity of its magnetic moment for over 135 years of recorded worldwide measurements. As with other known decay processes (e.g., radioactive decay), the magnetic decay data fit best on an exponential curve, with a half-life of 1,400 years. That is, the intensity of the earth's dipolar field would have been twice as strong 1,400 years ago as it is today.

If extrapolated back to 7,000 years (that is, 5 x 1,400), which is the approximate age of the earth that is suggested by known human history, human population statistics and atmospheric radiocarbon build-up, the strength of the field would have been $(2)^5$, or 32, times as strong as it is today! It could hardly ever have been much greater than that, as the earth's structure itself would have disintegrated with a much stronger field.

At any given location on the earth, the local magnetic field may represent a combination of the over-all dipole field with local effects that may change its local direction and intensity. Barnes limited his analysis, however, to the dipole field, as determined by integration of measurements all over the world. Later criticisms of his results on the basis of local-field effects are, therefore, irrelevant. There is no doubt that the dipole field of the earth as a whole is decaying.

> The dipole component of the earth's field was considerably stronger 2,000 years ago than it is today. . . . In the next two millennia, if the present rate of decay is sustained,

---

[12] See the second edition of Barnes' monograph *Origin and Destiny of the Earth's Magnetic Field* (San Diego, CA: Institute for Creation Resaerch, 1983), for a detailed exposition of this evidence.

[13] "Magsat Down, Magnetic Field Declining," *Science News*, vol. 117 (June 28, 1980), p. 407.

the dipole component of the field should reach zero.[14]

When and if the earth's magnetic field strength reaches zero, its shielding effect on the earth will also be removed, with possibly harmful effects on human and animal health and longevity, as the incidence of cosmic radiation on the earth's surface is increased.

Of more interest to our immediate discussion is the implication that the earth's magnetic field was much stronger in the recent past, which is impressive evidence that the earth itself is very young — an age measured in thousands of years, rather than millions or billions of years. Evolutionists generally have tried to dismiss this evidence with a reference to the many past reversals of magnetic polarity in the earth, asserting that the present decline is merely a phase in the repeating cycle of reversals.

This answer is far from satisfactory, however. As discussed in chapter 10, the main evidence for global magnetic-field reversals (the so-called magnetic "stripes" on the sea floor on the two sides of the Mid-Atlantic Ridge) has been seriously questioned, if not positively refuted, by the grid of vertical stripes as well as horizontal stripes now known to characterize the sea floor magnetization pattern.

Furthermore, these reversals have supposedly been "dated" to occur at intervals of 500,000 to 700,000 years. But if the present decay cycle — which is scheduled to reach zero in the next 1,000 to 2,000 years — has been going on for 500,000 years, the earth long since *would have been vaporized* under the intense heat generated by the decaying electric currents, or dynamo motions, or whatever is producing the magnetic field in the earth's deep interior.

It is true that there is much evidence of former magnetic reversals now preserved in various basaltic rocks and other igneous formations at a number of places around the earth, including some that suggest much shorter periods of reversal (e.g., reversed polarity within a single lava-flow rock), but there is as yet no compelling evidence that any of these represent *global* reversals of the magnetic field, rather than ephemeral local phenomena.

> In all the thousands of years that people have lived in the aura of the earth's magnetic field, no one has ever discovered why it exists. . . . It took until the middle of this century for geophysicists to arrive at the idea that the swirling dance of the earth's liquid iron core somehow generates the magnetic

---

[14] Jeremy Bloxham and David Gubbins, "The Evolution of the Earth's Magnetic Field," *Scientific American*, vol. 261 (December 1989), p. 71.

field. But the detailed choreography of this motion, what energy source drives it and how it gives rise to the field, remain stubbornly out of reach.

There are all sorts of sources outside the earth — ionospheric currents and magnetic storms, for example — that induce currents to flow in the mantle, setting up magnetic fields that merge with that generated by the core.[15]

Evolutionists generally explain the earth's dipolar magnetic field by a great "dynamo" in the earth's core, with great masses of molten iron "swirling" around, and perhaps reversing directions at intervals. No one knows whether such a dynamo really exists, of course, or what gives it the tremendous energy to keep swirling around, if it does exist, and especially to change directions. How this would generate a magnetic field at the surface or how it could cause the polarity to reverse (either instantly or gradually) is also highly speculative.

For that matter, it is not even known whether the earth's core consists of iron *or* of some completely different state of intensely pressurized matter. It is also believed by evolutionists that this presumed dynamo in some unexplained way provides the massive energies required to move whole continents around on the earth's surface.

This remarkable (and relatively new, since about 1965) paradigm of deep dynamos, magnetic reversals, plate tectonics, spreading sea floors, drifting continents, emerging and subducting mantle materials, is sufficiently flexible to explain a wide variety of geophysical and geological phenomena (just as is the evolutionary paradigm); but that is not to say that any part of it has ever been observed occurring, any more than evolution has ever been observed. There are, in fact, still many reputable geophysicists and geologists (not just creationists) who question the whole concept.[16]

Creation has never been observed occurring either, of course, but the creation paradigm is also flexible enough to explain these and all other phenomena (if they are real phenomena), and to do so much more simply and directly. For example, the present exponential decay of the magnetic dipolar field is easily explained by circulating electrical

[15] Steffi Weisburd, "The Earth's Magnetic Hiccup," *Science News*, vol. 128 (October 5, 1985), p. 218.

[16] See, for example, the symposium *New Concepts in Global Tectonics*, eds. S. Chatterjee and N. Holton (Lubbock, TX: Texas Tech University Press, 1992), This compilation contains 23 papers by geophysicists and other scientists who reject the plate-tectonics paradigm, and propose various other theories to explain the same phenomena.

currents in the earth's deep interior. These were *created* by the earth's Creator at the time that the earth was created, and they have been decaying ever since, generating heat as they flow against resistance, resulting both in heat flow to the surface and an exponentially decaying magnetic field.

In fact, the theory as developed by Dr. Barnes is quite an elegant theory, explaining many other phenomena associated with the magnetic field, and adequately accounting for the local phenomena associated with reversals and similar matters. One should refer to his monograph previously cited (see footnote 12) for more details.

One more difficulty should be mentioned in relation to the idea of dipole reversals. There is a titanic amount of energy associated with the generation of the earth's magnetic field, no matter how it is generated, and that energy will have been dissipated when the field decays to zero strength. How then could it ever start up again? The basic energy conservation law would seem to preclude it, unless there is some great (but unknown) source of energy to start up the "motor" again. And even if there were such a giant "crank" somewhere in the earth, why would it start it up in the *opposite direction*?

> During the past 10 million years the earth's magnetic field has reversed polarity once every 500,000 years or so. Yet the dipole field decays on a much shorter time scale. These facts suggest that the dipole field does not reverse polarity after every period of dipole decay.[17]

So the subject continues to grow in complexity — and confusion.

> It is interesting . . . that there is no accepted explanation of the origin and physical significance of earth's magnetic polarity changes.[18]

It is simpler, of course, and more in accord with actual scientific observations, to conclude that the present dipolar decay of the magnetic field is real and permanent, and that it essentially tells the whole story. This means that the earth must be only a few thousand years old!

Decaying Comets

Another decay process of significance to the age of the earth is the gradual disintegration of the comets of the solar system. It is well-known

---

[17] Bloxham and Gubbins, "Evolution of the Earth's Magnetic Field," p. 75.

[18] J. C. Pratsch, "Petroleum Geologist's View of Oceanic Crust Age," *Oil and Gas Journal,* vol. 84 (July 14, 1986), p. 114.

that the comets, like planets, orbit the sun, and so presumably are of an age comparable to that of the solar system as a whole, including the earth. The problem is that they are all disintegrating. Many have already died out, and the ones that are still active (both short-period comets and long-period comets) are also known to be breaking up.

This is true of even the most famous comet of all, Halley's Comet, as well as all other known comets.

> Indeed the rate at which comets such as Halley lose material near perihelion is so great that they cannot have been in their present orbits for very long, either. . . . Their [planetary physicists] conclusion is that the time Halley's comet has spent in the Inner solar system is a mere 23,000 years, perhaps enough for fewer than 300 revolutions of the orbit.[19]

Now even if the above rather extravagant extrapolation were correct, evolutionists cannot settle for anything like 23,000 years as the age of the solar system. It would be far too brief a time for any evolution to occur.

Accordingly, they have invented an imaginary "Oort Cloud" of "wannabe" comets somewhere on the distant edges of the solar system. Every now and then, the gravitational pull of some nearby star, or of something else, supposedly pulls one of these comets-in-waiting out of the cloud, and sends it spinning into orbit around the sun. When that comet eventually disintegrates and falls into the sun, another will be fortuitously released from the cloud, thus keeping the cometary component of the solar system more or less constant.

This convenient Oort Cloud, however, has never been observed through any telescope. The only evidence for its existence is the evolutionary *need* for it, to keep from admitting that the solar system is young. Its name comes from the name of the otherwise relatively unknown astronomer who invented it.

> In this accepted view of the appearance of comets, the existence of the Oort Cloud itself is not a firm reality, but is inferred, essentially from calculations of the chance that such an object will be catapulted into the inner solar system and from the number of known comets. In the circumstances many people would be happier if there were more objective

---

[19] John Maddox, "Halley's Comet is Quite Young," *Nature*, vol. 339 (May 11, 1989), p. 95.

evidence for the reality of the Oort Cloud.[20]

Evolutionists would be happier, no doubt, but creationists are quite satisfied with the evidence as it stands. Most known comets are already gone and the ones that remain are breaking up. *The obvious conclusion is that they are young.* Therefore, the solar system to which they belong is young, and the earth is even younger!

Down to the Sea

The same Edmund Halley after whom the famous comet was named back in the 17th century, is believed to be the first to suggest that the age of the ocean (and, therefore, the age of the earth) could be determined by dividing the salt in the sea by the annual influx of salt from rivers carrying it down to the sea. From such calculations, a popular figure for the age of the earth during the 19th century was about 50 million years.

Even allowing for known egress of salt from the ocean because of sea spray, deposition in salt marshes, or whatnot, the known data could not bring the age up to more than about 100 million years, and this was not enough to satisfy the Darwinians, who needed more time to make evolution appear feasible. Accordingly, they abandoned all such methods as soon as radiometric dating came in and enabled them to upgrade the earth's age, first to about 2 billion years, and then eventually to 4.6 billion years.

Nevertheless, the influx of chemicals (not only salt, but a host of other substances) into the ocean from rivers still provides many valuable age-indicators for the ocean. One can calculate the age from at least 30 different chemicals, and all of them — with no exception — will yield an age far too small for evolution.

The chemical composition of sea water is quite well known, and so is that of rivers emptying into the ocean. It is a matter of simple arithmetic — dividing the amount of a given chemical *in* the ocean by the average annual inflow of that chemical *into* the ocean — to get the number of years required for the process.

The results are extremely variable, all the way from 100 years for aluminum to 45 million years for magnesium. However, this variability is only to be expected, because all such calculations are based on the unrealistic assumptions of uniformitarianism. The rates of influx of most chemicals were probably greater in the past, because the rivers carried more water, and the continents were higher and more easily eroded. This

---

[20] John Maddox, "Halley's Comet is Quite Young," *Nature*, vol. 339 (May 11, 1989), p. 95.

would reduce all age estimates, of course. Some ages are abnormally small, however, because of man-derived additions of chemicals to the rivers (e.g., wastes from riverside aluminum plants during the past century).

The most unrealistic assumption, however, is that the oceans had only fresh water when first created. Since multitudes of organisms seem specifically designed for life in salt-water environments, this is an unrealistic assumption that makes most age estimates from such calculations far too high.

Evolutionists dismiss such evidence, however, with the naive and hasty argument that this type of computation merely yields the "residence time" of the given chemical in the ocean rather than the time required to build up the ocean's component of that chemical from a zero base.

Actually, the same calculation would yield *both* the build-up time and *also* the residence time once the "build-up" had reached a "steady-state" with the "out-go." For the idea of residence time to have any meaningful basis, however, it first needs to be shown that there is actually an efflux of the given chemical from the ocean (through atmospheric recycling, sea floor deposition, or other "sinks") sufficient to achieve the postulated steady state.

This, however, the evolutionists have not been able to show. In the few cases where enough real measurements have been made to enable such calculations to be made, the results have always contradicted the steady-state assumption. Consider, for example, the quantities of *metallic* elements in the ocean:

> The startling conclusion . . . is that most trace metals are at extremely low concentrations in the oceans and have rather unspectacular variations in their concentrations. The calculated theoretical concentrations of cooper, nickel, silver, gold, lead and other metals in the oceans are many orders of magnitude higher than the best currently measured values.[21]

The reason that these concentrations are all so low is undoubtedly because the rivers and oceans are only thousands of years old, instead of millions or billions, so they have not yet reached their natural steady state. Turekian guesses:

---

[21] Karl K. Turekian, "The Fate of Metals in the Oceans," *Geochimica et Cosmochimica Acta*, vol. 41 (1977), p. 1139.

The secret lies in the role particles play as the sequestering agents for reactive elements during every step of the
transport process from continent to ocean floor.[22]

Exactly what these particles are and how they manage to "seques-
ter" so much copper, nickel, silver, gold, and lead along the way is a
matter of speculation — not of observation.

At least one rather detailed study of one important element —
uranium — was made a number of years ago, in an attempt to quantify
all such sequestering agents and sinks along the way.

The ocean contains over 4 billion tons of dissolved
uranium, at a concentration of 3.3 parts per billion. . . . A
detailed mass-balance calculation has shown that only
about 10% (0.2×10^{10} grams per year) of the present-day
river input of dissolved uranium can be removed by known
sinks.

The mean uranium concentration in world rivers is
about 0.6 parts per billion. This value multiplied by the
total river flux of water of 0.32×10^{20} grams per year gives
1.92×10^{10} grams per year as the total riverine influx of
dissolved uranium.[23]

In addition to the 10 percent of this uranium influx that is removed
by sinks in the ocean itself (presumably, deposition on the ocean floor),
there are a number of removal agents en route to the ocean.

Low and high-temperature alteration of basalts, organic-rich sediments and co-existing phosphorites on continental margins, metalliferous sediments, carbonate sediments, and sediments in anoxic basins deeper than 200
meters remove about three-fourths of the present-day riverine supply to the ocean.[24]

Thus, about 85 percent of the 19.2 billion grams coming to the
ocean each year is removed, leaving 15 percent (or 2.88 billion grams)
to be added to the ocean itself. The 4 billion tons *already* in the ocean is
equal to 3,640 trillion grams.

Therefore, the maximum age of the ocean in terms of uranium

---

[22] Karl K. Turekian, "The Fate of Metals in the Oceans," *Geochimica et Cosmochimica Acta*, vol. 41 (1977), p. 1139.

[23] Salman Block, "Some Factors Controlling the Concentration of Uranium in the World Ocean," *Geochimica et Cosmochimica Acta*, vol. 44 (1980), p. 373.

[24] *Ibid.*, p. 376.

content is 1,250,000 years. This seems like a long time, but it would take us back only into the Pleistocene Age (the time of the glacial period) according to standard geologic chronology. Furthermore, it assumes that there was no uranium in the ocean to begin with, and it also allows an extremely generous extraction of uranium by various possible sinks and sequestering agents. Without the latter, the maximum age would be calculated as (1,250,000)(0.15), or only 187,000 years.

A similar, very detailed calculation of the maximum age of the ocean, based on its sodium content (the main component of the ocean's salt), has been made by Dr. Steve Austin and Dr. Russell Humphreys. Both are creationists with impeccable credentials, Austin a geologist, Humphreys a geophysicist.

After calculating in full detail all possible sources of both sodium input and output, they concluded that the maximum possible age for the ocean (even assuming *no* sodium in the ocean to begin with) was 32 million years.[25]

Therefore, the evolutionist's dodge of an imagined "residence time" for the chemicals in the ocean, assuming a steady-state situation for all these chemicals, fails to check out whenever detailed measurements are made of all sources of output and input and are carefully considered. This evidence cannot prove what the actual age of the ocean may be, since there is no way of knowing its initial composition, but it *does prove* rather conclusively that the earth is far too young for organic evolution.

It can even be shown, based on present rates of continental erosion and sea floor deposition (again based on uniformitarian assumptions and on present rates) that neither the present continents nor the ocean bottom sediments can be older than about 15 million years.

Furthermore, based on the present average influx of juvenile water from the earth's deep interior, all the water in the ocean could have been produced by volcanism in 340 million years, which would take us back, geologically speaking, to only the Silurian "period," the age of fishes. In fact, the entire crust of the earth could have been produced by volcanism at present rates in 500 million years, *less than one-ninth the present assumed age of the earth.*

There are many other indicators of a young earth (or, at least an earth too young to allow evolution as a viable theory of origins) that are discussed in more detail in many other books by creationist scientists.

---

[25] Steven A. Austin and Russell D. Humphreys, "The Sea's Missing Salt: A Dilemma for Evolutionists," *Proceedings of the Second International Conference on Creationism*, vol. 2 (1991), p. 17-33.

For the most part, the documentation in this book has been restricted to citations from articles and books written by evolutionary scientists, in order to forestall the charge of biased quoting from only those of like mind to that of the writers.

There are, however, numerous scientific discussions of evidences for recent creation available in books and articles by creationists. A few relevant book titles by the writers and their colleagues at the Institute for Creation Research are listed below for those who want further information on the *scientific evidences for recent creation*. There are many others, of course, but it is impracticable to list them all here, as well as injudicious to list only selected titles from other creationists. Hence, only ICR-related books are listed below.

Scientific Creationism, ed. Henry M. Morris (Master Books, 1985), p. 91-170.

What is Creation Science? by Gary E. Parker and Henry M. Morris (Master Books, 1987), p. 3, 223-296.

The Young Earth, by John D. Morris (Master Books, 1994), p. 45-117.

The Biblical Basis for Modern Science, by Henry M. Morris (Baker Book House, 1984), p. 260-269, 304-335, 414-426.

Science, Scripture and the Young Earth, by Henry M. Morris and John D. Morris (Institute for Creation Research, 1989), p. 25-82.

The Genesis Flood, by John C. Whitcomb and Henry M. Morris (Presbyterian and Reformed Pub. Co., 1961), p. 331-437.

Age of the Earth's Atmosphere, by Larry Vardiman (Institute for Creation Research, 1990), 32 p.

Radiocarbon and the Genesis Flood, by Gerald E. Aardsma (Institute for Creation Research, 1991), 82 p.

Origin and Destiny of the Earth's Magnetic Field, by Thomas G. Barnes (Institute for Creation Research, 1983), 132 p.

Studies in Flood Geology, by John Woodmorappe (Institute for Creation Research, 1993), 208 p.

Grand Canyon: Monument to Catastrophe, by Steven A. Austin (Institute for Creation Research, 1994), 288 p.

Ice Cores and the Age of the Earth, by Larry Vardiman (Institute for Creation Research, 1993), 87 p.

In two of the above books (*What is Creation Science?* and *The Biblical Basis for Modern Science*), one of the writers (H. Morris) has listed some 68 worldwide natural processes which, with the standard uniformitarian assumptions, will yield a young age for the earth, *far too young for evolution.*

However, the average person never learns about these works, for that very reason: they would not justify the evolutionary paradigm. Conversely, the handful of radiometric dating methods that *do* allow billions of years for certain rocks are very widely publicized. It is *these* dating techniques, based on radioactive transmutation of certain elements into others, which operate so very slowly that they can be made to yield billion-year-type ages, that are widely believed to provide the time needed by evolutionists for their model. These are considered briefly in the following section.

The Uncertain Sound of Radiometric Dating

A number of dating methods are based on the radioactive decay of one element into one or more other elements, and these decay process rates have been measured very precisely. The ratio of "parent" elements to "daughter" elements in a given system is therefore considered, when properly calibrated, to measure the "age" of that system.

The main radiometric decay processes used in dating are as follows:

Uranium 238 decays through a long chain of elements into non-decaying Lead 206 and Helium 4, with a half-life of 4.5 billion years.

Uranium 235 decays into Lead 207 and Helium 4 with a half-life of 0.7 billion years.

Thorium 232 decays into Lead 208 and Helium 4 with a half-life of 14.1 billion years.

Potassium 40 decays into Argon 40 and Calcium 40 with a half-life of 1.3 billion years.

Rubidium 87 decays into Strontium 87 with a half-life of 49 billion years.

Other similar processes are used occasionally, as well as various sub-processes based on the five noted above. The latter are the most significant, however, and most widely used. The types of fallacies that can be noted in these are typical of those that could apply to all of them. All are based fundamentally on *uniformitarianism, which is itself invalid*, rendering all such pre-historic age guesses essentially meaningless.

First of all, there is no certainty that the radioactive decay rates have always been the same, although this is not the most questionable assumption. More to the point is the "closed-system" assumption. In the real world of real physical processes, there is no such thing as a true closed system. Either the parent element or daughter element or both can more or less easily move in or out of a radioactive mineral, thereby completely upsetting any desired age-reading. In fact, most such radioactive age measurements turn out to be "discordant" or "anomalous" for this very reason, and are rejected.

However, in the context of the creation-evolution issue, neither of these questionable assumptions is the real problem. With such long half-lives, if the mineral contains any of the daughter element *at all*, it suggests a very old age. Even if the system yields an anomalous age (that is, an age that disagrees with the assumed geologic age), or a suite of discordant ages (that is, different ages calculated from different decay processes operating in the same rock formation), whatever "ages" are suggested will all tend to be very great — and that is why evolutionists favor radiometric dating over all other processes.

The real problem, however, is the arbitrary rejection of the *very possibility* of initial special creation, when that is the very question under debate. If there is a Creator (as the abundant evidence of complex design in the universe would indicate, as well as the utter absence of any real evidence of macro-evolution), it is eminently reasonable that He would create a complete and fully functioning universe right from the start. It follows then, that the mere presence of a so-called "daughter element" in a mineral would not at all have to mean that it had been derived over long ages by decay from its supposed "parent element." It could just as well — in fact much more likely — have been *created* there to begin with. At the very least, it would be impossible to prove otherwise.

Thus, the "apparent age" of a given radioactive mineral would have no relation whatever to its true age. At the very moment when the granite rock, for example, was created, the uranium-bearing minerals contained in it could have indicated an apparent age of, say, a billion years. The Creator, as Creator, surely has the right to set the "clock" to read whatever "time" He chooses.

The fact that different minerals and different rocks in different parts of the world now all read different times can be accounted for by mixing and distributing processes occurring during later geophysical catastrophes of either a regional or a global nature, even if they were all set to read the same "zero time" to begin with.

To the evolutionist, such suggestions are abhorrently unscientific, because it would make it impossible ever to determine the true age of the earth by scientific observation and calculation.

Exactly! That is the point! If an evolutionist has determined to deny *even the possibility of creation*, he is espousing atheism, whether he intends to do so or not. As noted before, if any entity of any sort whatever is supernaturally *created*, it necessarily will appear to have been there *before* it was created. Therefore, it necessarily will have an "appearance of age," so to speak. And if creation is a possibility, then the most logical thing for the Creator to do would be to create the entire cosmos — including the earth and all its living creatures — *complete and functioning right from the start*.

He surely would have some high purpose in creation — after all, an omnipotent Creator would not be uncertain or capricious in His actions — so He would definitely not waste eons of time in trial-and-error evolutionary meandering, involving incredible waste and cruelty, before beginning, to accomplish that purpose! Vast ages of evolution may make some sense to an atheist or to a pantheist, but surely not to anyone who believes in an omniscient, omnipotent Creator — a Creator who would surely know a better way to do it, and then be fully able to carry it out.

* * *

In this volume, we have reviewed many scientific evidences and arguments against evolution and in favor of special creation. Creation is at least a very viable alternative to evolution as a model of origins. If creation is even possibly true, then uniformitarianism would necessarily be invalid if projected back into the creation period, and it would be completely impossible to determine just *when* creation took place.

That does not mean that we will never be able to know the date of creation, but it *does* mean that we can learn it only if the Creator chooses to tell us when it was. That would require a special revelation from God himself, however, and a discussion of revelation is beyond the scope of this volume. *That* topic, of course, is fully treated in Volume 1 of this Trilogy.

Even apart from revelation, however, and even using the uniformitarian approach, we have seen much evidence that the earth is quite young, with *no good evidences* that the long geological ages ever took place at all! Radiometric dating can be applied only to individual minerals, and it is subject to many errors, whereas population growth, radiocarbon build-up, magnetic-field decay, growth of ocean chemicals, and other processes that we have discussed are all global processes much less influenced by any local changes. Furthermore, the great geological deposits all speak of a single global cataclysm, not long ages of evolution.

Therefore, the weight of all truly scientific evidence is not only opposed to evolution *per se*, but also to the concept of the vast ages that might allow evolution to appear possible. Genuine *science* — as distinct from naturalism and scientism — thus adds its testimony of the recent special creation of all things to that of the divine revelation of the One who created all things, as recorded in the Bible, and as shown compellingly in Volume 1.

This should not be surprising, for the God who made the world is the One who wrote the Word! Naturally, the two will agree.

Index of Subjects

Uniformitarianism
  Assumed as basic for evolutionism
    20-21
  Historical geology, Basis of
    258-262
  Modern repudiation 274-276

See also: Catastrophism
Variation, Biological 30-31
Vestigial organs 47, 233-235, 254
Whales, Supposed evolution of 76-79
Worldwide flood, *See*: Catastrophism

Index of Names